ANALYTIC GEOMETRY:
A Vector Approach

FLOYD WILLMORE
University of Illinois

DONALD BARR
Naval Postgraduate School

DONALD VOILS
Wisconsin State University

ALLYN AND BACON, INC.   *BOSTON*

LIBRARY OF CONGRESS CATALOG CARD NUMBER: 79-155309   74-155309

PRINTED IN THE UNITED STATES OF AMERICA

CONTENTS

iii

V VECTORS IN THREE-DIMENSIONAL SPACE

PREFACE

Analytic Geometry has reappeared separately in mathematics curricula for two apparent reasons: because it does not fit naturally in many calculus programs, and because high schools are now teaching mathematics that were once reserved for colleges. We believe it is both mathematically and pedagogically sound to teach Analytic Geometry as a separate entity. We have found it convenient and natural to introduce and apply notions of Linear Algebra simultaneously with the more traditional topics of Analytic Geometry.

In this book, notions of vectors are introduced early. Throughout, the connections and interrelations between algebra and geometry are emphasized. Geometry is used in interpreting and visualizing algebraic notions such as the determinant of a matrix and its relation to solutions of systems of equations and to intersections of lines or planes. Vectors are used in the development of Analytic Geometry notions such as translations and rotations, and fundamental facts about lines and planes. Concepts of linear algebra, such as matrix multiplication, are used to develop coordinate changes. We have endeavored to make clear the distinction between a point and its coordinate, so that the student may fully understand transformations of coordinates and the use of various coordinate systems. The notion of an equivalence relation is established and applied to vectors in order that the often neglected difference between coordinate-free vectors and position vectors may be understood.

Throughout the text we study classic topics such as conic sections in a context related to other elementary but independent notions such as symmetry, asymptotes, and coordinate changes. The conic sections are studied both in terms of algebraic structure (by a study of the general second–degree equation) and geometric structure (by taking the intersections of planes and right circular cones), the connections being shown as vector applications. In spite of the fact that we have introduced many topics of linear algebra, they are never taken out of the geometric setting of two and three dimensional spaces.

The material is separated into five chapters. In turn, each chapter consists of smaller units, each of the latter being followed by a lengthy exercise set. Chapter I is a summary of certain elementary mathematical notions which are used throughout. Chapter II introduces basic graphing ideas and some standard relations and functions. Chapter III discusses two dimensional vectors. In Chapter IV, the notions of coordinate transformations are applied to the case of translating and rotating conic sections into standard form. Chapter V is a consideration of vectors and their applications in three–dimensional space.

1

FOUNDATIONS

INTRODUCTION

In this chapter we shall review certain topics about which the student very likely has a working knowledge. One purpose of this review is to establish a common basis upon which we can develop our main topic. A second purpose is to establish the notation that we are to use throughout the book. We also introduce some topics the students may not previously have studied, most notably, the relationship between partitions and equivalence relations, and the idea of coordinatizations.

In our development we have attempted to strike a reasonable balance between brevity and the reader's assumed mathematical experience. Fundamental concepts of set theory and logic are treated very briefly in Sections 1.1 and 1.2. Functions and related topics are given a somewhat more lengthy treatment.

Before we proceed, let us discuss the general nature of mathematics and its applications in science. A mathematical system is usually made up of several identifiable types of objects. These objects can be classified roughly in the following categories: (1) A logic (generally unspecified). (2) Undefined terms (necessary to avoid logically unsatisfactory circular definitions, that is, defining a word ultimately in terms of itself). (3) Axioms and definitions (statements of assumed facts about the undefined terms). (4) Theorems (statements concerning the terms and relations derived from the axioms using logical reasoning).

A good example of this kind of mathematical system is the system of plane (Euclidean) geometry. In that system, the logic used is the familiar type.

Some of the undefined terms are "between" and "coincident." When studying a mathematical system, the investigator often formulates a "real-world" analogue that parallels, at least to some extent, the terms and axioms adopted in the system. Thus, in the case of geometry, one may view the term "point" as a dot on paper, and one may have some intuitive notion about how he might expect the relation "between" to behave in the system. It is understood, however, that the real-world interpretation is only a method of gaining intuition and insight. The structure of the mathematical system is an entity in itself, independent of any physical interpretation.*

On the other hand, the application of mathematics to the physical and social sciences depends on making useful real-world interpretations. The basic idea is to formulate mathematical models of phenomena that are observed to occur in the physical universe. That is, we wish to use a mathematical system (which in some sense is analogous to the particular physical process under consideration) to gain information about the process under investigation. The usefulness of formulating such a "mathematical model" depends on many factors. If the model reflects faithfully in mathematical terms the attributes of the physical process, then we may be able to use mathematical methods in our model to arrive at conclusions about the model that also may be interpreted as conclusions about the physical process. The procedure of using a mathematical model can be schematically diagrammed as follows:

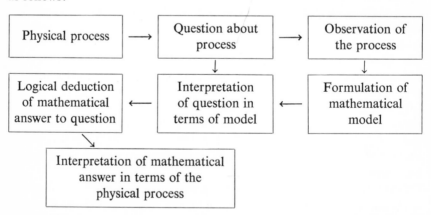

A good example of the use of models to explain observed phenomena is associated with the problem of accounting for observed planetary motion. An early model of our solar system, the Ptolemaic model, used the assumption that the earth was the center of the system. Planetary motion and the motion of the sun were interpreted by the use of circles and epicycles, with the earth as the center of the system. This view was held by educated men for several

---

* For further discussion of the *Philosophy of Mathematics*, see S. Barker (Englewood Cliffs, N. J.: Prentice Hall, Inc., 1964.)

centuries, until it was superseded by a model of Copernicus, in which the sun was assumed to be the center of the system. This led to later developments by Kepler and Newton in which mathematics was readily applied to the study of the solar system. The point of this is that each model can be used to explain the observed motions of the planets, but the system developed earlier becomes very complicated in the attempt, whereas the newer system is relatively simple. Thus, in adopting the system initiated by Copernicus, we rule in favor of the simpler and more workable of these alternative "explanations" of the observed motion.

There are many phenomena that have several alternative models, each of which has merits and drawbacks. Consider the case of explaining the observed phenomena associated with light. The main models are called the *wave theory* and the *corpuscular theory* of light. Each model can be used to explain certain phenomena that the other cannot; hence, no clear choice between the two can be made. Since each of the models is useful, each is used. To use one of the models is not to claim that light *is* actually of the particular form involved. Thus, a very important distinction exists between a useful *model* of light and a claim as to what light actually *is*.

Most mathematical systems are invented with a particular physical problem in mind. In many cases, they are later applied to other sciences in which the processes involved are quite different from the original problem. One such outstanding case is the application of trigonometry to electrical phenomena, whereas the subject grew out of the needs of surveying and astronomy.*

1.1 SETS: AN INTRODUCTION

We shall now proceed with a brief exploration of certain elementary set concepts. These concepts will be used throughout the development of the text.

The idea of a set is taken to be a primitive concept. We thus make no formal definition of this term. The basic notion, however, is a common one, even outside of mathematics. Various everyday words such as collection, bunch, and herd are used to express the set idea.

Example: You are familiar with the following sets of numbers:

    N: The set of *natural numbers* (1, 2, 3, . . .),

    Z: The set of *integers* (. . . -3, -2, -1, 0, 1, 2, 3, . . .),

    Q: The set of *rational numbers* (all ratios of integers a/b, $b \neq 0$).

The objects making up a set are called *members* (or, synonymously, *elements*) of the set. Thus, $\frac{1}{2}$ is a member of **Q** but is not a member of **Z**. A

---

* See Thomas Kuhn, *Copernican Revolution* (New York: Vintage Press, 1959); and Thomas Kuhn, *Scientific Revolution* (Chicago: Chicago Press, 1962).

common notation for this relationship between an object and a set is to write "$a \in S$" to denote that a is an element of the set S. Similarly, we write "$a \notin S$" to indicate that a is *not* a member of S. Thus, $\frac{1}{2} \in \mathbf{Q}$, whereas it is not true that $\frac{1}{2} \in \mathbf{Z}$ (written $\frac{1}{2} \notin \mathbf{Z}$).

In general, sets are specified by a list or some other descriptive device. We wish to emphasize that it is important, in using a given set description, to keep in mind the following two facts: (1) One should be able (at least theoretically) to determine whether or not any given object is an element of the set. (2) One should not "read into" the set description any additional information, such as an "order" in which elements occur, or "the number of times" an element occurs.

Example: $\{1, 2, 3\}$ is a *list description* of a set that has as elements (members) the numbers 1, 2, and 3. The description $\{2, 3, 1, 2\}$ is a different description for the same set. It distinguishes precisely the same objects as members, and that is all one should expect of the description. Thus, we could also write $\{1, 2, 3\} = \{2, 3, 1, 2\}$.

One of the most common and useful types of set descriptions involves specifying a property satisfied by certain elements of some *universal set*. (A universal set can be viewed as the set of all objects under consideration in a given context, and is usually denoted by U.) These descriptions are of the form:
$$S = \{x \in U : p(x) \text{ is true}\}$$
or, more simply,
$$S = \{x : p(x)\}.$$
These symbols are read "the set of all x in U such that $p(x)$ is true" and "the set of all x such that $p(x)$" respectively. When used in this way, $p(x)$ is called an open sentence. (We shall discuss open sentences in more detail in the next section.) If b is a member of the universe U (the set of objects under consideration) and $p(b)$ results in a true statement, then b is a member of the set S. If $p(b)$ results in a false sentence, then b is not a member of S.

Example: Suppose the universal set is N. Then
$$\{x : x < 5\} = \{1, 2, 3, 4\}.$$
$$\{s : s \text{ is prime and } s < 20\} = \{2, 3, 5, 7, 11, 13, 17, 19\}.$$
$$S = \{t : t^2 - 3t - 10 = 0\} = \{5\}.$$

Question: Why is -2 not an element of S?

Set Operations

Next, we introduce several useful set notions, which can be formally defined in terms of the ideas discussed above.

1.1-1 **Definition:** Given sets A and B, we write $A \subset B$ (read "A is a *subset* of B" or "A is *contained* in B") iff (if and only if) every element in A is also an element of B. If it is not the case that $A \subset B$, we write "$A \not\subset B$" (read "A is not contained in B").

Example: $\{1, 2, 3\} \subset \{1, 2, 3, 4\}$, and $\{x : x > 3\} \subset \{x : x > 0\}$, but $\{-1, 1\} \not\subset \{1, 2, 3\}$.

Remark: Every set is a subset of itself. For example, $R \subset R$, where R denotes the set of real numbers.

Question: Suppose $\{1, 2, 3, 4\} = A$. Then $\{1, 2\} \subset A$. What other sets are contained in A? Is $\{1, 3, 4, 3\}$ contained in A? Is $\{1, 3, 5\}$ contained in A?

Example: $\mathbf{N} \subset \mathbf{R}, \mathbf{Q} \subset \mathbf{R}, \mathbf{N} \subset \mathbf{Q}, \mathbf{Z} \subset \mathbf{Q}, \mathbf{N} \subset \mathbf{Z}$. (Recall that we denote by $\mathbf{N}, \mathbf{Z}, \mathbf{Q}, \mathbf{R}$, the number systems known as the natural numbers, the integers, the rational numbers, and the real numbers respectively.)

Question: What must be true if $A \not\subset B$?

One of the most common mistakes made by the novice is to confuse the *elements* of a set with certain of its *subsets*. If $A = \{1, 2, 3\}$, it is true that $1 \in A$, but false that $\{1\} \in A$. Also notice that $\{1\} \subset A$, but $1 \not\subset A$.

Question: Is $\{2, 3\} \subset A$? Is $\{\{2\}, 3\} \subset A$?

A set may contain elements that are themselves sets, although a set cannot be an element of itself.

Example: Let $A = \{\{1\}, \{2, 3\}, \{1, 2, 3\}\}$.
$\{1\} \in A, 1 \not\in A, \{1\} \not\subset A, \{2, 3\} \in A, \{\{1\}, \{2, 3\}\} \subset A,$
$\{2, 3\} \not\subset A, 2 \not\subset A$.

We now consider three operations with sets.

1.1-2 **Definition:** The set $A \cap B = \{x : x \in A \text{ and } x \in B\}$ is called the *intersection* of A with B.

1.1-3 **Definition:** The set $A \cup B = \{x : x \in A \text{ or } x \in B\}$ is called the *union* of A with B.

Example: Let $A = \{1, 2, 3\}, B = \{2, 3, 5, 6\}$. Then

$$A \cap B = \{2, 3\} \quad \text{and} \quad A \cup B = \{1, 2, 3, 5, 6\}.$$

Example: Let $S = \{x : x > 5\}, T = \{x : x > 2\}$. Then

$$S \cap T = S \quad \text{and} \quad S \cup T = T.$$

Remark: It is useful (although at first shocking to some people) to use the notion of a set with no elements. We denote such a set by "ϕ," and call it the *empty set*.

Example: Let $A = \{1, 2, 3\}$, $B = \{7, 9\}$. Then

$$A \cap B = \phi$$

(i.e., the sets A and B have no members in common.)

Remark: Sets A and B with the property that $A \cap B = \phi$ are called *disjoint*. A collection of sets that has the property that any two are disjoint is called a collection of *pairwise disjoint* sets.

Question: Is it possible for a set to have no subsets?

Complementation

We will also utilize the notion of sets that contain members of one set that are not also members of a second set.

1.1-4   Definition: Suppose A and B are subsets of some universe U. Then the *complement of B in A* is the set

$$A - B = \{x : x \in A \quad \text{and} \quad x \notin B\}.$$

Example: If $S = \{a, b, c, d\}$ and $T = \{a, c, e\}$, then

$$S - T = \{b, d\}.$$

Remark: The special case $U - B$ arises sufficiently often that a special symbol and name are used. The set $U - B$ (the complement of B in the universal set) is denoted by $\bar{B}$, and is simply called the *complement of B*. Thus, if the universal set is understood in some discussion, then $\bar{B} = \{x : x \notin B\}$.

Example: The complement of the set of even numbers is the set of odd numbers, where it is understood that $U = N$.

Exercise: Show that $\bar{\bar{A}} = A$ for any set A.

Some Axioms

We are not attempting to make an axiomatic development of set theory nor even a complete constructive development. However, we wish to point out some of the critical assumptions needed to make a complete and consistent set theory.

In addition to the existence of the empty set ϕ, one needs to assume the existence of a universe U such that each set is a subset of U. It would appear at first that one could simply assume the universe to be the collection of all possible objects that one could define or construct using set notation. However, in order to avoid logical difficulties such as Russell's paradox, one must avoid "sets" that are elements of themselves.

We use *equality* as a fundamental notion, in much the same way that we introduced the terms "set" and "element of." When we write $P = T$, we mean that P and T are names for the same object. Thus, in any sentence where P occurs, we can substitute T. This, however, is all we assume concerning equality.

Due to the primitiveness of the three concepts, *equality*, *set*, and *element of*, it is necessary to axiomatize a sufficient condition for set equality.

1.1-5 **Axiom:** *The axiom of extent.* Let A and B be subsets of the universe U. If $A \subset B$, and $B \subset A$, then $A = B$.

The converse of this axiom is a theorem that can be proved using the definition of $\subset$.

1.1-6 **Theorem:** If $A = B$, then $A \subset B$, and $B \subset A$.

PROOF: Assume $A = B$. Every element of A is in A, and so $A \subset A$. It follows by appropriate substitutions that $A \subset B$, and $B \subset A$.

Venn Diagrams and De Morgan's Laws

A useful device for illustrating set properties is that of *Venn diagrams*. A Venn diagram usually consists of a region drawn on paper representing the universal set U, with smaller regions inside depicting subsets of U. As an example, let us illustrate the famous and important results known as De Morgan's laws.

1.1-7 **Theorem:** (De Morgan's laws). If A and B are subsets of the universal set, then

$$\text{(i)} \quad \overline{A \cup B} = \bar{A} \cap \bar{B},$$

and

$$\text{(ii)} \quad \overline{A \cap B} = \bar{A} \cup \bar{B}.$$

PROOF: We shall give a Venn diagram illustration (see Figure 1.1) of the first part and a formal proof of the second part. You should study the diagrams and explain why they illustrate the set property $\overline{A \cup B} = \bar{A} \cap \bar{B}$.

To prove the equality $\overline{A \cap B} = \bar{A} \cup \bar{B}$, we show that $\bar{A} \cup \bar{B} \subset \overline{A \cap B}$ and that $\overline{A \cap B} \subset \bar{A} \cup \bar{B}$, and apply the axiom of extent. The standard method for proving an *inclusion* (a subset relation), is to "trace an element from one set into the other."

Suppose that for an arbitrary (but fixed) $x \in U$, it is found that $x \in \bar{A} \cup \bar{B}$. Then $x \in \bar{A}$ or $x \in \bar{B}$, from which $x \notin A$ or $x \notin B$. It then follows that x cannot be in both A and B. That is, $x \notin A \cap B$, or equivalently, $x \in \overline{A \cap B}$. Since this argument works for *any* element of $\bar{A} \cup \bar{B}$, it must be the case that all elements of $\bar{A} \cup \bar{B}$ are also elements

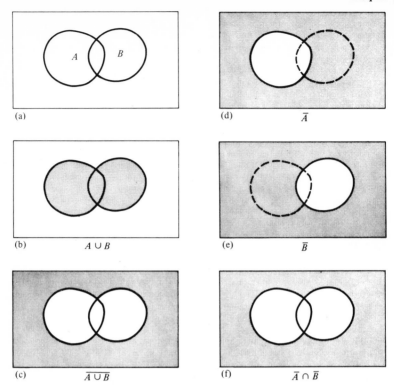

FIGURE 1.1

of $\overline{A \cap B}$. Hence, it follows that $\overline{A} \cup \overline{B} \subset \overline{A \cap B}$. Now let $x \in \overline{A \cap B}$; that is, $x \notin A \cap B$, from which x cannot be in both A and B, and thus $x \notin A$ or $x \notin B$. It then follows that $x \in \overline{A}$ or $x \in \overline{B}$, which is equivalent with $x \in \overline{A} \cup \overline{B}$. Thus, we have $\overline{A \cap B} \subset \overline{A} \cup \overline{B}$. We have shown that an element is in $\overline{A} \cup \overline{B}$ if and only if it is in $\overline{A \cap B}$, and hence we conclude equality of these sets; that is, the two descriptions $\overline{A} \cup \overline{B}$ and $\overline{A \cap B}$ describe the same set.

Remark: It should be noted that Venn diagrams and other geometric devices are useful primarily in gaining insight into the mathematical objects they are supposed to represent. One should not rely in an essential way on these devices in making formal (rigorous) proofs, although their use in an informal manner is quite acceptable and is encouraged.

Power Sets

Given a universe U, it is often desirable to discuss the subsets of U as being elements of some universe. One of the subsets of U is U itself, but as we have remarked, we cannot allow U to be one of its own elements. Thus we find it necessary to consider a second universe in this context.

1.1-8   Definition: Let A be a set. Then $2^A = \{B : B \subset A\}$. The collection 2^A of all subsets of A is called the *power set of A.*

A fact of interest is that if the number of elements in A is n, where n is some natural number, then the number of elements in 2^A is 2^n. The notation we have used to designate the power set was suggested by this fact.

Example: $2^{\{1,2\}} = \{\{1\}, \{2\}, \phi, \{1, 2\}\}$
$\qquad\quad 2^\phi = \{\phi\} \qquad (2^0 = 1)$
$\qquad\quad 2^N$ is a large set!

EXERCISES 1.1

1. Determine which of the following statements are true and which are false.
   a. $3 \in \{2, 3, 4, 3, 1, 5\}$.   b. $\{2\} \in \{2, 3, 4, 5\}$.
   c. $\{3\} \in \{\{2, 3\}, \{5, 6\}, 3\}$.   d. $\{5, 6\} \in \{\{2, 3\}, \{5, 6\}, 3\}$.

2. Let $U = \{1, 2, 3, 4, 5, 6, 7, 8, 9, 10\}$, $A = \{1, 3, 5, 7, 9\}$, $B = \{2, 4, 6, 8, 10\}$ $C = \{1, 3, 4, 6, 7, 9, 10\}$, and $D = \{1, 2, 4, 5, 7, 8, 10\}$. Find each of the following sets:

a. $A \cap B$.	b. $B \cup C$.	c. $C \cap D$.
d. $A \cap C$.	e. $A \cup C$.	f. $B \cap C$.
g. $C \cup D$.	h. $D \cup A$.	i. $A - B$.
j. $(A \cap D) - C$.	k. $(A \cup C) - (A \cap C)$.	l. $U - (A \cap D)$.
m. $\overline{A}$.	n. $\overline{B \cup C}$.	o. $\overline{D \cap C}$.

3. Write a brace description and a list description if possible for the set consisting of:
   a. All numbers larger than 5.
   b. All numbers larger than 7 and less than or equal to 12.
   c. All numbers whose square minus 17 is equal to 36.
   d. All numbers whose square is less than 2.

4. Let $U = R$, $A = \{x : x \geqslant 2 \text{ and } x \leqslant 7\}$, $B = \{x : x \leqslant 5 \text{ and } x > 3\}$, and $C = \{x : x > 0\}$. Are the following true or false?
   a. $A \subset A$.   b. $A \in B$.   c. $B \in A$.
   d. $A \subset B$.   e. $B \subset A$.   f. $B \subset C$.
   g. $A \subset C$ or $C \subset B$.   h. $A \subset C$ and $C \subset B$.

5. Complete each of the following sentences:
   a. If $A \not\subset B$, then for some $x \in A$, x _____.
   b. If $A \subset B$, then for every $x \in A$, x _____.
   c. If every $x \in A$ is also in B, then _____.
   d. If some $x \in A$ is not in B, then _____.
   e. If $x \in A$ and $A \subset B$, then x _____.

6. Let U be R, the real numbers. Let $A = \{x : x \geqslant 3\}$, $B = \{x : x \leqslant 18\}$,

$C = \{x : 3 < x \text{ or } x < -5\}$, and $D = \{x : x > 3 \text{ and } x < 5\}$. Give a brace description for each of the following:

a. $A - B$.
b. $C \cap D$.
c. $A \cup C$.
d. $B \cap C$.
e. $C - B$.
f. $D \cup B$.
g. $\overline{B}$.
h. $\overline{C}$.
i. $\overline{A} \cap B$.

7. Let $U = R$, $A = \{x : x \geqslant 3\}$, $B = \{x : x \geqslant 5\}$, and $C = \{x : x \geqslant 10\}$. Are the following true or false?

a. $A \subset B$.
b. $B \subset A$.
c. $A \subset C$.
d. $\{C\} \subset A$.
e. $B \subset C$.
f. $C \subset B$.
g. $5 \in B$.
h. $5 \in C$.
i. $A \in C$.
j. $C \in A$.
k. $\{10\} \in C$.
l. $C \in 10$.

8. Let $U = R$. Are the following true or false?
   a. $\{x : x \geqslant 5\} \subset \{x : x \geqslant 2\}$.
   b. $\{x : x \geqslant 5 \text{ and } x \leqslant 9\} \subset \{y : y \geqslant 6\}$.
   c. $\{x : x \geqslant 0 \text{ and } x \in Z\} \subset \{x : x \in Q \text{ and } x \geqslant 0\}$.

9. Investigate (prove or disprove):
   a. $A \subset A \cup B$.
   b. $A \cap B \subset A$.
   c. If $A - B = \phi$, then $A = B$.
   d. If $A \cap B = \phi$, then $B \cap \overline{A} = B$.
   e. $\overline{A} - \overline{B} = B - A$.

10. Investigate (prove or disprove):
    a. $A \subset B$ iff $\overline{B} \subset \overline{A}$.
    b. $A = B$ iff $\overline{A} = \overline{B}$.
    c. $A \subset \overline{B}$ iff $B \subset \overline{A}$.
    d. $A \subset B$ and $A = \phi \Rightarrow \overline{B} = \phi$.

11. Draw a Venn diagram for three nonempty sets, A, B, and C so they will have the following properties:
    a. $A \subset B$, $C \subset B$, and $A \cap C = \phi$.
    b. $A \subset C$, $A \not\subset B$, and $B \cap C = \phi$.
    c. $A \subset B$, $C \not\subset B$, $A \cap C \neq \phi$.
    d. $A \subset (B \cap C)$, $B \subset C$, $C \neq B$, and $A \neq C$.

12. Let $A = \{a, b, \{c\}, \{d, e\}, f, g, h\}$. Are the following true or false?
    a. $a \in 2^A$.
    b. $\{a, b\} \in 2^A$.
    c. $\{a, b\} \subset 2^A$.
    d. $\{\{a, b\}, \{f, g\}\} \subset 2^A$.
    e. $\{c\} \in 2^A$.
    f. $\{d, e\} \subset 2^A$.
    g. $\{a, b, c\} \in 2^A$.
    h. $\{\{c\}, \{d, e\}\} \in 2^A$.

13. a. Let $A = \{2, 1, 3\}$. Find all subsets of A including ϕ and A. How many subsets has A?
    b. Let $A = \{1, 2, 3, 4\}$. Find all subsets of A. How many subsets has A?
    c. Let $A = \{1, 2, 3, \ldots, b\}$. Argue that A has 2^n subsets. (HINT: Argue that by adding one element to a collection, the number of subsets is doubled.)

14. What is the difference between ϕ and $\{\phi\}$? (Note that writing *braces* around ϕ is not "making something out of nothing," since ϕ is *not* nothing! It is a set.) Designate each of the following as true or false.
    a. $\{\phi\}$ is empty.
    b. $\phi \in \{\phi\}$.
    c. $\phi \subset \{\phi\}$.
    d. $\phi \in \phi$.
    e. $\phi \subset \phi$.

15. Define $A \triangle B$ (called the *symmetric difference*) as follows:
    $$A \triangle B = (A - B) \cup (B - A).$$ Investigate (prove or disprove):
    a. $A \triangle B = B \triangle A$.
    b. $A \triangle (B \cup C) = (A \triangle B) \cup (A \triangle C)$.
    c. $A \triangle (A \cap B) = A - B$.
    d. $A \triangle (A \cap B) = A \cap \overline{B}$.
    e. $A \triangle (B \cap C) = (A \triangle B) \cap (A \triangle C)$.

1.2 LOGIC: A SUMMARY

In this section we shall review and discuss some terminology and notation associated with mathematical logic. Logic is the major tool of mathematics. We introduce here certain concepts of logic that we use throughout the text. From time to time, we may find it convenient to introduce additional logic and to elaborate on what has been given here.

Formation of Sentences

A mathematical sentence is a phrase that is considered to be either true or false. We do not allow a sentence to be both true and false. A true sentence is said to have truth value T, and a false one, F. We shall occasionally encounter an expression whose truth value cannot be determined due to its incompleteness or incoherence. We shall not call such an expression a sentence. A mathematical system usually involves many sentences. The logic we develop here deals with four ways of constructing new sentences from one or more given sentences. We wish to analyze the use of the words *not, and, or,* and *implies.* We should like to use these words in the construction of new expressions that are sentences in our system. Since this is done by using these words to join two or more sentences into one sentence, they are called *connectives.*

Negation ("Not")

If we consider a sentence "p", we wish to know what truth value to assign to the sentence "not p" (the *negation* of p). We intuitively feel that if "p" is true, then its negation "not p" should be false, and that if "p" is false, then "not p" should be true. Furthermore, our intuition tells us that there are no other possibilities. Let us construct a table (called a truth table) that summarizes this information.

Negation truth table

p	not p
T	F
F	T

In the case of negation, it is fairly easy to see how a truth value should be assigned to the newly constructed sentence, given the truth value of the original sentence. As we shall see later in the case of the connective "implies," this is not always so easy.

Conjunction ("and")

Let us now examine the *connective* "and." We want to decide how to assign a truth value to a new sentence constructed by placing the connective "and" between two given ones. If "p" and "q" are sentences, then the truth value of the new sentence "p and q" will depend on the truth values of "p" and "q." There are four possibilities to consider. Let us list these possibilities, and the truth value assigned to each new sentence, in a truth table.

Conjunction truth table

p	q	p and q
T	T	T
T	F	F
F	T	F
F	F	F

How do you feel about the way we have constructed this table? Does it seem reasonable in the first case that if "p" is true, and if "q" is true, then we should consider "p and q" to be a true sentence?

Example:

$$p = \text{New York is a state}.$$
$$q = \text{The President is a person}.$$

In this case "p" and "q" are each true and the sentence "New York is a state and the President is a person" is also true.

What about the next case? Here we have considered "p" to be true while "q" is false. The contention is that "p and q" is a false sentence.

Question: Would it be appropriate to connect two seemingly unrelated phrases with the word "and"?

Example:

$$p = \text{Wisconsin is a state}.$$
$$q = \text{New York is the capital of Maine}.$$

In this case, the statement "Wisconsin is a state and New York is the capital of Maine" is false.

Exercise: Think of other sentences using "and" that verify the rules of conjunction given in the truth table.

Disjunction ("or")

Next we consider the standard truth table for the connective "or." We leave it for the reader to convince himself that this is the "logical" way to construct this truth table. Notice that when a mathematician uses "or," he does not exclude the possibility of both sentences, being true. This is somewhat in contrast with common usage.

Disjunction truth table

p	q	p or q
T	T	T
T	F	T
F	T	T
F	F	F

Exercise: Think of some sentences using "or" and test your intuition with the table.

Implication ("If, Then")

In ordinary conversation when one uses the expression, "———— implies ————," or the equivalent expression, "if ———— then ————," the sentences being connected usually have a common context. However, we wish to assign a truth value to the sentence, "*p* implies *q*" that depends only on the individual truth values of "*p*" and "*q*" and that is independent of any common or uncommon context. This may seem a bit strange at first, but we should like to be able to combine any two arbitrary sentences using the connective "implies" as we did with "and" and "or." (When we have a sentence "*p* implies *q*," *p* is called the *hypothesis* and *q* the *conclusion*. The sentence "*p* implies *q*" is called an *implication*.)

In some cases, in the assignment of a truth value to a statement of implication, our intuition may fail us. Some expressions seem to make no sense, although the components from which we constructed the implication are perfectly sensible. (By perfectly sensible, we do not mean that the sentence is necessarily true.) For example, consider the statement: "If $5 < 2$, then some dogs have long hair." Thus, if we insist on being able to combine any two arbitrary sentences by implication, then we are forced to have some seemingly nonsense sentences in our system. Let us take the position that we shall allow these statements to be true provided that we are never confronted with phrases that apparently have both truth values.

Let us examine the way in which we intend to use an implication. A consistent mathematical system comprises a large body of true statements. We use our logic to gain knowledge about this collection. If the sentence "*p* implies *q*" is in our collection of truths, and if "*p*" is also in that collection, then we will deduce that "*q*" is among our collection of true sentences. In general then, if a statement "*p*" is not in the collection of truths (that is, if "*p*" is false), then allowing "*p* implies *q*" to be a true sentence can never introduce a contradiction, regardless of the truth value assigned to "*q*." That is, the statement "*p* implies *q*" would never in itself force us either to accept or reject the truth of "*q*." Implications in which the hypothesis is false are said to be *vacuously true*.

Keeping these things in mind, you should be willing to accept the following truth table for the implication connective.

Implication truth table

p	*q*	*p* implies *q*
T	T	T
T	F	F
F	T	T
F	F	T

Exercise: Think of some sentences that use the word "implies" and think about their truth values. Compare your intuition with the truth table.

Alternative Notation

Various notational devices are used to indicate the connectives we have discussed. It is common to negate a sentence by negating the verb of the sentence, often accomplished by drawing a slash through a symbol that acts as the verb in the sentence.

Example: The sentence "$5 = 6$" is negated by either of the following:
   a. Not $(5 = 6)$.
   b. $5 \neq 6$.

Other common expressions that are equivalent to "*p* implies *q*" are:
   a. If *p*, then *q*.
   b. $p \Rightarrow q$ (read "*p* implies *q*").
   c. *p* only if *q*.

A logical connective that is often used is the connective "if." This is related to "implies" in that the sentence "*q* implies *p*" is equivalent to "*p* if *q*." Other sentences that are equivalent to "*p* if *q*" are:
   a. $p \Leftarrow q$.
   b. *p* is implied by *q*.
   c. *p* is necessary for *q*.
The following is a truth table for the connective "if."

p	q	$p \Leftarrow q$
T	T	T
T	F	T
F	T	F
F	F	T

Another connective that is constructed by combining "if" and "implies" (using conjunction) is the connective "if and only if." Other sentences equivalent to "*p* if and only if *q*" are:

  a. $p \Leftrightarrow q$.
  b. *p* iff *q* (we shall use this often so don't forget what it means).
  c. *p* is necessary and sufficient for *q*.

The following is a truth table for "if and only if."

p	q	$p \Leftrightarrow q$
T	T	T
T	F	F
F	T	F
F	F	T

Logical Equivalence

One can construct truth tables for compound sentences by a step-by-step application of the rules discussed above. For example, we include for you to follow, the construction of a truth table for "$(p \Rightarrow q)$ and $(p \Leftarrow q)$."

p	q	$p \Rightarrow q$	$p \Leftarrow q$	$(p \Rightarrow q)$ and $(p \Leftarrow q)$
T	T	T	T	T
T	F	F	T	F
F	T	T	F	F
F	F	T	T	T

Compare this with the truth table for $p \Leftrightarrow q$.

  If two sentences have the same truth table (ignoring any intermediate steps taken in the construction), then the sentences are said to be *logically equivalent*.

  Example: We construct a truth table for "not $(p \Rightarrow q)$."

p	q	$p \Rightarrow q$	not $(p \Rightarrow q)$
T	T	T	F
T	F	F	T
F	T	T	F
F	F	T	F

We then compare it with a table for "p and (not q)."

p	q	not q	p and (not q)
T	T	F	F
T	F	T	T
F	T	F	F
F	F	T	F

We deduce that the sentences "not $(p \Rightarrow q)$" and "p and (not q)" are logically equivalent. Does this equivalence seem reasonable?

Exercise: Construct a truth table for "(not q) implies (not p)." Compare it with the truth table for "p implies q."

Exercise: If p and q are true and s is false, what is the truth value of each of the following?

  a. (Not p) and (not s).
  b. If p then (q or s).
  c. Not not p.
  d. p and q and s.
  e. p or q or (not s).

Vacuous Arguments

Let us demonstrate some of the logic principles discussed above by discussing the proofs of two simple theorems concerning the empty set ϕ.

1.2-1 Theorem: For any set A, $\phi \subset A$.

PROOF: According to the definition, we must show that every element in ϕ is also an element of A, where A is any set whatsoever. Since ϕ has no element, it is true that every element of ϕ is also in A.

This proof may at first seem confusing. The argument uses the fact that a false statement implies any statement. In particular, for any set A,

$$x \in \phi \Rightarrow x \in A$$

is a true implication, since "$x \in \phi$" is a false premise: x cannot be an element of ϕ since ϕ has no elements. Thus, no matter which element x is chosen, it is vacuously true that $x \in \phi \Rightarrow x \in A$.

Contrapositive Arguments

1.2-2   Theorem: $A \subset \phi \Rightarrow A = \phi$.

PROOF: A must be the empty set, for if it were not, A would contain some element. But this element of A cannot also be an element of ϕ since by definition ϕ contains no element. Thus, if A were not the empty set, the premise $A \subset \phi$ wouldn't be true.

Remark: Note that in order to prove this theorem, we are required to prove an implication of the form $p \Rightarrow q$; p denotes the statement "$A \subset \phi$" and q denotes the statement "$A = \phi$." One way to do this would be to start with the statement p and through logic derive statement q, thus deducing $p \Rightarrow q$. The actual proof above succeeds in establishing instead the implication

$$\text{not } q \Rightarrow \text{not } p.$$

This implication is called the *contrapositive* of the original one and is logically equivalent to the former.

It is extremely important that one does not confuse this with

$$q \Rightarrow p,$$

which is called the *converse* of $p \Rightarrow q$.

Remark: An implication is not logically equivalent to its converse.

Quantifiers

You have already seen how we use open sentences to describe sets. An open sentence $p(x)$ takes on a truth value when the name for some element in the universe replaces the variable x. It might be, in some cases, that each substitution gives rise to a true statement. In these cases, the statement "for every x, $p(x)$" is a true sentence. On the other hand, if for some b in the universe $p(b)$ is false, then the statement "for every x, $p(x)$" is false. Thus, a truth value can be assigned to the expression "for every x, $p(x)$" in spite of the "blanks" left by the variable x.

Example: Let $U = \{4, 2, 3\}$ and consider the open sentence "x is a natural number." We notice in this particular case that every element in the universe makes the statement true. That is, "4 is a natural number," "2 is a natural number," and "3 is a natural number" are all true sentences. Therefore, the statement "for every x, x is a natural number" is also true with the understanding that "for every x" means "for every x in the universe U."

We call the expression "for every x" the *universal quantifier*. Other expressions that have the same meaning as "for every" are "for each" and "for all."

We also frequently use the expression "for some x," called the *existential quantifier*.

Example: Let $U = \{1, 2, 3, 4, 5\}$ and let $p(x)$ be the open sentence "$x + 1 \in U$." The sentence "for all x, $x + 1 \in U$" is false, since $5 + 1 \notin U$. However, the sentence "for some x, $x + 1 \in U$" is true.

Note that in each quantifier there is a variable, but in neither case could we use the quantifier itself for an open sentence. Let us now describe how the truth value is determined for sentences involving quantifiers.

1.2-3   Quantification Rule: If $p(x)$ is an open sentence, then the sentence "for every x, $p(x)$" is called a *universal generalization*. If "for every x, $p(x)$" is a true sentence, then it will follow that "$p(a)$" is true, independently of the particular element a in the universe. Conversely, if one can verify that "$p(a)$" is true independently of the particular element a in the universe, then he can conclude that "for every x, $p(x)$" is also a true sentence.

1.2-4   Quantification Rule: If $p(x)$ is an open sentence, then the sentence "for some x, $p(x)$" is called an *existential assertion*. If "for some x, $p(x)$" is a true sentence, then it will follow that for at least one member b of the universe, the sentence "$p(b)$" is true. (There may be more than one such member, or there may be exactly one.) Conversely, if one can verify the existence of some element b in the universe with the property $p(b)$, then he may conclude that "for some x, $p(x)$" is a true sentence.

Example: Let $U = \{1, 2, 3, 4\}$. Then the sentence "for some x, $x + 2 = 4$" is a true sentence. The sentence "for some x, $x + 4 = 3$" is a false sentence.

We are now in a position to make more concise descriptions of ϕ (the empty set) and $\subset$ (the inclusion relation).

1.2-5   Description: For every x, $x \notin \phi$.

1.2-6   Description: $A \subset B$ iff for all x, $x \in A \Rightarrow x \in B$.

Example: Let

$$U = \{1, 2, 3, 4, 5, 6, 7, 8\}, A = \{1, 2, 3\}, \text{ and } B = \{1, 2, 3, 4, 5\}.$$

Then "for all x, if $x \in A$, then $x \in B$" is true since all of the following sentences are true:

$$\text{If } 1 \in A, \text{ then } 1 \in B.$$
$$\text{If } 2 \in A, \text{ then } 2 \in B.$$
$$\text{If } 3 \in A, \text{ then } 3 \in B.$$
$$\text{If } 4 \in A, \text{ then } 4 \in B.$$

If $5 \in A$, then $5 \in B$.
If $6 \in A$, then $6 \in B$.
If $7 \in A$, then $7 \in B$.
If $8 \in A$, then $8 \in B$.

Therefore, $A \subset B$. Notice that some of these sentences are vacuously true (have a false premise). Some of the vacuously true sentences have a true conclusion, while others have a false conclusion.

Example: Let $U = N$, $A = \{4, 7, 5\}$, and $B = \{1, 2, 3, 5, 7, 4\}$. The sentence "for all x, if $x \in A$, then $x \in B$" is true since each of the following is true:

If $1 \in A$, then $1 \in B$.
If $2 \in A$, then $2 \in B$.
If $3 \in A$, then $3 \in B$.
If $4 \in A$, then $4 \in B$.
If $5 \in A$, then $5 \in B$.

.
.
.
.

Even though we cannot list all the statements that must be true in order that this generalization may hold, we do need to know they are true. With our knowledge of the set of natural numbers, we can predict that the complete list contains only true sentences. Therefore, we conclude that the generalization "for any x, if $x \in A$, then $x \in B$" is also true, and thus by definition that $A \subset B$. Notice that it is necessary to check only those sentences in which the hypothesis is true, since any sentence with a false hypothesis is vacuously true.

In order to prove an existential assertion, we need find only one true statement in the list; however, there may be more than one.

Example: Let $U = N$, $A = \{1, 2, 3\}$, and $B = \{2, 3, 6, 8, 10\}$. Then

"for some x, $x \in A$ and $x \in B$"

is a true sentence since "$2 \in A$ and $2 \in B$" is a true sentence; (in addition, "$3 \in A$ and $3 \in B$" is true), although the sentences

$1 \in A$ and $1 \in B$,
$4 \in A$ and $4 \in B$,
$5 \in A$ and $5 \in B$,
$6 \in A$ and $6 \in B$,

.
.
.
.

are all false.

De Morgan's Laws (Again)

It is interesting to note that negation of a statement can be interpreted in terms of complementation of a certain set. Consider for example, an open sentence $p(x)$, where x may vary over some universe U and the set T where

$$T = \{x : p(x) \text{ is true}\}.$$

Any element $b \in A$ that satisfies $p(b)$ is in T, and if not, it is in $\bar{T}$; that is,

$$T = \{x : p(x)\} \qquad \text{if and only if } \bar{T} = \{x : \text{not } p(x)\}.$$

We can use this information formally to deduce De Morgan's laws. Recall Theorem 1.1-7, in which we claim that:

If A and B are subsets of some universe, then (a) $\overline{A \cup B} = \bar{A} \cap \bar{B}$, and (b) $\overline{A \cap B} = \bar{A} \cup \bar{B}$.

We prove this as follows: $A \cup B = \{x : x \in A \text{ or } x \in B\}$ has as its complement

$$
\begin{aligned}
\overline{A \cup B} &= \{x : \text{not } (x \in A \text{ or } x \in B)\}, \\
&= \{x : \text{not } (x \in A) \text{ and not } (x \in B)\}, \\
&= \{x : x \notin A \text{ and } x \notin B\}, \\
&= \{x : x \in \bar{A} \text{ and } x \in \bar{B}\}, \\
&= \bar{A} \cap \bar{B}.
\end{aligned}
$$

Note that the assertion $\overline{A \cup B} = \bar{A} \cap \bar{B}$ rests directly upon the fact that not (p or q) iff not p and not q. This logic analogue of the set theoretic result is also called De Morgan's law.

The proof for the (b) part is analogous, resting directly on the fact that not (p and q) iff (not p or not q), and is omitted.

EXERCISES 1.2

1. a. Consider the expression "not (p or q)" where p and q are sentences. Would the expression be a sentence? Fill in the truth values for the following table:

p	q	(p or q)	not (p or q) :
T	T		
T	F		
F	T		
F	F		

Compare this with a table for "not p and not q." What can you now deduce regarding these two sentences?

b. Make a table for "not (p and q)" and compare it with a table for "not p or not q." Deduce a logical equivalence.

c. Construct a table for "q or not p" and compare it with the "implies" table. What can you now deduce?

d. Construct a table for "p and not q" and compare it with the "p implies q" table. What can you deduce from this? (HINT: Construct a table for "not (p implies q).")

2. Suppose p, q, r, and s are true statements and that t, u, and v are false. Determine the truth value of each of the following sentences:

a. not p.

b. p or r.

c. p and not q.

d. $p \Rightarrow$ not q.

e. $s \Leftarrow t$.

f. v if not r.

g. if not t, then v.

h. u or not t.

i. p and not not s.

j. not p but (not q or r). (Logically, *but* is equivalent to *and*.)

k. r while v and t. (What do you think is meant by *while*?)

3. Let $U = \{1, 2, 3, 4\}$, $A = \{1, 2, 3\}$, and $B = \{1, 2\}$.

a. List all statements that are asserted to be true by the statement "for all x, if $x \in B$, then $x \in A$."

b. List all the statements that are asserted to be true by the statement "for all x, if $x \in A$, then $x \in B$."

c. Is the statement "for all x, $x \in A$" true or false? Why?

4. Decide in each case whether the statement is true or false. Let $U = R$, the reals.

a. For every $x \in R$, $x + 1 > 0$. b. For some $x \in R$, $x + 7 = 0$.

c. For some $x \in N$, $x + \frac{1}{3} > -1$. d. For all $x \in N$, $5 + x > 7$.

e. For all x, if $x \in Q$, then $5x = 7$. f. For some x, if $x \in N$, then $(\frac{1}{3})x \in N$.

g. For all $x > 2$, $x - 1 \geqslant 2$.

5. Let $U = \{1, 2, 3, 4\}$, $A = \{1, 2, 3\}$, and $B = \{1, 2\}$. Determine in each case whether the statement is true or false:

a. For all x, $x \in A$ and $x \in B$. b. For some x, $x \in A$ and $x \in B$.

c. For all x, if $x \in A$, then $x \in B$. d. For all x, if $x \in B$, then $x \in B$.

e. For some x, if $x \in B$, then $x \in A$. f. For any x, $x \in A$ or $x \in B$.

g. For any x, if $x \notin A$, then $x \notin B$. h. If $4 \in B$, then $4 \in A$.

6. Given that the statement "for all x, $x \in A \Rightarrow x \in B$" is true, where the universe is the set $\{1, 2, 3\}$. Of the following sentences, decide which are true, which are false, and which do not have enough information to decide:

a. $(1 \in A \Rightarrow 1 \in B)$ and $(2 \in A \Rightarrow 2 \in B)$ and $(3 \in A \Rightarrow 3 \in B)$.

b. $2 \in A$ or $2 \in B$.

c. $2 \in A$ and $2 \notin B$.

d. $2 \in B$ and $2 \notin A$.

e. $(1 \in A \Rightarrow 1 \in B)$ or $(2 \in A \Rightarrow 2 \in B)$

f. $3 \notin A$ or $3 \in B$.

g. Not $(1 \in A$ and $1 \notin B)$.

7. Let $U = R$, the real numbers. Let $A = \{x : x \geqslant 0$ and $x < 5\}$, and $B = \{x : x \geqslant 2\}$. Answer true, false, or not enough information to decide.

a. $0 \in A$.

b. If $1 \in A$, then $1 \in B$.

c. If $2 \in A$, then $2 \in B$.

d. For some x, $x \in A$ and $x \in B$.

e. For some x, if $x \in A$, then $x \in B$.   f. If $5 \in A$, then $5 \in B$.

g. If $0 \in A$, then $0 \in B$.   h. If $-\frac{1}{2} \in A$, then $-\frac{1}{2} \in B$.

8. Let $U = \{1, 2, 3, 4, 5, 6\}$, $A = \{1, 2, 3\}$, and $B = \{1, 2, 3, 4\}$. Prove that for any x, if $x \in A$, then $x \in B$.

9. Let $U = \{a, b, c\}$, where a, b, and c are all distinct. Let $A = \{a\}$, $B = \{a, b\}$, and $C = \{b, c\}$. Are each of the following true or false?

   a. For all x, if $x \in A$, then $(x \in B$ and $x \in C)$.

   b. For all x, if $x \in A$, then $(x \in B$ or $x \in C)$.

   c. For all x, $x \in B$ or $x \in C$.

   d. For some x, $x \in A$ and $x \in C$.

   e. For some x, $x \in B$ or $x \in C$.

   f. For some x, if $x \in B$, then $x \in A$.

(Explain where and why it would change the answers if we had not indicated specifically that a, b, and c were all distinct.)

10. Let $U = \{a, b, c, d\}$, where a, b, c, and d are not necessarily distinct. Let $A = \{a, b\}$, $B = \{b, c\}$, and $D = \{a, b, d\}$. Answer true, false, or undecidable for the following.

   a. $A \subset B$.   b. $B \subset A$.   c. $B \not\subset A$

   d. $A \subset D$.   e. $D \not\subset B$.

1.3   ORDERED PAIRS, RELATIONS, FUNCTIONS

One of the most important ideas throughout mathematics is that of a function. In order to develop this notion properly, we shall first introduce a more basic class of objects, ordered pairs. It is possible to define an ordered pair in terms of the set ideas introduced in the first section. Such a definition would allow us to avoid the introduction of an additional primitive notion. However, we shall be content here simply to discuss attributes of ordered pairs without a formal introduction. The important fact about ordered pairs is given in the following theorem, which we state without proof:

1.3-1   Theorem: An *ordered pair* (denoted by (x, y), where x and y are elements of a suitable universe) has the following property:

$$(a, b) = (c, d) \qquad \text{if and only if } a = c \text{ and } b = d.$$

Question: What is the difference between the ordered pair (a, b) and the set $\{a, b\}$?

These objects allow us to introduce the idea of order into a system. Indeed, many elaborate mathematical objects can be introduced using the relatively elementary notions of ordered pairs, sets, and equality.

1.3-2   Definition: Let A and B be subsets of a universe. Then

$$A \times B = \{(x, y) : x \in A \text{ and } y \in B\}.$$

1.3-3 **Definition:** Any subset of $A \times B$ is called a *relation in $A \times B$*. If $B = A$, it is often called a *relation in A*.

Example: $\{1, 2\} \times \{2, 3, 4\} = \{(1, 2), (1, 3), (1, 4), (2, 2), (2, 3), (2, 4)\}$.

Example: $\{(1, 2), (5, 4)\}$ is a relation in N (subset of $N \times N$.)

Example: $L = \{(x, y) : x < y,$ where $x \in Z$ and $y \in R\}$ is a relation in $Z \times R$.

Example: Let $A = \{a, b, c\}$ and $B = \{1, 2\}$. Then

$$A \times B = \{(a, 1), (a, 2), (b, 1), (b, 2), (c, 1), (c, 2)\}$$

is a relation in $A \times B$. Some other relations in $A \times B$ are

$$S_1 = \{(a, 2), (b, 1), (b, 2), (c, 1)\}$$

and

$$S_2 = \{(b, 1), (c, 2)\}.$$

Note that in general, $A \times B \neq B \times A$, since in general $(x, y) \neq (y, x)$.

Question: How many relations are there in $A \times B$ of the previous example? (Be sure to consider ϕ and $A \times B$.)

Using sets of ordered pairs in this fashion allows us carefully to describe certain relationships between sets. For example, if we wish to express the fact that in the sets of the above example a is related to 1 and b is related to 2 but no other relationships exist (under the relation in mind), then we could convey this by indicating the set $S = \{(a, 1), (b, 2)\}$.

When discussing relations, it is common to write aTb to mean $(a, b) \in T$. For example, in the ordinary order relation on numbers, we write $2 < 3$ to mean $(2, 3) \in L$, and so forth.

Functions

A *function* is a special type of relation. Functions are used to describe assignments from one set into another (not necessarily different) set. In order to describe a relation in $A \times B$ in which each element of some set S ($S \subset A$) is related to exactly one element in B, we use relations in which each element of S appears exactly once as a first component of an ordered pair.

1.3-4 **Definition:** A *function* in $A \times B$ is a relation $F \subset A \times B$ such that $((a, b) \in F$ and $(a, c) \in F) \Rightarrow b = c$.

Example: S_2 above is a function in $A \times B$, whereas S_1 is not.

It is useful to give names to the sets of first members and second members of the ordered pairs in a function or relation.

1.3-5 **Definition:** Let F be a relation in $A \times B$. Then

$$\mathfrak{D}_F = \{x : (x, b) \in F \text{ for some } b\} \qquad \text{(called the } \textit{domain of F} \text{),}$$
and

$$\mathfrak{R}_F = \{y : (a, y) \in F \text{ for some } a\} \qquad \text{(called the } \textit{range of F} \text{).}$$

Example: Let $A = \{a, 2, 7\}$ and $B = \{4, 7, 9, 10\}$. Then

$$F = \{(a, 4), (2, 4), (7, 9)\}$$

is a function in $A \times B$ with $\mathfrak{D}_F = A$ and $\mathfrak{R}_F = \{4, 9\}$.

Remark: Observe that if $F \subset A \times B$, then $\mathfrak{D}_F \subset A$ and $\mathfrak{R}_F \subset B$.

We continue now with our discussion of functions.

1.3-6   Definition: If F is a function in $A \times B$, and $\mathfrak{D}_F = S$, then we write

$$F : S \rightarrow B.$$

(This symbol is read "F is a function from S into B.")

Example: $G = \{(x, y) : y = x\}$ is a function with domain R. Thus we can write $G : R \rightarrow R$. (What is the range of G?)

Remark: If we write $F : S \rightarrow B$, then $\mathfrak{D}_F = S$ and $\mathfrak{R}_F \subset B$, but it is not necessarily the case that $\mathfrak{R}_F = B$.

1.3-7   Definition: If $F : A \rightarrow B$ and $\mathfrak{R}_F = B$ then F is said to be a function from A *onto* B. We denote this by

$$F : A \xrightarrow[\text{onto}]{} B.$$

Example: The function $G = \{(x, y) : y = x\}$ is onto R (that is, $G : R \xrightarrow[\text{onto}]{} R$). The function $C = \{(x, y) : x = 2\}$ in $R \times R$ has range $\{2\}$, hence C is not from R onto R.

If $(x, y) \in F$, then we write $y = F(x)$ (F evaluated at x). Notice that if $x = y$, then $F(x) = F(y)$ since (x, a), $(y, b) \in F$, and $x = y$ gives (x, a), $(x, b) \in F$, which implies that $a = b$. In fact, the notation $F(x)$ would be illogical if this were not the case. (Why?) The converse of this statement is not true. That is, if $F(x) = F(y)$, then it need not be the case that $x = y$. A function may assign more than one element of its domain to a given member of its range. However, functions that assign no more than one domain element to any range element are of importance so we give special attention to them.

1.3-8   Definition: If $F : A \rightarrow B$, and if

$$F(x) = F(y) \Rightarrow x = y,$$

then F is called a *one to one function* and we write

$$F : A \xrightarrow{1\text{-}1} B.$$

Example: Suppose $U = \{1, 2, 3, 4, 5\}$, and consider the following functions in U.

Let $F = \{(1, 2), (2, 2), (3, 2)\}$. Then F is not 1–1, but

$$F : \{1, 2, 3\} \xrightarrow[\text{onto}]{} \{2\} \, .$$

Let $G = \{(4, 5), (3, 4)\}$. Then G is not onto U, but $G : \{4, 3\} \xrightarrow{\text{1--1}} U.$
Let $H = \{(1, 1), (2, 1), (3, 5)\}$. Then $H : \{1, 2, 3\} \to U$ is neither 1–1 nor onto.
Let $K = \{(x, y) : x = y\} = \{(1, 1), (2, 2), (3, 3), (4, 4), (5, 5)\}$. Then $K : U \xrightarrow[\text{onto}]{\text{1--1}} U.$

This example shows that the concepts of 1–1 and onto are independent: that is, there are functions that are one type and not the other, and functions that are both types, and still others that are neither.

You should observe that a 1–1 and onto function from A into B establishes a pairing of the elements in A with those of B. Such a function is often called a *one-to-one correspondence* between A and B.

We shall have occasion to consider the inverse of a relation. This is the relation formed by interchanging (inverting) the first and second components in all the ordered pairs of the relation.

1.3-9 Definition: The *inverse of a relation* T in $A \times B$ is a relation T^{-1} in $B \times A$ defined by

$$T^{-1} = \{(x, y) : (y, x) \in T\} \, .$$

Example: $\{(1, 2), (3, 4)\}^{-1} = \{(2, 1), (4, 3)\} \, .$

Example: Let f be the function from R to R defined by:

$$\text{For every } x, \, f(x) = 2x + 1 \, .$$

Some particular values of f are

$$f(0) = 1, \quad f(2) = 5, \quad f(3) = 7 \, .$$

We may even compute a formula for f^{-1} in this case by solving the equation $y = 2x + 1$ for x. Thus,

$$\text{for every } y, f^{-1}(y) = \tfrac{1}{2}y - \tfrac{1}{2} \, .$$

Note the particular values of f^{-1}:

$$f^{-1}(1) = 0, \quad f^{-1}(5) = 2, \quad f^{-1}(7) = 3 \, .$$

Exercise: Show in the preceding example that f is a 1–1 function.

Remark: Note that $(T^{-1})^{-1} = T$. Note that the inverse of a function is not necessarily a function. Note that $\mathfrak{D}_{T^{-1}} = \mathfrak{R}_T$ and $\mathfrak{R}_{T^{-1}} = \mathfrak{D}_T$.

We shall now show that under certain circumstances, the inverse of a function is itself a function.

1.3-10   Theorem: If $F : A \xrightarrow[\text{onto}]{1-1} B$, then $F^{-1} : B \xrightarrow[\text{onto}]{1-1} A$.

PROOF: We need to know the following: (1) F^{-1} is a function. (2) $\mathfrak{D}_{F^{-1}} = B$. (3) $\mathfrak{R}_{F^{-1}} = A$. (4) F^{-1} is one-to-one. We show these as follows: (1) $(y, x) \in F^{-1} \Rightarrow (x, y) \in F$, and so if (y, a) and $(y, b) \in F^{-1}$, then (a, y) and $(b, y) \in F$, but since F is a 1-1 function, then $a = b$. (2) This follows since F is onto. (3) This follows since $\mathfrak{D}_F = A$. (4) (y, b), and (z, b) in $F^{-1} \Rightarrow y = z$, since F is a function.

EXERCISES 1.3

1. Let $A = \{3, 4, 5\}$ and $B = \{1, 2, 3\}$. List $A \times B$.

2. Let $T = \{(1, 1), (1, 5), (1, 3), (4, 4), (4, 5)\}$. Find T^{-1}. List the sets $\mathfrak{D}_T$, $\mathfrak{D}_{T^{-1}}$, $\mathfrak{R}_T$, $\mathfrak{R}_{T^{-1}}$.

3. Which of the following relations are functions?

$$T = \{(1, 3), (5, 7), (7, 4), (3, 4)\} .$$
$$P = \{(1, 4), (1, 5), (1, 6), (6, 1)\} .$$

4. List the domain and range of each of the relations in Exercise 7.

5. Consider the following relations in $A \times B$, where

$$A = \{1, 3, 7, 5\} \qquad \text{and} \qquad B = \{2, 4, 6, 8\} ;$$

$R_1 = \{(1, 2), (3, 2), (5, 2), (7, 2)\}$, $R_2 = \{(1, 2), (1, 4), (1, 6), (1, 8)\}$,
   $R_3 = \{(1, 2), (3, 4), (5, 6)\}$, $R_4 = \{(1, 4), (3, 2), (7, 8), (5, 6)\}$.
   a. Which are functions?
   b. Which are functions from A into B?
   c. Which are 1-1?
   d. Which are 1-1 correspondences between A and B?

6. If $F = \{(1, 2), (2, 5), (3, 9), (5, 7)\}$, then F is a function. What is $F(1)$, $F(2)$, $F(3)$, $F(5)$?

7. Consider $f \subset R \times R$ defined by $f(x) = x^2 + 1$ for all $x \in R$. Find (a) $f(2)$; (b) $f(3)$; (c) $f(7) - f(4)$; (d) $f(2 + 3)$; and (e) $f(b + 2)$ for an arbitrary b.

8. Consider $f \subset R \times R$ defined by: for all $x \in R$, $f(x) = 2x - 4$. Find (a) $f(2)$; (b) $f(3)$; (c) $f(2 + 1)$; and (d) $f(2) + f(1)$.

9. Suppose $A = \{a, b, c\}$ and $B = \{1, 2\}$.
   a. How many functions are there in $A \times B$? (Don't forget ϕ.)
   b. How many 1-1 functions are there in $A \times B$?
   c. How many are functions onto B?
   d. How many 1-1 and onto functions from A to B?

10. a. Argue that any function from a nonempty set A into a singleton set B is onto. (A *singleton set* is a set with only one member, such as $\{2\}$.)
    b. When can such a function also be 1-1?

11. If $A \times B = \{(1, 1), (2, 5), (3, 4), (9, 1), (1, 5), (9, 5)\}$, then find A and B. (Double check this. This is a trick question!)

12. a. How many elements are there in $A \times B$ if A contains m elements and B contains n?

     b. How many relations in $A \times B$ are there? (HINT: How many subsets of $A \times B$ are there?)

1.4 ADDITIONAL TOPICS ABOUT FUNCTIONS AND RELATIONS

Binary Operations

There is a particular class of functions known as *binary operations*, which will interest us a great deal when we begin to develop vector systems. You are familiar with the operation of adding (subtracting, multiplying, dividing) two numbers and obtaining a third number. We would like to decide precisely what we mean by such operations and then extend the concept to a more general setting.

The operations we have in mind deal with one set and have the following properties:

1. If a pair of (not necessarily distinct) elements is selected from the set, then the operation assigns the pair to some element of the set.

2. For some operations, the order in the pair is important (for example, in subtraction) while for others it is not (for example, in addition).

We wish to make a definition that will allow addition, subtraction, multiplication, and division (if 0 is excluded) to be binary operations. This definition will also allow us to generalize the underlying ideas involved.

1.4-1 Definition: Let S be a set. Then any function

$$\varphi : S \times S \to S$$

is called a *binary operation* on S.

Usually, if φ is a binary operation on S, and if

$$(a, b) \in \mathfrak{D}_\varphi,$$

then the unique value that φ takes at (a, b) is designated by

$$a \, \varphi \, b.$$

Thus, if $\varphi((a, b)) = c$, then we write $a\varphi b = c$.

Example: The operation "$+$" on N is a binary operation. That is,

$$+ : N \times N \to N.$$

Thus,

$$+((5, 3)) = 8, \qquad +((4, 1)) = 5, \qquad +((1, 4)) = 5,$$

but one usually writes

$$5 + 3 = 8, \qquad 4 + 1 = 5, \qquad 1 + 4 = 5.$$

Example: The operation "$-$" on Z is a binary operation. Thus,

$$-((5, 3)) = 2, \qquad -((4, 1)) = 3, \qquad -((1, 4)) = -3,$$

which is usually written

$$5 - 3 = 2, \qquad 4 - 1 = 3, \qquad 1 - 4 = -3.$$

Example: Let $S = \{a, b\}$ and * be defined by

$$a*a = a, \qquad a*b = b, \qquad b*a = a, \qquad b*b = b.$$

The ordered pairs in * are given in the list

$$* = \{((a, a)a), ((a, b), b), ((b, a), a), ((b, b), b)\} .$$

(On looking at a binary operation as a set of ordered pairs, we see that the simpler notation is desirable.)

It is sometimes of interest to determine whether a subset of a binary operation is itself a binary operation (on a smaller set.)

1.4-2   Definition: If $\varphi : S \times S \to S$, and $A \subset S$, we say that the set A is *closed* under φ, provided that φ maps points in $A \times A$ to images in A. The function φ' obtained by restricting the domain of φ to $A \times A$ is called the *restriction* of φ to A.

Example: Let $S = \{a, b, c\}$ (all distinct). Let * be an operation on S defined by the following table. (That is, to find $x*y$, one looks at the entry in the row labeled x and the column labeled y.)

*	a	b	c
a	b	a	c
b	a	b	b
c	c	a	a

Let *' be * *restricted* to $\{a, b\}$. That is, use the same values as before, but consider only elements in the smaller set. Then *' is given by the following table.

*'	a	b
a	b	a
b	a	b

Now *' is a binary operation on $\{a, b\}$ since *' is a function from $\{a, b\} \times \{a, b\} \to \{a, b\}$. Hence, $\{a, b\}$ is closed under *. Let *'' be * restricted to $\{a, c\}$. Then *'' is given by the following table.

*''	a	c
a	b	c
c	c	a

Clearly $\{a, c\}$ is not closed under *.

Question: What about closure of $\{b, c\}$ under *?

Example: Addition is a binary operation on Z. If we select only elements in $N \subset Z$ and add them, we always get sums in N. Thus, the subset N is closed under addition.

Example: Subtraction is a binary operation on Z, but if we select any two elements from $N \subset Z$, we cannot be certain that the difference is in N. Thus, N is not closed under subtraction.

Binary Operations with Special Properties

There are in general many binary operations on any given set. Some special properties of some binary operations make them more interesting and more useful than other operations. We list here two such special properties.

1.4-3   Definition: Let φ be a binary operation on S. If

for all $x \in S$ and   for all $y \in S$, $x \varphi y = y \varphi x$,

then we say φ is a *commutative operation*. If

for all $x, y, z \in S$, $x \varphi (y \varphi z) = (x \varphi y) \varphi z$,

then we say that φ is an *associative operation*.

Exercise: Verify that addition on Z is both commutative and associative whereas subtraction is neither.

Example: The operation * on $\{a, b, c\}$ given in the following table is commutative but not associative.

*	a	b	c
a	a	b	b
b	b	a	c
c	b	c	a

Note that $(a*b)*c = b*c = c$, but $a*(b*c) = a*c = b$.

Composition of Relations

Recall that a relation in $A \times B$ "relates" A and B by "connecting" or pairing some of their respective elements. Consider that a set A is related to B by a relation S and that B is in turn related to a set C by a relation T.

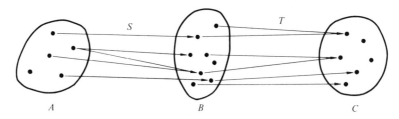

FIGURE 1.2

The diagram (Figure 1.2) suggests that in a very natural way a relation is induced between A and C. If there is a path from an element in A to an element of C, then these elements may be taken to be related. The following definition makes this idea precise.

1.4-4 Definition: If $S \subset A \times B$ and $T \subset B \times C$, then $T \circ S \subset A \times C$ is given by

$$T \circ S = \{(x, z) : (x, y) \in S \quad \text{and} \quad (y, z) \in T \text{ for some } y \in B\}.$$

("$T \circ S$" is read "T composed with S" or "S followed by T.")

Example: Let $A = \{a, b, c\}$, $B = \{1, 2, 3\}$, $C = \{5, 10, 15\}$, and

$$S = \{(a, 1), (a, 2), (b, 3)\} \quad \text{and} \quad T = \{(1, 5), (1, 10), (3, 10)\}.$$

Then $T \circ S = \{(a, 5), (a, 10), (b, 10)\}$.

Composition of Functions

Since a function is a relation, composition of functions is automatically defined. It is not difficult to show that the collection of functions is closed under composition. That is, if f and g are functions, then $f \circ g$ is a function.

It is common in dealing with composition of functions to express the functional value of $f \circ g$ by $f(g(x))$ rather than by $f \circ g(x)$. This is natural, since in order to determine $f \circ g(x)$, one first finds the value $y = g(x)$ and then evaluates f at y. That is, $f \circ g(x) = f(y)$, where $y = g(x)$. Notice, that $f \circ g(x) = f(g(x))$ is defined only if $g(x)$ lies in the domain of f.

Example: Consider functions f and g in $R \times R$ defined by

$$f(x) = 2x + 1 \quad \text{and} \quad g(x) = x^2 - 1.$$

Now

$$f(2) = 5 \quad \text{and} \quad g(5) = 24,$$

hence

$$g \circ f(2) = g(f(2)) = g(5) = 24.$$

Example: Give formulas that describe $g \circ f(x)$ and $f \circ g(x)$ where $f(x) = 2x + 1$ and $g(x) = x^2 - 1$. We solve this as follows. Given an arbitrary $a \in R$, we trace a through f and g:

$$g \circ f(a) = g(f(a)) = g(2a + 1) = (2a + 1)^2 - 1 = 4a^2 + 4a.$$

Hence,

$$\text{for each } x, \, g \circ f(x) = g(f(x)) = 4x^2 + 4x.$$

Similarly, if $b \in R$, then

$$f \circ g(b) = f(g(b)) = f(b^2 - 1) = 2(b^2 - 1) + 1 = 2b^2 - 1.$$

Hence

$$f \circ g(x) = f(g(x)) = 2x^2 - 1 \quad \text{for all } x \in R.$$

EXERCISES 1.4

1. Let $S = \{a, b, c\}$ and define the binary operation $\oplus$ on S by the following table.

$\oplus$	a	b	c
a	a	b	a
b	b	a	c
c	a	c	a

  a. Determine:

    $a \oplus b$ $b \oplus c$ $\oplus((b, b))$

    $c \oplus c$ $\oplus((a, c))$ $\oplus = \{\text{———}\}$

  b. Is $\oplus$ a commutative operation? Is $\oplus$ an associative operation?

  c. Make a table for $\oplus$ restricted to $\{a, b\}$. Is $\{a, b\}$ closed under $\oplus$?

2. Let $S = \{a, b\}$ and define $*$ by

$$a*b = a, \quad a*a = a, \quad b*a = a, \quad b*b = b.$$

  a. Make a table for $*$.   b. Is $*$ commutative or associative?

3. Define $*$ on $\{A, B\}$ by

$*$	A	B
A	B	B
B	A	A

  a. Show that $*$ is neither associative nor commutative.

  b. Show that no nonempty proper subset of $\{A, B\}$ is closed under $*$.

4. a. Is Z closed under division? b. Is Q closed under division?

5. Let $Z_5 = \{0, 1, 2, 3, 4\}$. Define $+$ by the following table.

+	0	1	2	3	4
0	0	1	2	3	4
1	1	2	3	4	0
2	2	3	4	0	1
3	3	4	0	1	2
4	4	0	1	2	3

    a. Is $+$ associative or commutative?

    b. Does Z_5 have any subsets that are closed under $+$?

6. Let $T = \{(1, 2), (5, 7), (5, 5), (6, 7), (7, 9)\}$ and $S = \{(9, 5), (6, 3), (7, 7), (4, 1)\}$, then give a list description of: (a) $T \circ S$; (b) $S \circ T$.

7. If T and S are defined by: aTb, $1Ty$, $5Ta$, $7Tb$, $7T9$, and $5Sa$, $bS7$, $bS48$, $9S9$, then list the ordered pairs in $S \circ T$ and $T \circ S$.

8. Let $f : R \to R$ and $g : R \to R$ be defined by $f(x) = 6x + 3$, and $g(x) = 9x^2 + 1$. Determine (a) $f \circ g(x)$; (b) $g \circ f(x)$.

9. Determine a formula for $f \circ g(x)$ and $g \circ f(x)$, where

    a. $f(x) = 6x + 2$, and $g(x) = 3x^2 + x + 1$;

    b. $f(x) = 4 - x^2$, and $g(x) = 2x + 2$;

    c. $f(x) = x$, and $g(x) = 7x^2 - 4$;

    d. $f(x) = 3 + x^3$, and $g(x) = 2x$.

10. Let $y = f(x)$ and $z = g(x)$. Determine $f \circ g(3)$ and $g \circ f(3)$, where

    a. $y = 7x - 3$, and $z = x^2 + 2$;   b. $y = 6x^2$, and $z = x + 1$;

    c. $y = 2 - 3x^2$, and $z = 4x^2 - 1$;   d. $y = 4$, and $z = 7x$.

11. Show that if f and g are 1–1 functions, then (a) $f \circ g$ is 1–1, and (b) $(f \circ g)^{-1} = g^{-1} \circ f^{-1}$.

1.5 PARTITIONS AND EQUIVALENCE RELATIONS

Many mathematical ideas concerning a universe U can be examined by looking at the universes 2^U (the collection of all subsets of U) and $2^{U \times U}$ (the collection of all relations on U). In this section we shall develop an important and useful result that makes a direct connection between these two universes. That is, we shall show that a certain fundamental structural concept can be studied by either looking at 2^U or $2^{U \times U}$, whichever appears convenient in the specific problem under examination.

Partitions

We have defined an operation (complementation) that associates with a subset A of U another subset $\bar{A}$ of U with the following properties: $A \cap \bar{A} =$

ϕ, and $A \cup \bar{A} = U$. Thus, A and $\bar{A}$ constitute a nonoverlapping division of U into two parts. This type of division of U into disjoint subsets can be generalized to a division into various numbers of subsets. Such a division is called a *partition*.

1.5-1 Definition: A class $\mathcal{P}$ of nonempty sets is called a *partition* of the set U provided that:

  i. for each $A \in \mathcal{P}$, $A \subset U$;
 ii. if A and B are in $\mathcal{P}$ and $A \neq B$, then $A \cap B = \phi$; and
iii. $\{x : x \in A \text{ for some } A \in \mathcal{P}\} = U$.

Example: Let $U = \{1, 5, 6, 11\}$. Then $\{\{1\}, \{5\}, \{6, 11\}\}$ is a partition of U. Also, $\{\{1, 5, 6\}, \{11\}\}$ is a partition of U. But $\{\{1, 5\}, \{6\}\}$ is not, since $\{1, 5\} \cup \{6\} \neq U$. Also, $\{\{1, 5\}, \{6\}, \{6, 11\}\}$ is not, since $\{6\} \cap \{6, 11\} \neq \phi$.

Example: Let $S = \{a, b, c\}$, where a, b, and c are all distinct. Then $\{\{a\}, \{b\}, \{c\}\}$ is a partition of S. Also $\{\{a, b, c\}\}$ is a partition. But $\{\{a, b\}, \{b\}, \{b, c\}, \{a\}\}$ is not. Why?

Example: In general, there are many distinct partitions of a nonempty set U. For example, if $U = \{0, 1, 2\}$, then all possible partitions of U are: (a) $\{U\}$; (b) $\{\{0\}, \{1\}, \{2\}\}$; (c) $\{\{0\}, \{1, 2\}\}$; (d) $\{\{1\}, \{0, 2\}\}$; (e) $\{\{2\}, \{1, 0\}\}$.

Equivalence Relations

We now define a special kind of relation, and show that any such relation is very closely associated with a partition of the universal set. This is an important fundamental concept that is of great use in mathematics.

1.5-2 Definition: A relation E in $U \times U$ is an *equivalence relation* provided that the ordered pairs in E satisfy the following three conditions:

1. (Reflexive property)   for all $a \in U$, $(a, a) \in E$.
2. (Symmetric property) $(a, b) \in E \Rightarrow (b, a) \in E$.
3. (Transitive property) $(a, b) \in E$ and $(b, c) \in E \Rightarrow (a, c) \in E$.

Remark: Using the alternative notation of relations, the above definition can be stated as: A relation $\sim$ defined on U is an *equivalence relation*, provided that

  a. For all $a \in U$, $a \sim a$ (read "a is equivalent with a").
  b. $a \sim b \Rightarrow b \sim a$.
  c. $a \sim b$ and $b \sim c \Rightarrow a \sim c$.

Note that if $\sim$ is interpreted as the ordinary equals sign, then the three properties of an equivalence relation are satisfied. Thus, $\{(a, b) : a = b\}$ is an equivalence relation. Historically, it was an attempt to examine the abstract properties of equality that led to the notion of an equivalence relation.

Example: Let $U = \{a, b, c\}$, where a, b, and c are all distinct. Then $\sim = \{(a, a), (a, b), (b, a), (b, b), (c, c)\}$ is an equivalence relation on U (that is, $a \sim a$, $a \sim b$, $b \sim a$, $b \sim b$, $c \sim c$).

Example: Let S be the set of all lines in the plane, and define two lines m and t to be equivalent ($m \sim t$) iff they are parallel. Then it is easily seen that $\sim$ is an equivalence relation provided that we use the convention that a line is parallel to itself.

Example: Define a relation K in $Z \times Z$ by $(a, b) \in K$ iff $a - b$ is a multiple of 3 (that is, $(a, b) \in K$ iff $a - b = 3n$ for some $n \in Z$). Thus $(1, 4)$, $(-7, -13)$, $(42, 0)$ are members of K. We prove that K is an equivalence relation by showing that it is reflexive, symmetric, and transitive, as follows.

Reflexive condition: For any integer $m \in Z$, we have $m - m = 0 \cdot 3$, so that $m - m$ is a multiple of 3 and so (by definition), $(m, m) \in K$. Thus, we have shown that $m \in Z \Rightarrow (m, m) \in K$.

Symmetric condition: Suppose $(a, b) \in K$. Then $a - b = n \cdot 3$ for some n. But then $b - a = -(a - b) = (-n) \cdot 3$, so $b - a$ is also a multiple of 3, and $(b, a) \in K$. Thus, $(a, b) \in K \Rightarrow (b, a) \in K$.

Transitive condition: Suppose $(a, b) \in K$ and $(b, c) \in K$. Then $a - b = n \cdot 3$ and $b - c = m \cdot 3$. This implies in turn that $a - c = (a - b) + (b - c) = n \cdot 3 + m \cdot 3 = (n + m) \cdot 3$, so that $a - c$ is a multiple of 3, and $(a, c) \in K$. Thus, $(a, b) \in K$ and $(b, c) \in K \Rightarrow (a, c) \in K$.

Example: Let U be the set of points in the plane, and define the equivalence of any two points p and q as follows: $p \sim q$ iff p and q are at equal distances from the origin. It is easy to see that this relation satisfies the three conditions of an equivalence relation.

Exercise: Argue that congruence (and similarity) of triangles is an equivalence relation.

Equivalence Classes

The important aspect of an equivalence relation on U is that it naturally gives rise to a collection of subsets of U that forms a partition of U.

1.5-3   Definition: Let $\sim$ denote an equivalence relation in $U \times U$. Then for any element $a \in U$, the *equivalence class* C_a (with respect to $\sim$) is the set defined by

$$C_a = \{x \in U : x \sim a\}.$$

Remark: Note that $C_a \subset U$, and that the reflexive property ensures that $a \in C_a$. Thus, we know that for each element a, C_a is a nonempty subset of U.

Example: Let $U = \{a, b, d\}$ where a, b, and d are all distinct. Let $\sim$ be given by $a \sim b$, $b \sim a$, $a \sim a$, $b \sim b$, $d \sim d$. Then

$$C_a = \{a, b\}, \qquad C_b = \{b, a\}, \qquad C_d = \{d\}.$$

Notice that $C_a = C_b$ and that $\{C_a, C_d\}$ is a partition of U.

Example: Let $S = \{1, 2, 3, 4\}$ and let $\sim$ be given by $1 \sim 1$, $2 \sim 2$, $3 \sim 3$, $4 \sim 4$, $1 \sim 2$, $2 \sim 1$, $3 \sim 4$, $4 \sim 3$. Then

$$C_1 = \{1, 2\}, \qquad C_2 = \{2, 1\}, \qquad C_3 = \{3, 4\}, \qquad C_4 = \{4, 3\}.$$

Notice that the collection of equivalence classes forms a partition of S. Also note that $C_1 = C_2$ and that $C_3 = C_4$, which was a result of the fact $1 \sim 2$ and $3 \sim 4$.

Example: For the equivalence relation of a previous example in which parallel lines are equivalent, the equivalence classes are sets of parallel lines (sometimes called *families* of lines). To be more precise, suppose α denotes the line in the plane described by the equation $y = 0$. Then $C_\alpha = \{h : h$ is a horizontal line in the plane$\}$. Note that in this case there are infinitely many distinct equivalence classes, and that each equivalence class in turn contains infinitely many lines.

The fundamental connection between partitions and equivalence relations is given in the following theorem, which we state without proof.

1.5-4 Theorem: For any partition $\mathcal{P}$ of U, there is an equivalence relation $\sim$ such that the class of distinct equivalence classes with respect to $\sim$ is the partition $\mathcal{P}$. Further, this establishes a one–one correspondence between partitions and equivalence relations.

Example: Let $S = \{0, 1, 2\}$, and $0 \sim 0$, $1 \sim 1$, $2 \sim 2$, $0 \sim 1$, $1 \sim 0$. Then $\mathcal{P} = \{\{0, 1\}, \{1, 0\}, \{2\}\} = \{\{0, 1\}, \{2\}\}$ is the corresponding partition.

Example: Let $U = \{1, 2, 3, 4, 5\}$ and let $\mathcal{P} = \{\{1\}, \{2, 3\}, \{4, 5\}\}$. Then $\{(1, 1), (2, 2), (3, 3), (4, 4), (5, 5), (2, 3), (3, 2), (4, 5), (5, 4)\}$ is the corresponding equivalence relation.

Example: Consider the equivalence relation on Z defined by

$$a \sim b \Leftrightarrow a - b = 3n \qquad \text{for some } n \in Z.$$

There are exactly three distinct equivalence classes, which can be represented by C_0, C_1, C_2. These classes can be described as follows:

$$C_0 = \{\ldots, -6, -3, 0, 3, 6, 9, \ldots\} = \{x : x = 3n, \text{ where } n \in \mathbf{Z}\},$$
$$C_1 = \{\ldots, -5, -2, 1, 4, 7, \ldots\} = \{x : x = 3n + 1, \text{ where } n \in \mathbf{Z}\},$$
$$C_2 = \{\ldots, -4, -1, 2, 5, 8, \ldots\} = \{x : x = 3n + 2, \text{ where } n \in \mathbf{Z}\}.$$

The collection of subsets of $\mathbf{Z}$, $\{C_0, C_1, C_2\}$, partitions $\mathbf{Z}$ into three sets. Notice that the numbers in each class all leave the same remainder when divided by 3.

Remark: The preceding theorem shows, among other things, that equivalence relations are quite plentiful if U has many elements. For example, if U has only 3 distinct elements, there are 5 possible distinct partitions of U. Thus, there are exactly 5 distinct equivalence relations that can be defined in $U \times U$. Note that the number of ways in which U can be partitioned increases rapidly as the number of elements in U increases. For example, if U contains 4 elements, there are 15 ways to partition U and hence 15 distinct equivalence relations in $U \times U$.

EXERCISES 1.5

1. a. Determine all possible partitions of the set $\{0, 1\}$ and give the corresponding equivalence relations induced by the partitions.
   b. Do the same for $\{a, b, c\}$, where a, b, and c are all distinct.

2. Prove that if E is an equivalence relation in $U \times U$, then $\mathfrak{D}_E = \mathfrak{R}_E = U$.

3. Determine the equivalence classes (i.e., describe the partition) induced on Z by the relation $\sim$, where $x \sim y \Rightarrow x - y = 5n$ for some $n \in Z$.

4. List the ordered pairs in the equivalence relation induced by the following partition of $\{0, 1, 2, 3\}$: (a) $\{\{0, 1\}, \{2\}, \{3\}\}$; (b) $\{\{1\}, \{0, 2, 3\}\}$.

5. Give the partition induced by the equivalence relation E on $\{0, 1, 2, 3\}$, where

$$E = \{(0, 0), (1, 1), (2, 2), (3, 3), (0, 1), (1, 0)\} \,.$$

6. a. Construct the "smallest" equivalence relation on $\{2, 4, 9\}$ that contains at least the ordered pair $(2, 4)$.
   b. Construct the corresponding partition.

7. Suppose U is the Euclidean plane and we define two points on this plane to be equivalent iff they are the same distance from a given point P.
   a. Argue that this is an equivalence relation.
   b. Determine the equivalence classes of this relation.
   c. Argue that the set of these equivalence classes forms a partition of U.

8. For the given set and relation, determine whether an equivalence relation is defined.
   a. U is the set of all people in the world today; $a \sim b$ iff a and b have an ancestor in common.
   b. U is the set of all people in the world today, $a \sim b$ iff a lives within 100 miles of b.
   c. U is the set of all people in the world today; $a \sim b$ iff a and b have the same father.
   d. U is the set R; $a \sim b$ iff $a = \pm b$ (i.e., $a = b$ or $a = -b$.)
   e. U is the set Z; $a \sim b$ iff both $a < b$ and $b < a$.
   f. U is the set of all people in the world; $a \sim b$ iff a and b live in the same house.

9. Interpret a partition of U in terms of Venn diagrams.

10. How many distinct partitions are there of a set U containing five elements?

11. Show that $A \subset U, B \subset U \Rightarrow \mathcal{P}$ is a partition of U, where $\mathcal{P} = \{\overline{A \cup B}, A - B$
    $A \cap B, B - A\}$. Assume that these four subsets of U are nonempty.

12. Prove or disprove this statement: The composition of two equivalence relations S and T is an equivalence relation iff $S \circ T = T \circ S$.

1.6 THE REAL NUMBER SYSTEM AND SOME SPECIAL SUBSETS

We do not attempt here a thorough exploration of the properties of the real number system. Since most of the mathematics taught in elementary and early secondary school deals with properties and applications of real numbers, we assume the student has a working knowledge of this number system. We do however wish to state explicitly the basic properties of the real numbers and point out their relationship with familiar geometrical interpretations.

Algebraic Properties

The algebraic properties of the real number system **R** can be summarized by stating that **R** is a *field*. That is, **R** along with the two operations $+$ and $\cdot$ satisfy the following properties.

1.6-1 The Field Properties:

1. For all x, y, and z, $(x + y) + z = x + (y + z)$ and $(x \cdot y) \cdot z = x \cdot (y \cdot z)$.

    (The associative laws)

2. For all x and y, $x + y = y + x$ and $x \cdot y = y \cdot x$.

    (The commutative laws)

3. There is a 0 such that, for all x, $x + 0 = x$ and there is a 1 such that, for all x, $x \cdot 1 = x$.

    (The identity laws)

4. For each x, there is some $(-x)$ such that $x + (-x) = 0$ and for each $x \neq 0$, there is some (x^{-1}), such that $x \cdot x^{-1} = 1$.

    (The inverse laws)

5. For all x, y, and z, $x \cdot (y + z) = x \cdot y + x \cdot z$.

    (The distributive laws)

6. $1 \neq 0$.

The multiplicative operation, $\cdot$, is usually denoted merely by juxtaposition, except in cases where this would be confusing. The multiplicative inverse of a given nonzero number x is as often denoted by $1/x$ as by x^{-1}. The operation of subtraction is defined by $x - y = x + (-y)$, and the operation of division is defined by $x/y = x \div y = x(y^{-1})$. All of the familiar rules for handling fractions, solving equations, and simplifying expressions involving variables that are taught in elementary mathematics are logical consequences of these axioms and notational devices.

Example:

$$\tfrac{3}{11} + \tfrac{7}{11} = 3 \cdot (\tfrac{1}{11}) + 7 \cdot (\tfrac{1}{11}) \qquad \text{Definition of division}$$
$$= (\tfrac{1}{11}) \cdot 3 + (\tfrac{1}{11}) \cdot 7 \qquad \text{Commutative law for} \cdot$$
$$= (\tfrac{1}{11})(3 + 7) \qquad \text{Distributive law}$$
$$= (\tfrac{1}{11}) \cdot 10 \qquad \text{Addition of integers}$$
$$= 10 \cdot (\tfrac{1}{11}) \qquad \text{Commutative law for} \cdot$$
$$= \tfrac{10}{11} \qquad \text{Definition of division}.$$

The student undoubtedly has a sizeable knowledge of the algebraic results that follow from these rules. Also, he probably knows very little else regarding algebraic structure. This is not intended to deemphasize the knowledge gained in previous courses, but rather to emphasize the usefulness of the field properties. There are many important and useful fields other than **R**, and one might waste a great deal of time, if, on encountering such a field, he were not aware that he already knows a great deal about the system through the algebra governing the system (the field structure and its consequences).

Example: The set **Q** of rational numbers forms a field under ordinary addition and multiplication. In fact, the field structure was originally studied because the rational number system enjoys these properties.

Exercise: Determine which of the field properties are enjoyed by the integers **Z**.

Order Properties

In addition to the algebraic operations $+$ and $\cdot$, the real number system comes equipped with an order relation, $<$, which has the following properties and conventions.

1.6-2 Properties of the order relation $<$:

1. Exactly one of the following holds for any numbers x and y: $x < y$, $x = y$, $y < x$. (The trichotomy law)
2. If $x < y$ and $y < z$, then $x < z$. (The transitive law)
3. If $a < b$, then $a + x < b + x$, for any x.
4. If $a < b$, and $x > 0$, then $ax < bx$.
5. If $a < b$, and $x < 0$, then $ax > bx$.
6. If $a < b$ and $c < d$, where $a > 0$ and $d > 0$, then $ac < bd$.

The student is urged to remember these results. There are many other simple results that are immediate consequences of these properties, and any time a question arises concerning the manipulation of inequalities, one should return to these basic facts.

Remark: In addition to the convention that "$a > b$" means "$b < a$," we make use of the following conventions:

a. "$a \leqslant b$" means "$a < b$ or $a = b$." (Similarly for $a \geqslant b$.)

b. "$a < b < c$" means "$a < b$ and $b < c$." (This symbol indicates the simultaneous satisfaction of two inequalities.) Similar conventions hold for symbols of the form "$a \leqslant b \leqslant c$," "$a > b > c$," and so forth. Note that the symbols "$a < b > c$" and "$a > b < c$" are left undefined.

Geometric Interpretations and the Absolute Value Function

The ordering of **R** allows one to think of the numbers as lying in some sort of line. It is impossible, however, to determine the "length" of the line, or whether it is "straight" or "curved." Indeed, it is impossible even to determine what numbers *are*. However, the familiar properties of the order relation $<$ give us the intuitive feeling that they are "lined up."

In the next section we shall elaborate on the connection between geometry and certain geometric notions regarding the real numbers. We conclude the present section with a discussion of the *distance* between real numbers, and associated subsets of **R**. We first need to define the *absolute value* function.

1.6-3   Definition: If $x \in \mathbf{R}$, then $|x| = \begin{cases} x & \text{if } x \geqslant 0 \\ -x & \text{if } x < 0. \end{cases}$ ($|x|$ is called the *absolute value* of x.)

Example: $|2| = 2, |3| = 3, |-4| = -(-4) = 4, |-\pi| = -(-\pi) = \pi$.

Question: Why can't we say that $|-a| = a$?

Exercise: Verify that $|x| < b$ if and only if $-b < x < b$.

If we interpret **R** as the familiar line of numbers (small numbers on the left of zero and large ones on the right), then $|a - b|$ gives a measure of the *distance* from a to b. (See Figure 1.3.)

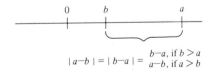

$$|a-b| = |b-a| = \begin{array}{l} b-a, \text{ if } b > a \\ a-b, \text{ if } a > b \end{array}$$

FIGURE 1.3

We will shortly associate this kind of distance between numbers with the measurement of lengths of line segments. In order to do this, we must first discuss coordinates and coordinatizations.

Intervals

We wish to define a collection of special subsets of **R**, called *intervals*. These sets arise often in mathematical discussions, so they have been given the standard names as follows.

1.6-4 Definition: Let a and b be real numbers. Then:

$$
\begin{aligned}
(a, b) &= \{x \in \mathbf{R} : a < x < b\} && \text{(an open interval).}\\
(a, b] &= \{x \in \mathbf{R} : a < x \leqslant b\} && \text{(a half open interval).}\\
[a, b) &= \{x : a \leqslant x < b\} && \text{(a half open interval).}\\
[a, b] &= \{x : a \leqslant x \leqslant b\} && \text{(a closed interval).}\\
(a, \infty) &= \{x : a < x\} && \text{(an open half-line).}\\
[a, \infty) &= \{x : a \leqslant x\} && \text{(a closed half-line).}\\
(-\infty, a) &= \{x : x < a\} && \text{(an open half-line).}\\
(-\infty, a] &= \{x : x \leqslant a\} && \text{(a closed half-line).}
\end{aligned}
$$

Remark: Note that the interval $[a, b] = \phi$ if $b < a$. Other similar situations also occur. Also, ∞ and $-\infty$ are not numbers, but are symbols which indicate that the set has no corresponding endpoint. CAUTION: The symbol (a, b) for an interval should not be confused with an ordered pair!

It is interesting to determine the set that results when every element in a given interval is multiplied by or added to a given fixed number.

Example: Consider the interval $[3, 5]$. Note that

$$x \in [3, 5] \Leftrightarrow 3 \leqslant x \leqslant 5 \Leftrightarrow 3 + 2 \leqslant x + 2 \leqslant 5 + 2 \Leftrightarrow 5 \leqslant x + 2 \leqslant 7;$$

or equivalently

$$x + 2 \in [5, 7].$$

Thus, if we add 2 to every member in $[3, 5]$ we obtain the interval $[5, 7]$.

Example: If we multiply every member of $[3, 5]$ by 2 we obtain $[6, 10]$ since

$$3 \leqslant x \leqslant 5 \Leftrightarrow 6 \leqslant 2x \leqslant 10.$$

Interval notation can be used to express various inequalities.

Example:

$$5 < 3x - 1 \leqslant 8 \Leftrightarrow 6 < 3x \leqslant 9 \Leftrightarrow 2 < x \leqslant 3.$$

Thus, we see that $5 < 3x - 1 \leqslant 8$ is equivalent with $x \in (2, 3]$.

Example: Let us give an interval description of the numbers that satisfy

$$|2x - 1| \leqslant 2.$$

Note first that for any y, $|y| \leqslant 2$ is equivalent with $-2 \leqslant y \leqslant 2$. That is, in this case, $-2 \leqslant 2x - 1 \leqslant 2$, which is equivalent with

$$-(\tfrac{1}{2}) \leqslant x \leqslant (\tfrac{3}{2}) \qquad \text{or} \qquad x \in [-\tfrac{1}{2}, \tfrac{3}{2}].$$

Example:

$$|x| > 2 \Leftrightarrow x > 2 \text{ or } -x > 2 \Leftrightarrow x \in (-\infty, -2) \cup (2, \infty).$$

It is common to discuss the *length of an interval*. This is related to the idea of the distance between two numbers.

1.6-5   Definition: Let $a < b$. Then the *length* of any of the intervals (a, b), $(a, b]$, $[a, b)$, and $[a, b]$, is $b - a$.

Example: The length of $[-2, 7)$ is 9. If every $x \in [-2, 7)$ is multiplied by 3, then the resulting interval $[-6, 21)$ has length $27 = 9 \cdot 3$. If every $x \in [-2, 7)$ is increased by 2 (that is, has 2 added to it), the resulting interval $[0, 9)$ has the same length as the original.

EXERCISES 1.6

1. Simplify each of the following, using only the field properties and notational conventions.

   a. $\dfrac{\frac{1}{2} + \frac{2}{3}}{\frac{1}{3} - \frac{7}{8}}$.

   b. $\dfrac{2^{-1} - 3^{-1}}{5 - \frac{1}{7}}$.

   c. $\dfrac{(xy)^{-1}x^{-1}y^{-1}}{(x^2 - y^2)x}$.

   d. $\dfrac{(x - y)(x^{-1} + y^{-1})}{x^2}$.

2. Determine the set of real numbers that results when each member of the interval $[-4, 3)$ is added to
   a. -3 b. 2   c. 4   d. -5.

3. Determine the set of real numbers that results when each member of the interval $[-4, 3)$ is multiplied by
   a. -3 b. 2   c. 4   d. -5.

4. Determine the sets that result when each member of the given interval is multiplied by 3 and by -3.
   a. $(2, 7)$ b. $[-3, 4]$ c. $[-7, -1]$ d. $(-1, 0]$.

5. Determine the set $\{x + y : x \in A \text{ and } y \in B\}$, where
   a. $A = [1, 2]$ $B = [0, 3)$.
   b. $A = (-3, 4)$ $B = [-2, 7)$.
   c. $A = (2, 7)$ $B = [-1, 6]$.

6. Determine the set $\{xy : x \in A \text{ and } y \in B\}$ where
   a. $A = [1, 2]$ $B = [0, 3)$.
   b. $A = (-3, 4)$ $B = [-2, 7)$.
   c. $A = (2, 7)$ $B = [-1, 6]$.

7. Give interval descriptions for the sets of numbers x for which
   a. $-3 < x + 1 < 5$.
   b. $2 \leqslant 4x - 6 \leqslant 28$.
   c. $-7 \leqslant 4x + 5 < -1$.
   d. $3x + 8 > -5$.
   e. $2x - 3 \leqslant 7$.

8. Give interval descriptions for the sets of numbers x for which
    a. $|x| < 5$.   b. $|2x| \geqslant 6$.
    c. $|3x - 5| > 2$.   d. $|2x + 6| \leqslant 2$.
    e. $|6 - 5x| \leqslant 4$.

9. Identify each of the following as **R**, ϕ, or $\{5\}$.
    a. $(-\infty, \infty)$.   b. $(5, 5)$.   c. $[5, 5]$.
    d. $(-\infty, 5) \cup [5, \infty)$.   e. $(-\infty, 5) \cap [5, \infty)$.   f. $(5, 5]$.

1.7 COORDINATIZATION OF A LINE

We shall find it useful to discuss the concept of coordinates and coordinatizations. In the study of Euclidean geometry, one studies relations between points, lines, and so on. Although the term "point" is left formally undefined, it is assumed that every one "knows" what a point is. Lines are taken to be sets of points satisfying a given collection of axioms. Of course, no one has ever seen the Euclidean plane, since it is not a physical object; however, in our imagination we usually expect it to be somewhat like a very thin, flat, unbendable, and unscratched piece of porcelain that is indefinitely extended. Lines (certain subsets of the plane) are imagined to lie in the plane, and are very closely related to a *betweenness* property for points. We wish to discuss certain kinds of one–one correspondences between lines and the set of real numbers. In this discussion, we shall assume a certain knowledge of Euclidean geometry, so the following definitions and assumptions are stated without excessive detail.

1.7-1 Definition: If a and b are real numbers, where $a \leqslant b$, then a number x is said to be *between* a and b (or between b and a) if $a \leqslant x \leqslant b$.

1.7-2 Definition: If $\mathcal{L}$ is a line in the Euclidean plane, and C a one–one function from $\mathcal{L}$ onto **R**, ($C : \mathcal{L} \xrightarrow[\text{onto}]{1-1} \textbf{R}$) then C is called a *coordinatization* of $\mathcal{L}$ provided betweenness is preserved. That is, if p is between r and s in the geometric sense, then $C(p)$ is between $C(r)$ and $C(s)$ in the sense of the ordering of real numbers.

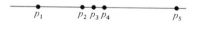

FIGURE 1.4

A coordinatization C could permit $C(p_5) = -1$, $C(p_4) = 0$, $C(p_3) = 20$, $C(p_2) = 20 + \pi$, and $C(p_1) = 10\pi$, but not $C(p_5) = -1$, $C(p_4) = 20$, $C(p_3) = 0$, where p_1, p_2, p_3, p_4, and p_5 are the points shown in Figure 1.4.

The Euclidean plane does not come equipped with a sophisticated measuring device. We have no way to determine "how far apart" two points lie from each other. However, we can presumably make certain "compass constructions," which enables us in some cases to determine when two points are the same distance from a third. (See Figure 1.5.)

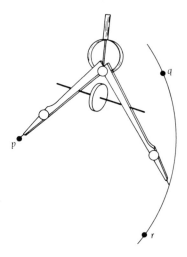

FIGURE 1.5

We wish to use our real number system with its notion of length to build more elaborate measuring devices for the plane. Hence, we should like to know exactly which kinds of coordinatizations of a line will preserve our compass notion of distance. For example, if we select a point p_0 on a line $\mathcal{L}$, (see Figure 1.6) then using a Euclidean (collapsible) compass we can construct

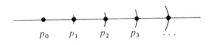

FIGURE 1.6

a sequence of points, $p_1, p_2, \cdots$ on $\mathcal{L}$ such that the directed distance (in the intuitive sense) between p_k and p_{k-1} remains the same for any k.

If we wish for our coordinatization to preserve these primitive distances, then C cannot assign p_0 to 1, p_1 to 5, p_2 to 6, and p_3 to 20, although such an assignment would not violate the betweenness property. Let us assume then that it is possible to make a coordinatization in which the distances are preserved in the sense described above. We formalize this by the following assumption, although we admit that the construction process as described is very vague.

1.7-3 **Assumption:** Suppose $\mathcal{L}$ is a line. Then there exists a *standard* co-ordinatization K of $\mathcal{L}$ ($K : \mathcal{L} \xrightarrow[\text{onto}]{\text{1-1}} \mathbf{R}$) such that given any sequence of distinct points p_0, p_1, p_2, $\cdots$ constructed on $\mathcal{L}$ using a compass, by proceeding from p_k to p_{k+1} constructing p_{k+1} the same distance and in the same direction as going from p_{k-1} to p_k, for any m and any n, we find

$$\frac{K(p_{n+1}) - K(p_n)}{K(p_{m+1}) - K(p_m)} = 1.$$

(See Figure 1.7.)

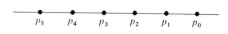

$$\begin{array}{cccccc} \bullet & \bullet & \bullet & \bullet & \bullet & \bullet \\ p_5 & p_4 & p_3 & p_2 & p_1 & p_0 \end{array}$$

FIGURE 1.7

Example: If $K(p_0) = 0$, $K(p_1) = \pi$, $K(p_2) = 2\pi, \ldots, K(p_k) = k\pi$, then

$$\frac{K(p_{n+1}) - K(p_n)}{K(p_{m+1}) - K(p_m)} = \frac{(n+1)\pi - n\pi}{(m+1)\pi - m\pi} = \frac{\pi}{\pi} = 1.$$

We shall call such a coordinatization a "rigid" coordinatization. We shall proceed from the assumption that there does exist at least one acceptable rigid coordinatization K as described above.

1.7-4 **Definition:** Any coordinatization C is called a *rigid coordinatization* provided that for any four points p_1, p_2, p_3, p_4, such that $p_3 \neq p_4$,

$$\frac{C(p_1) - C(p_2)}{C(p_3) - C(p_4)} = \frac{K(p_1) - K(p_2)}{K(p_3) - K(p_4)}.$$

(K is a standard coordinatization of the type we have assumed to exist.)

Remark: The points p_1, p_2, p_3, p_4 in the above definition do not necessarily represent successive compass steps as described previously, so the ratio would not necessarily be 1.

We will call $C(p_1) - C(p_2)$ a *directed distance* (with respect to the given coordinates) from p_2 to p_1. Although different rigid *coordinate systems* (coordinatizations) may exist, our definition ensures that the ratio of the lengths of two different line segments remains constant regardless of the coordinate system used. Intuitively, the real line has been "spread evenly" along the line being coordinatized.

Example: Let p_1, p_2, p_3, p_4 be points on $\mathcal{L}$ and let C and C' be coordinatizations of $\mathcal{L}$ such that $C(p_1) = 2$, $C(p_2) = 6$, $C(p_3) = -1$, $C(p_4) = 0$, whereas $C'(p_1) = 3$, $C'(p_2) = 1$, $C'(p_3) = 6$, $C'(p_4) = 5$. We know that one (or both) of these coordinatizations is not rigid since

$$\frac{C(p_1) - C(p_2)}{C(p_3) - C(p_4)} = \frac{2 - 6}{-1 - 0} = 4,$$

but

$$\frac{C'(p_1) - C'(p_2)}{C'(p_3) - C'(p_4)} = \frac{3 - 1}{6 - 5} = 2.$$

If we knew that the standard rigid coordinatization K has $K(p_1) = 7$, $K(p_2) = 3$, $K(p_3) = 13$, and $K(p_4) = 11$, then we could conclude that C is not rigid, because

$$\frac{K(p_1) - K(p_2)}{K(p_3) - K(p_4)} = \frac{7 - 3}{13 - 11} = 2.$$

However, we cannot tell for sure about C' without additional knowledge, because the equal-ratio property may not hold for all points.

The following very important theorem describes a fundamental relation between different rigid coordinate systems for a line.

1.7-5 **Theorem:** If C is a rigid coordinatization and if C' is defined by

$$C'(p) = aC(p) + b \qquad (a \text{ and } b \text{ real numbers}, a \neq 0),$$

then C' is also a rigid coordinatization.

PROOF: It is sufficient to show that for any four points p_1, p_2, p_3, p_4, such that $p_3 \neq p_4$,

$$\frac{C(p_1) - C(p_2)}{C(p_3) - C(p_4)} = \frac{C'(p_1) - C'(p_2)}{C'(p_3) - C'(p_4)}.$$

Now,

$$\frac{C'(p_1) - C'(p_2)}{C'(p_3) - C'(p_4)} = \frac{(aC(p_1) + b) - (aC(p_2) + b)}{(aC(p_3) + b) - (aC(p_4) + b)}$$

$$= \frac{a(C(p_1) - C(p_2))}{a(C(p_3) - C(p_4))} = \frac{C(p_1) - C(p_2)}{C(p_3) - C(p_4)},$$

which establishes this fact.

Question: Do you think the converse is true?

Essentially, the theorem asserts that if one changes coordinates by any linear map (a linear function $f : \mathbf{R} \to \mathbf{R}$ is one described by $f(x) = mx + b$), then the important rigidity property is preserved.

Remark: Note that "changing coordinates by a linear map" is the same as coordinatizing by the composition of f and C, $(f \circ C : \mathcal{L} \xrightarrow[\text{onto}]{\text{1-1}} \mathbf{R})$.

Example: Assume we have coordinatized a line $\mathcal{L}$ as shown in Figure 1.8. Note that we don't explicitly describe the mapping, but rather "identify" points and numbers in a loose fashion. If we change coordinates by the map $f(x) = 2x + 1$, then the coordinatization would look like that shown in Figure 1.9.

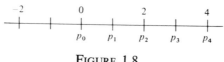

FIGURE 1.8

FIGURE 1.9

The point p_0, which had coordinate 0, now has coordinate $2(0) + 1 = 1$, and p_2, which previously had coordinate 2, now has coordinate $2(2) + 1 = 5$.

Distances on a Line

Let P and Q be two points on some line $\mathcal{L}$ that has coordinatization K. Thus $K(P) = p$ and $K(Q) = q$, where p and q are some real numbers. It is sometimes convenient to identify the points P and Q with the numbers p and q respectively. We then speak of the points p and q (always keeping in mind that these identifications are with respect to a particular coordinatization K of $\mathcal{L}$).

An important tool we derive from this relationship is the distance between two points on a line $\mathcal{L}$. We like to treat *length of a segment* as a positive real number. Since we have already defined the length of the interval $[p, q]$ to be $|p - q|$, it seems reasonable then to say that the distance from P to Q is the real number

$$|K(Q) - K(P)| = |q - p|.$$

Clearly, this distance is dependent upon the coordinatization being used. (See Figure 1.10.)

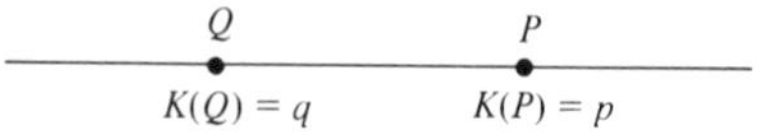

$$
\begin{array}{ccc}
\overset{\bullet}{Q} & & \overset{\bullet}{P} \\
K(Q) = q & & K(P) = p
\end{array}
$$

The distance from P to Q is $|K(Q) - K(P)| = |q - p|$.

FIGURE 1.10

1.7-6 Definition: If P and Q are points on a line $\mathcal{L}$ that is coordinatized by K, then the *distance from P to Q* is the real number

$$|K(Q) - K(P)|,$$

sometimes denoted by $d_K(P, Q)$. (The subscript will be dropped if no confusion is likely to result.)

Let $\mathcal{L}$ be a line and K be a coordinatization for $\mathcal{L}$ in the following examples:

Example: Find the set of all points whose distance from P is less than 4, where $K(P) = 3$. The distance from P to a point Q (let $K(Q) = q$) will be less than 4 if $d(P, Q) < 4$ (that is, $|q - 3| < 4$). Graphically, the set is pictured in Figure 1.11. This set could also be described as the interval $(-1, 7)$, or more precisely by $\{X : K(X) \in (-1, 7)\}$.

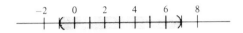

FIGURE 1.11

Example: Assume the line $\mathcal{L}$ has been coordinatized and graph

$$\mathcal{Q} = \{x : |x + 5| > 3\}.$$

$\mathcal{Q}$ is the set of all points whose distance from -5 ($d(x, -5) = |x - (-5)| = |x + 5|$) is greater than 3. From the properties of real numbers we know that if $|x + 5| > 3$, then $x + 5 > 3$ or $-(x + 5) > 3$. This implies that $x > -2$ or $-8 > x$. The graph of $\mathcal{Q}$ is Figure 1.12. (Note in this example how we fail to make the distinction between a point and its coordinate!)

FIGURE 1.12

From properties of the real numbers we can obtain the following properties for distances between points on a line.

1.7-7 Theorem:
    a. $d_K(P, Q) = d_K(Q, P)$
    b. $d_K(P, Q) \geqslant 0$
    c. $d_K(P, Q) = 0 \Leftrightarrow P = Q$
    d. $d_K(P, Q) + d_K(Q, S) \geqslant d_K(P, S)$ (Triangle inequality)

The coordinatization process is the very heart of analytic geometry. It allows one to study geometry by considering the coordinates (numbers) associated with the points. The usefulness of this lies in the fact that the numbers, having a sophisticated algebraic structure and an ordering, admit a large body of strong theorems that can be brought to bear upon problems having their origin in a geometric system. In the next section, we shall discuss coordinatizing the plane by matching points with ordered pairs of real numbers.

EXERCISES 1.7

1. If K is the standard coordinatization of a line $\mathcal{L}$ such that $K(p_1) = 0$, $K(p_2) = 2$, $K(p_3) = 6$, $K(p_4) = 9$, then which of the maps C_i cannot be rigid coordinatizations?

   a. $C_1(p_1) = 1$, $C_1(p_2) = 5$, $C_1(p_3) = 13$, $C_1(p_4) = 19$.
   b. $C_2(p_1) = 1$, $C_2(p_2) = 4$, $C_2(p_3) = 7$, $C_2(p_4) = 10$.
   c. $C_3(p_1) = 1$, $C_3(p_2) = -7$, $C_3(p_3) = -15$, $C_3(p_4) = -21$.

2. Show that if C and C' are rigid coordinatizations, then for any four points p_1, p_2, p_3, p_4,

$$\frac{C(p_1) - C(p_2)}{C(p_3) - C(p_4)} = \frac{C'(p_1) - C'(p_2)}{C'(p_3) - C'(p_4)}.$$

3. Let K be a rigid coordinatization of a line such that: $K(p_1) = -1$, $K(p_2) = 2$, $K(p_3) = 4$, $K(p_4) = 5$. Also let C be a rigid coordinatization such that $C(p_1) = 5$, $C(p_2) = 2$, and $C(p_3) = 1$. Find the C coordinate of p_4. (That is, find $C(p_4)$.)

4. Define the *cross ratio* of four points (ordered) p_1, p_2, p_3, p_4, $p_3 \neq p_4$, to be the common number $r = \mathrm{CrsRat}(p_1, p_2, p_3, p_4)$ such that for any rigid coordinatization K,

$$\frac{K(p_1) - K(p_2)}{K(p_3) - K(p_4)} = r.$$

   Show that if one knows the coordinates of three distinct points, and the cross ratio $\mathrm{CrsRat}(p_1, p_2, p_3, X)$, for any point X, then the coordinate of X can always be determined.

5. Draw a line and mark some points with numbers that might be a rigid coordinate system. Change coordinates according to the map:

   a. $f(x) = \frac{1}{2}x - 1$.   b. $f(x) = 3x + 2$.
   c. $f(x) = 2x$.   d. $f(x) = \frac{1}{4}x - 4$.

6. Describe in general the influence of the numbers a and b on the coordinates under the change of coordinates map $f(x) = ax + b$.

7. Investigate (prove or disprove) the converse of Theorem 1.6-5.

8. a. Show that if Q and I are two distinct points on a line, then there is exactly one rigid coordinatization C such that $C(Q) = 0$ and $C(I) = 1$.
   b. What image does C assign to a point halfway between Q and I?

9. In the following, assume that the points are on some line coordinatized by K.
   a. Graph each of the following sets:
      i. Set of all points whose distance from -6 is less than 2.
      ii. Set of all points whose distance from 3 is greater than or equal to 3.
   b. Use set notation, inequalities, and absolute values to describe each of the above sets.

10. a. Graph each of the following:
      i. $|x + 3| \geqslant 3/2$.   ii. $|5 - x| < 2$.   iii. $-2 \leqslant 5x + 3 < 7$.
   b. Describe each of the above sets in terms of distance between points.

11. Let $A = \{x : |x - 3| \leqslant 5\}$ and $B = \{x : |x + 1| < 2\}$.

a. Graph $A \cap B$ and $A \cup B$.
b. Describe $A \cap B$ in terms of distance to some point.

1.8   COORDINATIZING THE PLANE

The Euclidean plane studied in high school geometry, as we intuitively imagine it, has no marks or scratches, and thus has a rather uninteresting "geography." We shall now discuss ways in which we can add some "geography" by identifying points in the Euclidean plane E_2 with ordered pairs in $R \times R = R^2$. We do this in a manner that gives rise to appealing distance and betweenness notions like those for the line.

Select any pair of nonparallel lines, $\mathfrak{X}$ and $\mathfrak{Y}$. Since the lines are on a plane and are not parallel, they must intersect in a unique point. Let Q denote the point of intersection of these lines, the *origin*. Select a point I on $\mathfrak{X}$ different from Q, and a point J on $\mathfrak{Y}$ different from Q. Give $\mathfrak{X}$ the unique rigid coordinatization X having $X(Q) = 0$, and $X(I) = 1$, and give $\mathfrak{Y}$ the rigid coordinatization Y having $Y(Q) = 0$ and $Y(J) = 1$. (See Figure 1.13.)

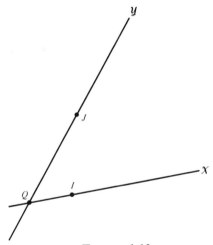

FIGURE 1.13

If P is some point in the plane, then there is a unique line $\mathcal{L}$ passing through P that is parallel to $\mathfrak{X}$. Similarly, there is a unique line $\mathfrak{M}$ passing through P that is parallel to $\mathfrak{Y}$. These lines are sometimes called "lattice lines." (See Figure 1.14.)

Now $\mathfrak{M}$ intersects $\mathfrak{X}$ in a point A having X coordinate x, (that is, $X(A) = x$) and $\mathcal{L}$ intersects $\mathfrak{Y}$ at the point B having Y coordinate y (that is, $Y(B) = y$). We then say that P has the *affine coordinate* (x, y) with respect to the chosen

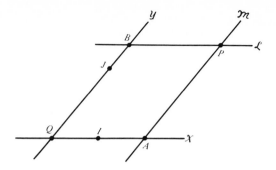

FIGURE 1.14

points and lines. (We also call (x, y) the x-y coordinate.) The line x is called the *x-axis*, and the line y is called the *y-axis*. In the discussion above, we were very liberal in the coordinatization of each axis. A very popular class of affine coordinatizations, which we shall call *Cartesian coordinate systems*, is made up of those having perpendicular axes, and the same unit distances on each axis.

Example: To construct a Cartesian coordinate system, we do the following: Choose two lines, x and y, which are perpendicular, and call their point of intersection Q. With a compass, swing an arc which crosses each line, calling the points of intersection I and J. We may then coordinatize the plane according to the preceding discussion. (See Figure 1.15.)

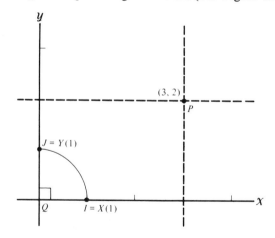

FIGURE 1.15

Having coordinatized the plane, it is convenient to "identify" a point and its coordinate. Actually, we have described a one–one correspondence between points in the plane and ordered pairs in $R \times R$. It seems natural to name each point by its coordinate (ordered pair). Thus, we may refer to the point P in Figure 1.15 as the point (3, 2). However, the distinction between a point and its coordinate under a given coordinatization should be borne in mind, as we shall see when we consider transformations of coordinates later on. Let us elaborate on this with an example.

Example: Suppose the plane has been coordinatized by a Cartesian system, as shown in Figure 1.16.

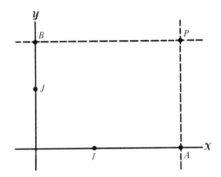

FIGURE 1.16

The point P has plane coordinate $(X(A), Y(B)) = (x, y)$, since A has linear coordinate $X(A) = x$, and B has linear coordinate $Y(B) = y$. The point P having coordinate (x, y) is often called the "point (x, y)," but this is acceptable only if there is no more than one coordinate system in the discussion. It could be the case that under a different coordinate system, the point P has coordinate $(x', y') \neq (x, y)$.

Let us now proceed to a consideration of analytic geometry. This will entail the use of number system properties to analyze and discuss geometric properties and figures. For example, assume the plane has been given Cartesian coordinates (that is, some Cartesian coordinate system), and consider the subset of $R \times R$ described by $\mathcal{K} = \{(x, y) : x \geqslant 2\}$. The set of ordered pairs in $\mathcal{K}$ is identified (through the coordinate mapping) with points in the plane. As long as no confusion arises, we shall also call the corresponding set of points in the plane $\mathcal{K}$. (See Figure 1.17.)

The analytic description of the set $\mathcal{K}$ is far easier to state than a geometric description of the corresponding set of points in the plane would be. This is one reason that analytic geometry is so useful.

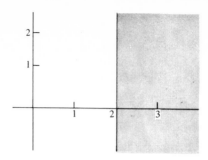

FIGURE 1.17

Example: The set of points $S = (1, 2] \times (2, 3]$ is "graphed" in Figure 1.18, using a Cartesian coordinate system.

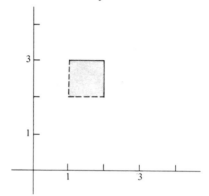

FIGURE 1.18

A solid line on the boundary indicates points that are in the set and a dotted line indicates points lying outside of the set. (See Figures 1.18 and 1.19.)

Example: The x-axis $\mathfrak{X}$ for a given coordinatization is identified with its corresponding set of coordinates $\{(x, 0) : x \in \mathbf{R}\}$. Similarly for the y-axis, we write: $\mathfrak{Y} = \{(0, y) : y \in \mathbf{R}\}$.

Let us now graph the set S of the above example using a *rectangular coordinate system*, which is not Cartesian since the *unit distances* differ on the two axes. It is not skewed, however, since the axes are perpendicular. (Compare Figures 1.18 and 1.19.)

Clearly, the set $S = (1, 2] \times (2, 3]$ does not correspond to the same set of points in the plane through the two different coordinatizations. This points out again the importance of realizing the difference between a point and its coordinate, even though we will very often not emphasize the distinction in a given discussion involving a single coordinatization. We shall in fact

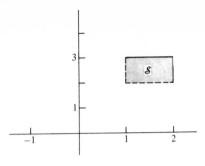

FIGURE 1.19

deemphasize the distinction. We will often speak of the "point (a, b)," when we actually mean the "point whose coordinate is (a, b) with regard to the given coordinate system."

The set of points in the plane identified with its set of coordinates $\mathcal{C}$ (through a given coordinate mapping) is called the *graph* of $\mathcal{C}$. The "picture" we draw of such a set is only a sketch of the graph of $\mathcal{C}$, but it is often referred to loosely as "the graph of $\mathcal{C}$." The context should make this dual usage of the word *graph* acceptable.

Example: Draw a sketch of the graph of $\mathcal{V} = \{(x, y) : x \geqslant 1 \text{ and } y < 3\}$, under a skewed coordinate system (that is, use axes that are not perpendicular, such as those in Figure 1.20.)

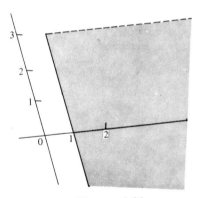

FIGURE 1.20

Later we will discuss methods that will enable us to find the coordinates of a set of points under one coordinate system by looking at its coordinates under another. For now, we content ourselves with graphing some simple sets under various interrelated coordinate systems.

1.8-1 Definition: Given a coordinatization of the plane, the set $(0, \infty) \times (0, \infty)$ is called the *first quadrant*. The set $(-\infty, 0) \times (0, \infty)$ is called the *second quadrant*, $(-\infty, 0) \times (-\infty, 0)$, the *third quadrant*, and $(0, \infty) \times (-\infty, 0)$, the *fourth quadrant*. (See Figure 1.21.)

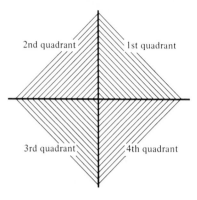

FIGURE 1.21

Remark: It is common practice to refer to the origin, the point whose coordinate is $(0, 0)$, of a coordinate system by the letter O (oh). This is not to be confused with the number 0 (zero). Thus, $\mathcal{X} \cap \mathcal{Y} = \{O\}$ or equivalently $\{(x, 0) : x \in \mathbf{R}\} \cap \{(0, y) : y \in \mathbf{R}\} = \{(0, 0)\}$.

We conclude this section with the following example and discussion.

Example: Draw a Cartesian coordinate system (call it C) and graph the set $\mathcal{S} = [1, 2] \times [1, 2]$. Draw a second Cartesian system C', with origin Q' at the point with C coordinates $(2, 2)$, and having unit distance half as long as the unit distance in C. (See Figure 1.22.)

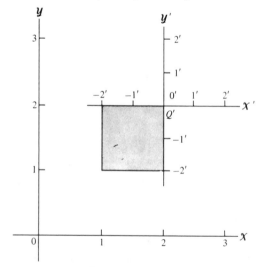

FIGURE 1.22

Question: What subset of $\mathbf{R} \times \mathbf{R}$ would have the same graph in the C' system as $[1, 2] \times [1, 2]$ does in the C system?

Answer: The set $[-2, 0] \times [-2, 0]$.

In this example, we can easily write formulas that give the C' coordinate (x', y') in terms of the C coordinate (x, y). They are:

$$x' = 2(x - 2) = 2x - 4$$

and

$$y' = 2(y - 2) = 2y - 4,$$

as you should verify. That is, $C'(P) = f \circ C(P)$, where $f(x, y) = (x', y') = (2x - 4, 2y - 4)$. Hence, f changes coordinates from the C system to the C' system.

EXERCISES 1.8

1. By selecting three different pairs of nonparallel lines in the plane, draw three coordinate systems.
   a. Sketch the graph of the ordered pair (1, 2) in each.
   b. Select one point P in the plane and determine the coordinate (x, y) of P in each of the three systems.

2. Graph the sets $A = [-1, 2) \times [2, 4]$ and $B = (0, 5) \times [2, 4]$ in (a) a Cartesian system; (b) a rectangular system with different units on the axes; and (c) in an affine system with nonperpendicular axes.

3. Draw a Cartesian coordinate system C. Draw a Cartesian coordinate system C', having origin at the point P whose C coordinate is (1, 1) (that is, $C(P) = (1, 1)$ or $C^{-1}(1, 1) = P$), but whose unit length is twice the unit length in the C system.
   a. Determine the C' coordinate of the point whose C coordinate is (2, 3) (that is, $C'(C^{-1}(2, 3)) = $ __?__).
   b. Sketch the graph of the set $S = [0, 2] \times [-1, 3]$ under the C coordinatization (that is, sketch the set $C^{-1}[S] = \{P : C(P) \in S\}$).
   c. What subset of $\mathbf{R} \times \mathbf{R}$ corresponds with $C^{-1}[S]$ via the C' coordinate system? (That is, identify $\{C'^{-1}(P) : P \in C^{-1}[S]\}$.)

4. Sketch two Cartesian systems C and C' with the same unit length, but with C' having origin Q' at the point with C coordinate $(-1, 3)$ (that is, with $C(Q') = (-1, 3)$.) Determine formulas involving x, y, x', and y' that will give (a) the C' coordinate (x', y') of a point P having C coordinate (x, y); (b) the C coordinate (x, y) of a point P' having C' coordinate (x', y').

5. Sketch two Cartesian systems C and C', both having the same axes but such that the unit length in C is four times that in C'. Determine formulas that will yield the C' coordinate (x', y') of a point having C coordinate (x, y).

6. Sketch two Cartesian systems C and C', with C' having as origin the point $C^{-1}(2, -3)$, and unit length three times that of the C system. Determine formulas giving the C' coordinates of a point in terms of the C coordinates.

7. Make a geometric sketch in some Cartesian coordinate system of the points whose coordinates are in the set given.
   a. $\{(x, y) : 5 \leqslant x \text{ and } -1 < y \leqslant 3\}$.

    b. $\{(x, y) : -3 \leqslant x \leqslant -1\}$.

    c. $\{(x, y) : 4 < x < 6$ and $-2 < y < -1\} \cup \{(x, y) : -1 \leqslant x < 0$ and $2 < y\}$.

    d. $\{(x, y) : x < -1$ and $y > 2\}$.

8. Give brace descriptions of the sets sketched in Figure 1.23.

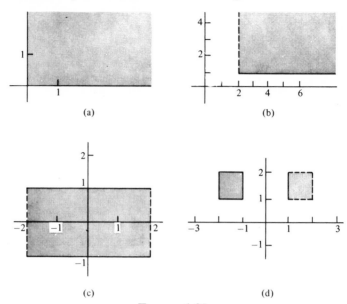

        (a)   (b)

        (c)   (d)

FIGURE 1.23

9. Draw a Cartesian coordinate system C, then draw the coordinate system $C' = f \circ C$; that is, change coordinates according to the map f.

    a. $f(x, y) = (\frac{1}{2}x - 1, \frac{1}{2}y - 1)$.   b. $f(x, y) = (3x + 2, 2y - 1)$.

    c. $f(x, y) = (2x, \frac{1}{4}y)$.   d. $f(x, y) = (\frac{1}{4}x - 4, 3x + 2)$.

10. Describe in general the influence of the numbers a, b, c, and d on the coordinates under the change of coordinates map $f(x, y) = (ax + b, cy + d)$.

11. If the regions of Exercise 8 are given in coordinates C, determine their analytic descriptions for each of the coordinate systems C' of Exercise 9.

II

GRAPHING TECHNIQUES
AND SOME SPECIAL RELATIONS
AND FUNCTIONS

Elementary analytic geometry has two major goals: (1) to allow the use of analytic "machinery" such as the field and order properties of the real numbers on geometric problems, and (2) to facilitate a geometric interpretation of analytic problems. In a sense, these are inverses differing primarily in the origin and point of view of the problem. We shall discuss problems from each point of view.

2.1 SOME FUNDAMENTAL NOTIONS

The Distance Function

In the preceding chapter we discussed distances on a line. We shall now extend this idea to the plane. For the line, distance was defined using the absolute value function. Distances on the plane will rely on the Pythagorean theorem,* which yields an important connection between geometry and number systems.

2.1-1 Theorem: (The Pythagorean theorem). The sum of the squares of the lengths of the legs of a right triangle is equal to the square of the length of the hypotenuse. (See Figure 2.1.)

---

* For a historical account of Pythagorean mathematics, read T. L. Heath, *A History of Greek Mathematics*, Vol. I (London: Oxford Press, 1965).

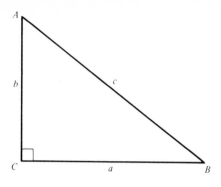

FIGURE 2.1

Let $\mathfrak{X}$ and $\mathfrak{Y}$ be perpendicular lines intersecting at O having coordinatizations X and Y respectively. We assume that we have given the plane a Cartesian coordinatization, so that X and Y have the same unit distances. Let P and Q be points in the plane with coordinates $(X(P), Y(P)) = (p_1, p_2)$, and $(X(Q), Y(Q)) = (q_1, q_2)$ respectively. We would like to determine the distance between P and Q. Let $\mathcal{P}$ be a line through P parallel to $\mathfrak{Y}$, and $\mathcal{Q}$ be a line through Q parallel to $\mathfrak{X}$. Since $\mathfrak{X}$ and $\mathfrak{Y}$ are perpendicular, so are $\mathcal{Q}$ and $\mathcal{P}$. Further, $\mathcal{P}$ and $\mathcal{Q}$ intersect at the point $R = (p_1, q_2)$, as shown in Figure 2.2.

Remark: By convention, $P = (a, b)$, means that the point P and the ordered pair (a, b) are matched up (identified) under the coordinatization in mind. We apologize for this abuse of the equals sign, but continue its practice so long as only one coordinatization is involved in the discussion.

The length of segment PR is $|p_2 - q_2|$ and the length of segment QR is $|p_1 - q_1|$. Thus, by the Pythagorean theorem, the distance from P to Q is

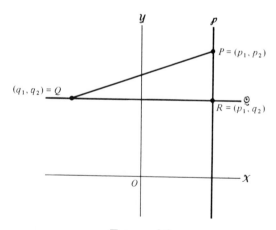

FIGURE 2.2

$$\sqrt{|p_1 - q_1|^2 + |p_2 - q_2|^2} = \sqrt{(p_1 - q_1)^2 + (p_2 - q_2)^2}.$$

This suggests the following definition.

2.1-2 Definition: If P and Q are points in the plane with coordinates (p_1, p_2) and (q_1, q_2) respectively, relative to a Cartesian coordinatization, then the *distance from P to Q* denoted by $d(P, Q)$ is given by

$$d(P, Q) = \sqrt{(p_1 - q_1)^2 + (p_2 - q_2)^2}.$$

Notice that the distance between two points P and Q will differ under different coordinatizations. Recall that the Euclidean plane does not come equipped with a very sophisticated measuring device. It is subject to compass measure of equal distances, enabling us to construct a Cartesian coordinate system, but it does not allow us to measure distances as with a ruler. However, with a Cartesian coordinate system and use of the Pythagorean theorem, we are able to introduce a more sophisticated measure related to the particular coordinatization.

As is the case for distances on a line, the following theorem holds for distances in the plane.

2.1-3 Theorem: For any points P, Q, and S,
    a. $d(P, Q) = d(Q, P)$.
    b. $d(P, Q) \geqslant 0$.
    c. $d(P, Q) = 0$ iff $P = Q$.
    d. $d(P, Q) + d(Q, S) \geqslant d(P, S)$.

Remark: Property d is called the *triangle inequality*. If P, Q, and S form a triangle, this statement is equivalent to the geometric statement that "the sum of the lengths of two sides of a triangle is greater than the length of the third side." Equality occurs when the points lie on a single line, in which case one says the triangle formed is *degenerate*.

Midpoint of a Segment

Notice that when restricted to points on an axis, the distance between points is the same as previously defined for points on a line in Chapter I.

Example: Suppose P and Q have coordinates $(a, 0)$ and $(b, 0)$. Then

$$d(P, Q) = \sqrt{(a - b)^2 + (0 - 0)^2} = \sqrt{(a - b)^2} = |a - b|.$$

This is in agreement with the distance between two points A and B on the x-axis, as discussed earlier.

Example: Find the "midpoint" of the segment PQ, where $P = (1, -2)$ and $Q = (3, 1)$. (See Figure 2.3.)
Using congruent triangles, we find that $(x - 1) = (3 - x)$ and $(1 - y) = (y + 2)$. Thus

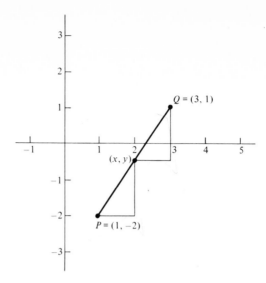

FIGURE 2.3

$$x = 2 = \frac{(3+1)}{2}$$

and

$$y = -\frac{1}{2} = \frac{(1+(-2))}{2}.$$

We can generalize this to the midpoint of the segment between any two points. We thus make the following definition. (Why a definition instead of a theorem?)

2.1-4 Definition: The *midpoint of any segment PQ*, where $P = (x_1, y_1)$ and $Q = (x_2, y_2)$ is the point $\left(\dfrac{x_1 + x_2}{2}, \dfrac{y_1 + y_2}{2}\right)$.

Comments on Graphs

In Chapter I we saw that certain subsets of a line can be described algebraically and that certain algebraic statements can be interpreted geometrically. The same approach can be taken with regard to points in the plane. We follow tradition and where no confusion arises, make no distinction between a set of points in the plane and an algebraic statement that describes the set. If a set of ordered pairs is described by an equation or inequality, then the corresponding set of points in the plane is said to be "determined by the equation or inequality." The equation (or inequality) may be referred to as "the *constraining* equation (or inequality)" of the figure (or region) in the plane. Also, we shall sometimes refer to a constraining equation or inequality by the figure it describes. For example, we make statements concerning "the line $y = x$." What is meant, of course, is the set of ordered pairs $\{(x, y) : y = x\}$, or the corresponding set of points in the plane.

Let us now describe some simple geometric figures by subjecting the coordinates of the points on the figure to some *analytic constraint* (combinations of equations and inequalities).

Example: Describe the "baseball diamond" with bases at $(0, -1)$, $(1, 0)$, $(0, 1)$, and $(-1, 0)$. (See Figure 2.4.)

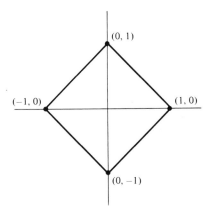

FIGURE 2.4

After some careful and deliberate consideration, one discovers that a point is on this figure if and only if its coordinate (x, y) satisfies the equation $|x| + |y| = 1$. (See Exercise 10.) The full description is given by

$$\{(x, y) : |x| + |y| = 1\} .$$

Example: A graph of the set of points (x, y) such that $y > 2$ and $x \leqslant 5$ is shown in Figure 2.5.

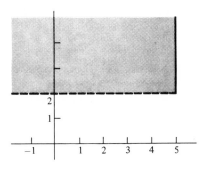

FIGURE 2.5

Example: Graph the set of points whose coordinates satisfy the equation $y = x^2$. That is, graph $\mathcal{P} = \{(x, y) : y = x^2\}$. Clearly, any ordered pair (x, y) that satisfies this equation will be on or above the x-axis since x^2 is never negative. Note first that $(0, 0) \in \mathcal{P}$. As x values are taken larger,

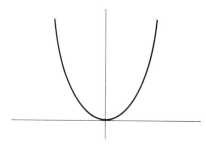

FIGURE 2.6

x^2 increases; however x^2 increases much faster than x does. If x is taken to be negative, the points are reflected across the y-axis since $x^2 = |x|^2 = (-x)^2$. Hence, the graph of $y = x^2$ must be similar to that shown in Figure 2.6.

EXERCISES 2.1

1. Find the distance between the following pairs of points.
   a. $(1, 2)$, $(-5, 7)$.
   b. $(0, 4)$, $(0, 3)$.
   c. $(2, 7)$, $(3, 6)$.
   d. $(-6, -6)$, $(7, -4)$.

2. Find the midpoints of the segments determined by the pairs of points in Exercise 1.

3. Graph the set of points (x, y) such that
   a. $x \geqslant 2$.
   b. $x = 1$ and $y \geqslant 2$.
   c. $y < 7$.
   d. $x < 5$ and $y < 4$.
   e. $-x = y$.
   f. $x < y$.

4. a. Graph the set of all points strictly inside the square with corners at $(0, 0)$, $(1, 0)$, $(1, 1)$, $(0, 1)$.
   b. Same as 4a except that the boundary of the square is included.
   c. Using equations or inequalities, describe the sets in 4a and 4b.

5. Describe the set of points (edges only) of the square with corners at $(-4, 0)$, $(0, 4)$, $(4, 0)$, $(0, -4)$.

6. Interpret graphically the property that a relation f is a function.

7. Graph
   a. $\{(x, y) : 2 < x < 3\}$.
   b. $\{(x, y) : -3 \leqslant y \leqslant 4\}$.
   c. $\{(x, y) : x > y\}$.
   d. $\{(x, y) : -x \leqslant y\}$.

8. Graph $\{(x, y) : y \leqslant x^2\}$.

9. Graph
   a. $(2, 3) \times [4, 2]$.   b. $[-3, 2] \times (2, \infty)$.
   c. $\{(x, y) : x \in [-2, 3)\}$.

10. Analyze the graph of $|x| + |y| = 1$ by considering separately (x, y) in each quadrant. One can thus ignore the absolute value signs in each separate case.

11. Graph
    a. $[(1, 2) \cup (3, 4)] \times (1, 3]$.   b. $[(-3, 2] \cup [1, 4)] \times (5, 6)$.
    c. $[(-1, 3) \cap (2, 4)] \times [5, 7)$.   d. $[(1, 2) \times (1, 3)] \cup [(3, 4) \times (1, 3)]$.

12. Investigate (prove or disprove): $(A \cup B) \times C = A \times C \cup B \times C$.

13. If $P = (a, b)$ and $Q = (c, d)$, try to find a general expression for a point (x, y) that is two-thirds the distance from P to Q.

14. Show that the distance from the midpoint to an endpoint of a segment is actually one-half of the length of the segment.

2.2 LINES IN THE PLANE

The Definition

We would now like to examine the general form of equations that determine lines. The first question that arises is how to tell a (straight) line from a gentle curve. We begin our study by attempting to make this distinction. We admit that we really can't tell; however, if we accept the fact that the lines used to construct a coordinate system (the *x*-axis and the *y*-axis) are "straight," then we can develop an analytic method for making the distinction.

First, we agree that any line parallel to either axis is a *straight line;* that is, the equations $x = c$ and $y = c$ describe straight lines, where c is any real number. Let us ask, What in particular characterizes a line in the plane and distinguishes it from other curves? The answer to this question is related to distances that are defined once a coordinatization is given. The property that characterizes a line and distinguishes it from other curves is the fixed relationship between what are called the "rise" and the "run." That is, if one imagines a point traveling at a fixed rate in one direction along a line, for any given time interval (or between any two points of the line) we should expect the ratio of the point's vertical increase to its horizontal increase to be the same as for any other time interval. (See Figure 2.7.)

Let us now examine this notion in terms of coordinates of points, thus allowing analytic machinery in our considerations. If (x_1, y_1) and (x_2, y_2) are the coordinates of two distinct points P_1 and P_2 on a line $\mathcal{L}$, then the *rise* from P_1 to P_2 is the number $y_2 - y_1$ and the *run* is $x_2 - x_1$. (See Figure 2.8.)
Hence, if the line is not vertical, the ratio $m = (y_2 - y_1)/(x_2 - x_1)$ exists, and the number m is independent of the two particular points P_1 and P_2. This

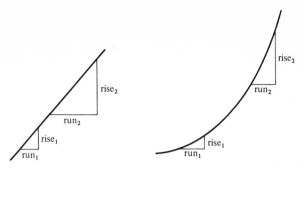

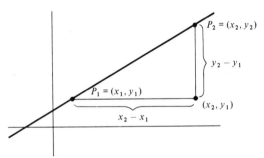

$$\frac{\text{rise}_1}{\text{run}_1} = \frac{\text{rise}_2}{\text{run}_2} = m \qquad\qquad \frac{\text{rise}_1}{\text{run}_1} \neq \frac{\text{rise}_2}{\text{run}_2}$$

FIGURE 2.7

FIGURE 2.8

number m is uniquely determined by the line, although the line is not uniquely determined by the number m. The number m is called the *slope* of the line.

2.2-0 Definition: The *slope* of a nonvertical line is the ratio

$$m = \frac{y_2 - y_1}{x_2 - x_1},$$

where (x_1, y_1) and (x_2, y_2) are any two distinct points in the line.

Members of the class of vertical lines (those parallel to the y-axis) have no slope since an attempt to form the rise-to-run ratio for a vertical line will involve division by zero.

Remark: Any two parallel lines are either both vertical or both of the same slope. Thus, we could define an equivalence relation on the class of all lines by defining a pair of lines to be equivalent if they have the same slope or are vertical. The equivalence classes would consist of families of parallel lines (see Figure 2.9). In order to distinguish any particular line, it is sufficient to know which class it belongs to and a point through which it passes.

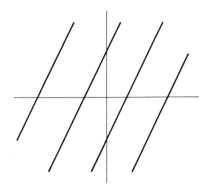

FIGURE 2.9

We thus decide that a *line* is a set of points whose Cartesian coordinates satisfy an equation $x = c$ for some c, or an equation $(y - y_0)/(x - x_0) = m$ for some m and some point $P_0 = (x_0, y_0)$. We state this formally as follows.

2.2-1   **Description:** A line is a set of points $\mathcal{L}$ whose Cartesian coordinates satisfy one of the following descriptions.

     i. For some $c \in \mathbf{R}$, $\mathcal{L} = \{(x, y) : x = c\}$; in this case $\mathcal{L}$ is called a *vertical line* passing through the point $(c, 0)$.

     ii. For some $m \in \mathbf{R}$ and $(x_0, y_0) \in \mathbf{R}^2$,

$$\mathcal{L} = \{(x, y) : y - y_0 = m(x - x_0)\};$$

in this case $\mathcal{L}$ is said to have *slope m* and to pass through the point (x_0, y_0).

Example: Graph the line passing through the point $(1, 2)$ having slope $-\frac{2}{3}$.

Solution: The slope $-\frac{2}{3}$ can be thought of as either the fraction $-2/3$ or $2/-3$. We interpret the first slope (rise-to-run) fraction as an upward increase of -2 (which is a downward increase of $+2$) for each rightward increase of $+3$. In the second case we interpret the slope fraction as an upward increase of $+2$ for each rightward increase of -3 (which is a leftward increase of $+3$). In either case we obtain the line in Figure 2.10.

Standard Forms

Certain *standard forms* for some functions and relations are useful in isolating pertinent information that is helpful in sketching graphs. Such standard

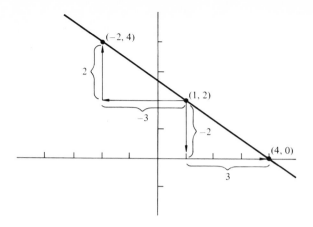

FIGURE 2.10

forms are also useful in determining an analytical description when certain geometric facts are known.

The equation $y - y_0 = m(x - x_0)$ for a line through the point (x_0, y_0) having slope m is called the *point slope form* for the equation of a line. This equation can be put into several other equivalent convenient standard forms. One of the most useful is obtained by solving for y, and obtaining $y = mx + (y_0 - mx_0)$. By setting $b = y_0 - mx_0$, we have the equation

$$y = mx + b.$$

This is known as the *slope intercept form*. When $x = 0$, we obtain $y = b$, which indicates that the line crosses the y-axis at the point $(0, b)$. The number b is called the *y-intercept*.

Example: Graph the line whose equation is $y = 4x - 2$. This line has slope 4 and crosses the y-axis at $(0, -2)$ and is shown in Figure 2.11.

If two points on a line are known, then the line is determined. If (x_1, y_1) and (x_2, y_2) are two points of a nonvertical line, then the slope m is given by $m = (y_2 - y_1)/(x_2 - x_1)$. Using this slope and the point (x_1, y_1) in the point slope equation, we obtain the equation

$$y - y_1 = \frac{y_2 - y_1}{x_2 - x_1}(x - x_1),$$

which is known as the *two-point-form* equation.

Example: Find the equation of a line passing through the points $(2, 1)$ and $(3, 5)$. (See Figure 2.12.)
Essentially the two-point form equates two ratios. The rise : run ratio from the given point $(3, 5)$ to the arbitrary point (x, y) is $(y - 5)/(x - 3)$ and the rise : run ratio from $(2, 1)$ to $(3, 5)$ is $(5 - 1)/(3 - 2) = 4$. An application of the two-point form merely consists of equating these two

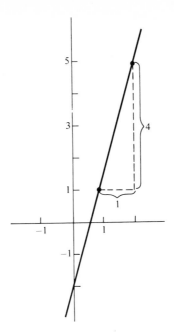

FIGURE 2.11

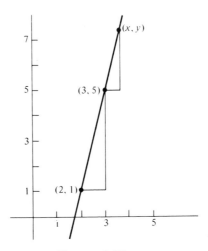

FIGURE 2.12

ratios. Our equation is thus $(y - 5)/(x - 3) = 4$. In slope intercept form it becomes $y = 4x - 7$.

One can easily see from the foregoing discussion that the equation for any line can be written in the form

$$Ax + By + C = 0,$$

where not both A and B are zero. This is called the *general linear equation in two variables.* A line is *vertical* when $B = 0$ and *horizontal* when $A = 0$. By putting this equation in the slope intercept form $y = -(A/B)x - C/B$, we see that the slope of the line (provided that $B \neq 0$; that is, provided that the line is not vertical) is $-(A/B)$ and the y-intercept is $-(C/B)$.

Exercise: Show that if $C = 0$ in the general form of a linear equation, then the line must pass through the origin.

Exercise: Consider the line $\mathfrak{L}$ given in general form by $-x + 3y = 4$.
    a. What is the slope of $\mathfrak{L}$?
    b. Find a point on $\mathfrak{L}$.
    c. What is the y-intercept of $\mathfrak{L}$?
    d. Give the point slope equation for $\mathfrak{L}$.
    e. Give a two-point equation for $\mathfrak{L}$.

Conditions for Parallelism and Perpendicularity

We are now prepared to formalize the notion that lines are *parallel.* Consider two lines having equations $A_1x + B_1y + C_1 = 0$ and $A_2x + B_2y + C_2 = 0$. The lines are "parallel" if both have the same slope or if both are vertical. In either case, a necessary and sufficient condition for the lines to be parallel is that

$$\frac{A_1}{B_1} = \frac{A_2}{B_2} \quad \text{or} \quad \frac{B_1}{A_1} = \frac{B_2}{A_2}.$$

This condition can be expressed more compactly as $A_1B_2 = A_2B_1$, or equivalently as $A_1B_2 - A_2B_1 = 0$.

2.2-2   **Definition:** Two lines having equations $A_1x + B_1y + C_1 = 0$ and $A_2x + B_2y + C_2 = 0$ are *parallel* if and only if

$$A_1B_2 - A_2B_1 = 0.$$

We would also like to derive a similar condition to determine when we will call two lines *perpendicular.* We will argue that the lines are perpendicular when

$$A_1A_2 + B_1B_1 = 0.$$

Let us first remark that, without loss of generality, we can consider only lines passing through the origin. (See Exercise 8.) Hence, in working with the linear equation $Ax + By + C = 0$, we will consider only the line given by $Ax + By = 0$.

Consider two "perpendicular" lines $\mathfrak{L}_1$ and $\mathfrak{L}_2$ having equations $A_1x + B_1y = 0$ and $A_2x + B_2y = 0$ respectively. Assume at first that neither is vertical. Assume that P_1 lies on $\mathfrak{L}_1$ but not on $\mathfrak{L}_2$, and has coordinate (x_1, y_1).

If P_2 lies on $\mathcal{L}_2$ an equal distance from $(0, 0)$, then P_2 has coordinate $(x_2, y_2) = (-y_1, x_1)$, as shown in Figure 2.13.

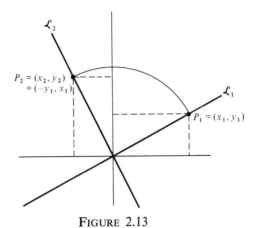

FIGURE 2.13

Substituting the coordinates into the equations of the lines, we have $A_1x_1 + B_1y_1 = 0$, and $A_2x_2 + B_2y_2 = A_2(-y_1) + B_2x_1 = 0$. Since neither line is vertical, we may assume that $x_1 \neq 0$ and $B_1 \neq 0$; hence we have the two equations

$$\frac{y_1}{x_1} = -\frac{A_1}{B_1} \quad \text{and} \quad \frac{y_1}{x_1} = \frac{B_2}{A_2},$$

from which

$$\frac{B_2}{A_2} + \frac{A_1}{B_1} = 0,$$

or equivalently

$$A_1A_2 + B_1B_2 = 0.$$

Question: What happens if one of the lines is vertical?

2.2-3 Definition: Two lines having equations $A_1x + B_1y + C_1 = 0$ and $A_2x + B_2y + C_2 = 0$ are said to be *perpendicular* iff

$$A_1A_2 + B_1B_2 = 0.$$

These conditions for parallelism and perpendicularity are important conditions and will be used later on in vector considerations. These conditions may also be stated in terms of slope. We have already noted that parallel lines having slope have equal slope; the following relationship exists for slopes of perpendicular lines having slope.

2.2-4 Theorem: Two lines $y = m_1x + b_1$ and $y = m_2x + b_2$ are perpendicular iff

$$m_1 = -\frac{1}{m_2}.$$

(Perpendicular lines have slopes that are negative reciprocals.) The proof is left to the reader (Exercise 11).

Half-Lines

We conclude this section with a definition for the *half-line*.

2.2-5   Definition: If $\mathcal{L}$ is a line having equation $y = mx + b$, and p is a real number, then the sets

$$\mathcal{H} = \{(x, y) : y = mx + b \text{ and } x \geqslant p\},$$

and

$$\mathcal{K} = \{(x, y) : y = mx + b \text{ and } x \leqslant p\}$$

are called *half-lines* with *initial point* $(p, mp + b)$. If $\mathcal{L}$ has equation $x = c$, then the sets

$$\mathcal{H} = \{(x, y) : x = c \text{ and } y \geqslant p\},$$

and

$$\mathcal{K} = \{(x, y) : x = c \text{ and } y \leqslant p\}$$

are called *half-lines* with initial point (c, p).

Example: The set $\mathcal{S} = \{(x, y) : y = 2x + 3 \text{ and } x \leqslant -1\}$ is the half-line shown in Figure 2.14.

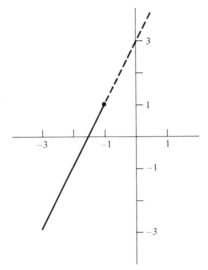

FIGURE 2.14

Example: The set of points on the *x*-axis associated with the interval $[a, \infty)$ is a half-line.

EXERCISES 2.2

1. Write an equation for a line having slope *m* passing through *P*. Give answers in slope intercept form and graph the line.

     a. $m = 2; P = (1, 4)$.   b. $m = -4; P = (-2, 3)$.

     c. $m = -\frac{1}{3}; P = (0, -2)$.   d. $m = \frac{2}{5}; P = (1, 1)$.

2. Write an equation for a line passing through the two given points. Give answers in slope intercept form and graph the line.

     a. $(2, 3); (-1, 4)$.   b. $(1, -1); (5, -2)$.

     c. $(-3, 2); (5, 2)$.   d. $(1, 1); (6, 6)$.

3. Graph the collection of lines passing through $(0, 0)$ having slope *m* in the interval given.

     a. $[0, 1]$.   b. $[1, \infty)$.

     c. $[-1, 0]$.   d. $(-\infty, -1]$.

4. For the point and line given, find the equation of a line through the point that is parallel to the line.

     a. $(3, -5); 3x + 2y = 10$.   b. $(-2, -1); x - y = 16$.

     c. $(6, 4); 3x - 5y = 20$.   d. $(1, 2); -4x + 2y = 7$.

5. For the point and line given in Exercise 4, find the equation of a line through the point perpendicular to the line.

6. Explain why

$$S = \left\{ (x, y) : \frac{y - y_0}{x - x_0} = m \right\}$$

is *not* the same as

$$\mathcal{L} = \{(x, y) : y - y_0 = m(x - x_0)\} .$$

7. Show that if the equation of a line can be written in the form $(x/a) + (y/b) = 1$, then *a* and *b* are the intercepts of the *x*-axis and *y*-axis respectively. Find the intercepts of the lines given. Use this information to graph the line.

     a. $2x + 7y = 14$.   b. $3x - 2y = 24$.

     c. $-4x + y = 7$.   d. $7x - y = 2$.

8. Let $\mathcal{L}_0$ denote the line passing through the origin that is parallel to $\mathcal{L}$. Similarly with S_0 and S. Argue that $\mathcal{L}$ and S are perpendicular iff $\mathcal{L}_0$ and S_0 are perpendicular.

9. Graph the following pairs of lines. Show that they are perpendicular.

     a. $2x + 3y - 3 = 0; 2x - \frac{4}{3}y + 1 = 0$.

     b. $-x + 2y + 2 = 0; 4x + 2y - 7 = 0$.

     c. $5x + 3y = 0; 2x - \frac{10}{3}y + 2 = 0$.

10. Graph the following pairs of lines. Show that they are parallel.

     a. $3x - y + 2 = 0; -6 + 2y + 3 = 0$.

     b. $4x + 2y = 7; 8x + 4y = 5$.

     c. $-x + 3y = 2; -3x + 9y = 6$.

11. Prove Theorem 2.2-4.

12. Graph the following half-lines.
   a. $y = 2x + 4$ and $x \geqslant 1$.   b. $y = -x - 2$ and $x \leqslant 0$.
   c. $x = 3$ and $y \leqslant 2$.

13. Graph each of the following pairs of half-lines.
   a. $y = 2x - 1$ and $x \geqslant 0$, $y = -x + 2$ and $x \leqslant 3$.
   b. $y = 3x + 4$ and $x \leqslant 1$, $y = 2x - 3$ and $x \geqslant 4$.

14. Find a half-line that has the same initial point as the half-line $y = -4x - 1$ and $x \geqslant 1$, and that is parallel to the line $y = 2x + 6$.

2.3   REFLECTION SYMMETRIES

In this section we examine some invariances under certain reflections that characterize some relations. These reflection invariances are called *symmetries* of various types.

Definitions of Symmetries

In Chapter I, we defined a relation T to be *symmetric* provided that $(a, b) \in T \Rightarrow (b, a) \in T$, or equivalently, provided that $T = T^{-1}$. This means that if you find a point of T, then the point obtained by interchanging the components of the coordinate of the given point is also in T. Geometrically this means that the graph of T can be reflected about the line $x = y$ without being changed. (See Figure 2.15.)

2.3-1   Definition: A relation $f \subset \mathbf{R} \times \mathbf{R}$ is *symmetric* iff

$$(x, y) \in f \Rightarrow (y, x) \in f.$$

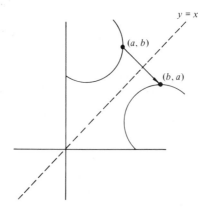

FIGURE 2.15

There are other symmetries of interest, and a knowledge of them can be very helpful in graphing.

2.3-2 Definition: A relation $f \subset \mathbf{R} \times \mathbf{R}$ is *symmetric through the origin* provided that

$$(x, y) \in f \Rightarrow (-x, -y) \in f.$$

The graph of a relation symmetric through the origin has the property that any point on the graph has a reflection through $(0, 0)$, which is also on the graph. (See Figure 2.16.)

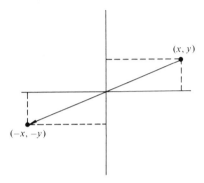

FIGURE 2.16

Example: The relations in $\mathbf{R} \times \mathbf{R}$ described by (a) $y = x^3$; (b) $\{(x, y) : x^2 + y^2 \leqslant 4\}$; and (c) $\{(1, 1), (-1, 1)\}$ are all symmetric through the origin. These relations are graphed in Figure 2.17.

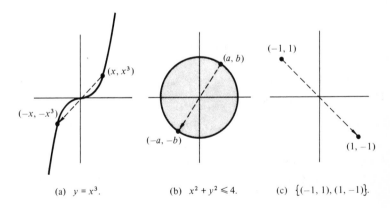

(a) $y = x^3$.   (b) $x^2 + y^2 \leqslant 4$.   (c) $\{(-1, 1), (1, -1)\}$.

FIGURE 2.17

Another type of symmetry is *symmetry about the ordinate* or *y*-axis.

2.3-3   Definition: A relation $f \subset \mathbf{R} \times \mathbf{R}$ is *symmetric about the ordinate* if and only if

$$(x, y) \in f \Rightarrow (-x, y) \in f.$$

Geometrically, this means the reflection of a point on the graph across the y-axis results in another point on the graph. (See Figure 2.18.) The graphs of

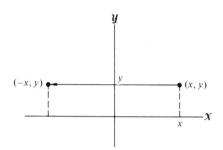

FIGURE 2.18

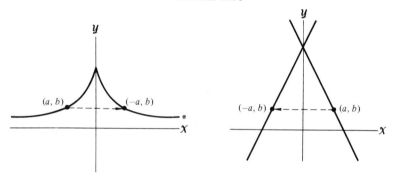

FIGURE 2.19

two relations with symmetry about the ordinate are shown in Figure 2.19. The last type of symmetry we mention here is *symmetry about the abscissa*.

2.3-4   Definition: A relation $f \subset \mathbf{R} \times \mathbf{R}$ is *symmetric about the abscissa* iff

$$(x, y) \in f \Rightarrow (x, -y) \in f.$$

A relation is thus symmetric about the abscissa provided the reflection of any point of the graph across the x-axis results in a point on the graph. (See Figure 2.20.)

Applications

Very often one can apply reflection symmetries to simplify the problem of graphing a given relation. For example, if one knows that a relation is

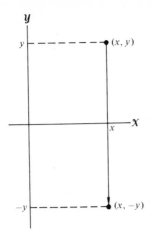

FIGURE 2.20

symmetric about the ordinate, then it is sufficient to compute points in the graph on the right (or left) of the y-axis, and reflect across the axis to obtain the remaining points.

Example: Graph the relation $x^2y^2 = 1$. We note that this relation has all of the symmetries mentioned in this section. (Verify this!) It is therefore adequate to consider the restricted values $x \geqslant 0$, $y \geqslant 0$, and $x \geqslant y$ (in which case, $x^2y^2 = 1$ iff $xy = 1$). Thus, let us graph $xy = 1$, or $y = 1/x$, where $x \geqslant y$. (See Figure 2.21.)

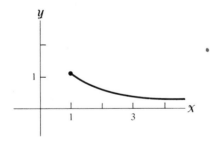

FIGURE 2.21

Thus, by applying the symmetries we know the relation possesses, we have the entire graph in Figure 2.22. (Explain!)

EXERCISES 2.3

1. Show that if a relation possesses any two of the following types of symmetry, then it possesses the third: (a) symmetry through the origin; (b) symmetry about the abscissa; (c) symmetry about the ordinate.

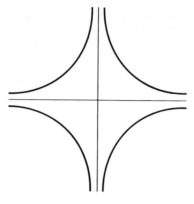

FIGURE 2.22

2. Graph the reflection of $y = x^2$ (a) through the origin; (b) through the ordinate; (c) through the abscissa; (d) through the line $x = y$; (e) through the line $y = -x$.

3. How would you state a definition for a relation to be symmetric through the line $y = -x$?

4. Develop a method for checking statements involving x and y to determine whether the relation described has (a) symmetry; (b) symmetry about the x-axis; (c) symmetry about the y-axis; (d) symmetry about the line $y = -x$. (For example, if on interchanging x and y throughout, a statement remains unchanged in meaning, then the relation is symmetric.)

5. Use the methods of Exercise 4 to test the following relations for symmetries.
   a. $5xy = 1$.   b. $xy^2 + x^2 = 3$.
   c. $x^3y^5 + x^2y = 3$.   d. $xy^3 + x^3y = 0$.
   e. $x^4 + 3y^3 = 1$.

6. Test each of the following relations for symmetries, and, as well as possible, graph the relation.
   a. $x^2y^2 = 4$.   b. $xy = 5 - x^2$
   c. $5 - xy = x^2$.   d. $y = 2 - 3x^2$.
   e. $xy = 5$.   f. $3xy = 1 - x^2$.
   g. $y = 2x$.   h. $-xy = 1$.

7. Show that $|x| + |y| = 1$ is the equation for the figure in Figure 2.4. (HINT: Consider the case $x \geqslant 0$ and $y \geqslant 0$ and apply symmetry techniques.)

2.4 CIRCLES AND ELLIPSES WITH CENTERS AT O

Circles

From elementary geometry we recall that a circle is the set of all points whose distance from a given point is a fixed number. We shall now adapt this definition to analytic geometry and study the constraining equations for circles.

2.4-1   **Definition:** A *circle* is a set $\mathcal{K}$ of points in $\mathbf{R} \times \mathbf{R}$ whose distance from a point $A = (x_0, y_0)$ is some fixed positive number r. The point A is called the *center* of $\mathcal{K}$. Any line segment between the center and a point on $\mathcal{K}$ is called a *radius*.

Remark: The number r is the common length of all the radii, but we will often refer (incorrectly) to r itself as the radius, instead of calling r the length of the radii.

Let us now find a constraining equation for a circle $\mathcal{K}$ with center O and radius r (See Figure 2.23.). The distance between two points (a, b) and (c, d) is $\sqrt{(a - c)^2 + (b - d)^2}$. Thus $\mathcal{K}$ can be described as follows:

$$\mathcal{K} = \{(x, y) : \sqrt{x^2 + y^2} = r\} \quad \text{or} \quad \mathcal{K} = \{(x, y) : x^2 + y^2 = r^2\}.$$

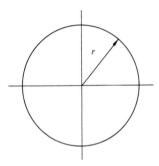

FIGURE 2.23

Suppose $(x, y) \in \mathcal{K}$, then $x^2 + y^2 = r^2$. But then we would also have $(-x, y)$, $(x, -y)$ and $(-x, -y)$ as points in $\mathcal{K}$. This tells us that $\mathcal{K}$ is symmetric with respect to the x-axis, the y-axis, and the origin. In fact, one can show that $\mathcal{K}$ is symmetric with respect to any line containing the center and that these are the only lines of symmetry. (See Figure 2.24.)

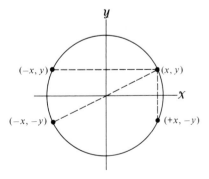

FIGURE 2.24

Question: What is the radius of the circle described by $x^2 + y^2 = 2$?

Ellipses

We now consider another important type of plane figure (subset of $\mathbf{R}^2$), called the ellipse. The ellipse differs from the circle in that we have two given points to which we consider distances.

2.4-2 Definition: Let $F_1 = (x_1, y_1)$ and $F_2 = (x_2, y_2)$ be two points in the plane and let $\mathfrak{IC}$ be the set of all points $X = (x, y)$ such that $d(X, F_1) + d(X, F_2)$ is a fixed positive number k. The relation $\mathfrak{IC}$ is called an *ellipse;* F_1 and F_2 are called the *foci* of $\mathfrak{IC}$ and $C = ((x_1 + x_2)/2, (y_1 + y_2)/2)$ is called the *center* of $\mathfrak{IC}$.

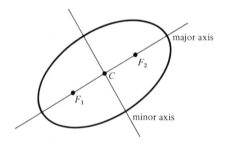

FIGURE 2.25

The line containing F_1 and F_2 is called the *major axis* of the ellipse and the line containing C, which is perpendicular to the major axis, is called the *minor axis.* (See Figure 2.25.)

Major Axis the X-Axis

Let us consider an ellipse $\mathfrak{IC}$ whose center is at the origin, whose major axis is the x-axis, and whose minor axis is the y-axis. Since the major axis is the x-axis and O is the center, the foci must be of the form $(c, 0)$ and $(-c, 0)$, where $c > 0$. Thus (See Figure 2.26.),

$$\mathfrak{IC} = \{(x, y) : d((x, y), (c, 0)) + d((x, y), (-c, 0)) = k\}.$$

The three points X, F_1, and F_2 are the vertices of a triangle, and since the sum of the lengths of two sides of a triangle is greater than the length of the third, we have

$$k = d(X, F_1) + d(X, F_2) > 2c.$$

Thus $k/2 > c$. It follows that $(k/2, 0) \in \mathfrak{IC}$, since

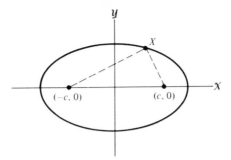

FIGURE 2.26

$$d\left(\left(\frac{k}{2},0\right),(c,0)\right) + d\left(\left(\frac{k}{2},0\right),(-c,0)\right) = \sqrt{\left(\frac{k}{2}-c\right)^2} + \sqrt{\left(\frac{k}{2}+c\right)^2}$$

$$= \left|\frac{k}{2}-c\right| + \left|\frac{k}{2}+c\right| = \left(\frac{k}{2}-c\right) + \left(\frac{k}{2}+c\right) = \frac{k}{2}+\frac{k}{2} = k.$$

Similarly, $(-k/2, 0) \in \mathfrak{IC}$.

For simplification of notation, let $a = k/2$. Thus $\mathfrak{IC}$ intersects $\mathfrak{X}$ the x-axis at $(a, 0)$ and $(-a, 0)$, as shown in Figure 2.27.

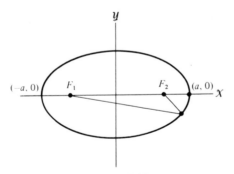

FIGURE 2.27

Consider a point on the ellipse that is on the y-axis; that is, suppose we let $x = 0$, and determine the corresponding values of y. Now

$$k = 2a = d((0, y), (c, 0)) + d((0, y), (-c, 0))$$

$$= \sqrt{c^2 + y^2} + \sqrt{y^2 + c^2} = 2\sqrt{c^2 + y^2}.$$

Therefore, $a^2 = c^2 + y^2$, from which $y^2 = a^2 - c^2$. Thus, if we let $b = \sqrt{a^2 - c^2}$, we see that $\mathfrak{IC}$ intersects $\mathfrak{Y}$ the y-axis at $(0, b)$ and $(0, -b)$.

Exercise: Read the above discussion again, interchanging x and y throughout.

2.4-3 **Definition:** The points of intersection of the major and minor axes with the ellipse ℑ𝒞 are called the *vertices*. The line segment between the vertices of ℑ𝒞 on the major axis is called the *major diameter* of ℑ𝒞, and the segment between the vertices on the minor axis is called the *minor diameter*. (See Figure 2.28.)

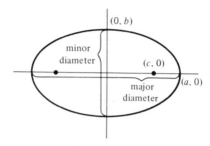

FIGURE 2.28

Let us now simplify the constraining equation for an ellipse with center at O. We have

$$2a = \sqrt{(x - c)^2 + y^2} + \sqrt{(x + c)^2 + y^2}.$$

Squaring both sides we have

$$4a^2 = [(x - c)^2 + y^2] + 2\sqrt{(x - c)^2 + y^2} \, \sqrt{(x + c)^2 + y^2} + [(x + c)^2 + y^2],$$

which simplifies to

$$2a^2 - x^2 - c^2 - y^2 = \sqrt{(x - c)^2 + y^2} \, \sqrt{(x + c)^2 + y^2}.$$

Now, squaring both sides again and simplifying, we have

$$a^4 - a^2x^2 - a^2c^2 - a^2y^2 + x^2c^2 = 0.$$

Thus

$$(a^2 - c^2)x^2 + a^2y^2 = a^2(a^2 - c^2).$$

Since $a^2 - c^2 = b^2 \neq 0$ and $a^2 \neq 0$, we can write this equation in the convenient *standard form* as

$$\frac{x^2}{a^2} + \frac{y^2}{b^2} = 1.$$

Major Axis the Y-Axis

If $\mathcal{L}$ is an ellipse whose major axis is the y-axis and whose minor axis is the x-axis with foci $(0, c)$ and $(0, -c)$, then it can be viewed as a reflection of ℑ𝒞 about the line $x = y$. Thus the equation of $\mathcal{L}$ can be obtained from the equation of $\mathcal{K}$ by interchanging x and y, yielding the standard form

$$\frac{y^2}{a^2} + \frac{x^2}{b^2} = 1.$$

General Comments

Since $a^2 > b^2$, we can always tell from the standard form whether the x-axis or the y-axis is the major axis by observing which denominator is the larger. In either case, if $(x, y) \in \mathcal{K}$, an ellipse with center at O having $\mathcal{X}$ or $\mathcal{Y}$ as major axis, then $(-x, y)$, $(x, -y)$, and $(-x, -y) \in \mathcal{K}$. Thus $\mathcal{K}$ is symmetric with respect to its center and each of its axes. These are the only lines or points through which $\mathcal{K}$ is symmetric. (See Figure 2.29.)

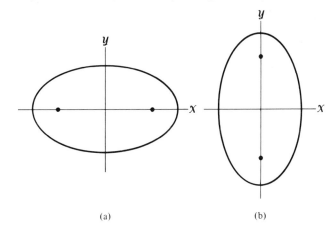

(a)   (b)

FIGURE 2.29

Remark: We should like to point out a useful interpretation of the relationship $b^2 = a^2 - c^2$. In general, if $2a$ is the length of the major diameter of an ellipse, $2b$ the length of the minor diameter, and $2c$ the distance between the focal points, then $b^2 = a^2 - c^2$, or equivalently, $a^2 = b^2 + c^2$. By the Pythagorean theorem, then a is also the length of the hypotenuse of the right triangle formed by the center K of the ellipse, a focal point F, and a vertex V on the minor axis. (See Figure 2.30.)

Example: Find the constraining equation and graph the ellipse whose center is O with a focus at $(-3, 0)$ and a vertex at $(0, -2)$.

Solution: Since one focus is $(-3, 0)$, the major axis is the x-axis, so the constraining equation will be of the form

$$\frac{x^2}{a^2} + \frac{y^2}{b^2} = 1.$$

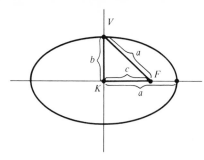

FIGURE 2.30

We know that a is the distance from the center to either vertex on the major axis, and that b is the distance from the center to either vertex on the minor axis. The distance of each focus from the center is given by c, where $b^2 = a^2 - c^2$. We are given that $c = 3$ and $b = 2$, from which $a = \sqrt{9 + 4} = \sqrt{13}$. Thus, the equation for $\mathcal{K}$ is $(x^2/13) + (y^2/4) = 1$, and its graph is shown in Figure 2.31.

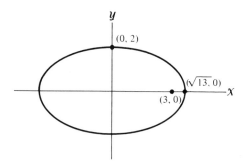

FIGURE 2.31

Example: Find the equation and graph the ellipse whose center is O, one of whose foci is $(0, 3)$ and whose minor diameter is 6 units long.

Solution: Since $(0, 3)$ is a focus and O is the center, the x-axis is the minor axis and the y-axis is the major axis, so the constraining equation is of the form $(y^2/a^2) + (x^2/b^2) = 1$. Now b is the distance from each vertex on the minor axis to the center, so $2b$ must be the length of the minor diameter. Thus $b = 3$. Since c is the distance from the center to a focus, $c = 3$. Therefore we have $c^2 + b^2 = 18 = a^2$, and hence an equation of the ellipse is $(y^2/18) + (x^2/9) = 1$, and the graph is shown in Figure 2.32.

Summary

We summarize our work here regarding ellipses by indicating how to graph the figure when the constraining equation is in standard form.

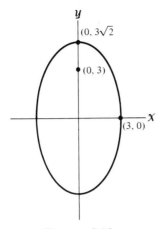

FIGURE 2.32

The equation for an ellipse with center at O takes the form

$$\frac{x^2}{\alpha^2} + \frac{y^2}{\beta^2} = 1.$$

When the equation is in this form, we know that it is the equation of an ellipse with center at O that crosses the x-axis at $\pm\alpha$ and crosses the y-axis at $\pm\beta$. (See Figure 2.33.) The relative size of α and β determines the major axis.

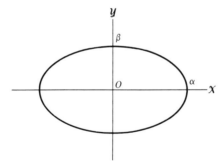

FIGURE 2.33

If one wishes to know the location of the focal points, he need only compute c^2 as discussed in the earlier remark.

Example: Graph the equation $6x^2 + 4y^2 = 24$.
    On dividing both sides of the equation by 24 we obtain

$$\frac{x^2}{4} + \frac{y^2}{6} = 1.$$

This equation can be written as

$$\frac{x^2}{2^2} + \frac{y^2}{(\sqrt{6})^2} = 1.$$

Thus, we have the ellipse in Figure 2.34.

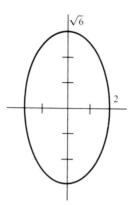

FIGURE 2.34

EXERCISES 2.4

1. Construct an ellipse with the use of a piece of string and two thumbtacks.
2. Graph the relation described by the given equation.

   a. $\frac{x^2}{9} + \frac{y^2}{16} = 1.$ b $x^2 + 25y^2 = 100.$

   c. $12x^2 + 75y^2 = 1.$ d. $x^2 + y^2 = 25.$

   e. $3x^2 = -3y^2 + 25.$ f. $\frac{x^2}{6} + \frac{y^2}{4} = 6.$

   g. $x^2 + y^2 = 0.$ h. $\frac{x^2}{16} + \frac{y^2}{9} = 0.$

3. Graph and give the constraining equation of the circles or ellipses whose center is the origin and that satisfies the following condition.
   a. The circle with radius $\frac{2}{3}$.
   b. The circle that contains the point $(-3, 5)$.
   c. The ellipse that has a major diameter is 8 and one focus at $(-3, 0)$.
   d. The ellipse that contains the points $(3, -2)$ and $(-2, 4)$.
   e. The ellipse whose major diameter is 12, whose minor diameter is 10, and whose major axis is the y-axis.
   f. The ellipse that has as vertices $(0, 4)$ and $(0, -4)$ and that has as focus $(0, 3)$.
4. a. Find the equations of a circle and an ellipse with major axis y, both having

centers at O and intersecting at $(10, 24)$, where the radius of the circle is equal the minor diameter of the ellipse.

   b. Find all other points of intersection.

5. A satellite travels around the earth in an elliptical orbit having the center of the earth as a focus. Assume the earth is of radius 4000 miles and the highest point (apogee) the satellite reaches is 350 miles and the lowest point (perigee) is 50 miles above the surface of the earth. What is an equation of its path?

6. Argue that two identical elliptical gears will "mesh," where each rotates on a bearing placed at its left focal point, as shown in Figure 2.35.

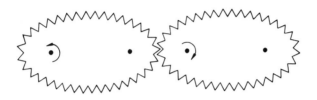

FIGURE 2.35

7. A *latus rectum* of an ellipse is a chord that passes through a focal point and that is perpendicular to the major axis. Show that the length of the latus rectum is $2b^2/a$, where the major diameter is $2a$ and the minor diameter is $2b$.

2.5 PARABOLAS WITH CENTERS AT O

In our study of the ellipse, we considered sets of points distinguished by the property that each point had the same total distance to two fixed points. We now consider a slightly different method of distinguishing interesting sets of points, using in this case a fixed line and a fixed point. These relations consist of sets of points in which each point has (perpendicular) distance to the given line equal to its distance to the fixed point. We shall see later that the ellipse could have been described using a similar method.

2.5-1   **Definition:** Let $\mathcal{L}$ be a line and F a point not on $\mathcal{L}$. A set $\mathcal{P}$ of points each of which has distance to F equal to its (perpendicular) distance to $\mathcal{L}$ is called a *parabola*. The point F is called the *focus* of $\mathcal{P}$ and the line $\mathcal{L}$ is called the *directrix*. The line $\mathfrak{M}$ perpendicular to $\mathcal{L}$ passing through F is called the *axis* of $\mathcal{P}$. The midpoint of the segment between F and $\mathcal{L} \cap \mathfrak{M}$ is called the *center* of $\mathcal{P}$. (See Figure 2.36.)

Axis Horizontal

Let us now find an analytic description of a parabola. We shall begin by finding an equation for a parabola $\mathcal{P}$ whose center is O and whose axis is the

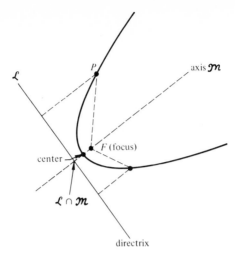

FIGURE 2.36

x-axis. We could have two cases; one where the focus is $(c, 0)$ and the other where the focus is $(-c, 0)$, $(c > 0)$. First consider the case in which the focus is $(c, 0)$. In this case, the directrix is the line $x = -c$, as shown in Figure 2.37.

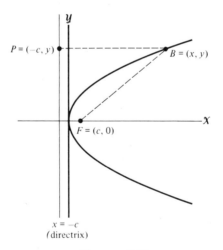

FIGURE 2.37

If $B = (x, y)$ is on $\mathcal{P}$ then B lies on the same side of the directrix as the focus, for otherwise the distance to the directrix would be less than the distance to the focus. Further, the distance from $B = (x, y)$ to the directrix $x = -c$ can be determined by computing the distance from B to the point $P = (-c, y)$. If $B \in \mathcal{P}$, then

$$d(B, P) = \sqrt{(x - (-c))^2 + (y - y)^2} = \sqrt{(x + c)^2} = |x + c|,$$

and

$$d(B, F) = \sqrt{(x - c)^2 + y^2}.$$

Since $d(B, F) = d(B, P)$, we have the equation

$$\sqrt{(x - c)^2 + y^2} = |x + c|.$$

Squaring both sides (a process that can be reversed since $x \geqslant -c$) we have

$$x^2 - 2cx + c^2 + y^2 = x^2 + 2cx + c^2,$$

which simplifies to the *standard-form* equation

$$y^2 = 4cx.$$

We see that $O \in \mathcal{P}$, verifying that the intersection of $\mathcal{P}$ with its axis is its center. The center of a parabola is also called its *vertex*, to carry over an analogy with the ellipse. If $(x, y) \in \mathcal{P}$, then so is $(x, -y)$; that is, we see that $\mathcal{P}$ is symmetric with respect to its axis. It possesses none of the other symmetries discussed earlier. A graph of $\mathcal{P}$ is shown in Figure 2.38.

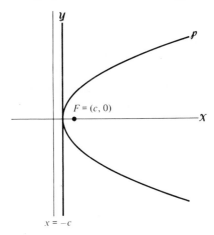

FIGURE 2.38

Suppose we now consider the case where $(-c, 0)$ $(c > 0)$ is the focus and the directrix is the line $x = c$. An argument similar to the one above may be used to establish that the constraining equation in this case is given by

$$-4cx = y^2.$$

A graph of this parabola is shown in Figure 2.39.

We have thus determined the standard form

$$y^2 = 4px$$

for a parabola with vertex at $(0, 0)$ and focus on the x-axis a distance $|p|$ from

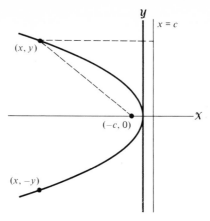

FIGURE 2.39

$O = (0, 0)$. If $p > 0$, then the parabola extends to the right and if $p < 0$, it extends to the left.

Axis Vertical

The case in which the center is O and the focus is $(0, c)$ can be obtained from our first case by reflecting about the line $x = y$. (See Figure 2.40.) The equation is thus obtained by simply interchanging x and y in the equation obtained with focus $(c, 0)$, and is given by

$$x^2 = 4cy.$$

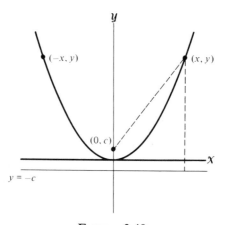

FIGURE 2.40

Similarly, the case in which the center is O and the focus is $(0, -c)$ can be obtained from our second case by reflecting about the line $x = y$. (See Figure 2.41.)

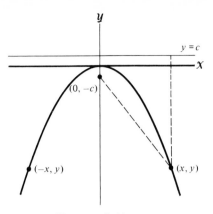

FIGURE 2.41

Thus, the standard form for a parabola with vertex at O and focus on the y-axis a distance $|p|$ from O is the equation

$$x^2 = 4py.$$

If $p > 0$, the parabola extends upward and if $p < 0$ it extends downward.

Example: Find an equation and graph of a parabola whose center is O, whose axis is the y-axis and whose focus is $(0, -2)$.

Solution: Since the center is O, the axis is the y-axis, and the focus is below the x-axis, the equation is of the form $x^2 = -4cy$. Since c is the distance

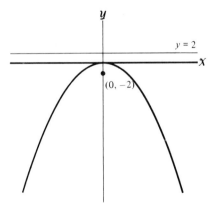

FIGURE 2.42

from the focus to the center, $c = 2$. Thus, a constraining equation is $x^2 = -8y$. The graph is shown in Figure 2.42.

Summary

We have determined how to graph equations

$$y = \alpha x^2 \quad \text{and} \quad x = \beta y^2.$$

These equations yield parabolas with center at O according to the previous discussion. We should like to make some general comments on the large family of parabolas given by $y = \alpha x^2$, each of which also determines a function. If $\alpha > 0$, then the parabola trails up into quadrants I and II. The larger α is, the steeper the curve for any particular value of x. The nearer α is to 0, the "flatter" the curve, and if $\alpha < 0$, the curve has "flipped" across the x-axis and thus extends into quadrants III and IV. (See Figure 2.43.)

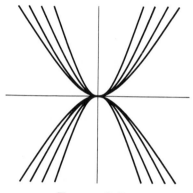

FIGURE 2.43

Example: Graph $y = -8x^2$. First observe that the curve must have symmetry about the y-axis. Also, we can put our equation in the form $y = 4(-2)x^2$ and deduce that the focus is $(0, -2)$. We can get a further feel for the steepness of the graph by noticing that the point $(1, -8)$ is in the parabola. Hence the graph is shown in Figure 2.44.

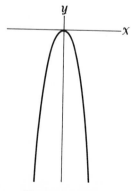

FIGURE 2.44

In a later chapter, we will consider the more general problem in which the center may be different from $(0, 0)$ and the directrix may be any line.

EXERCISES 2.5

1. Graph each of the following and locate the focus and the directrix.
   a. $y = x^2$.
   b. $12x - y^2 = 0$.
   c. $y = -6x^2$.
   d. $x^2 - 4y = 0$.
   e. $3y^2 + x = 0$.
   f. $2x^2 + y = 0$.
   g. $x^2 = 14y$.
   h. $4x^2 + y = 0$.

2. Graph and give the equation for the parabola that has its center at the origin and that satisfies the condition:
   a. The focus is $(-1, 0)$.
   b. The directrix is $y = -4$.
   c. Contains the point $(2, 32)$ and has the y-axis as its axis of symmetry.
   d. Contains the points $(1, -6)$ and $(-1, -6)$.
   e. The directrix lies to the right and is parallel to the y-axis, and the parabola passes through the intersection of the horizontal lines containing the foci of the ellipse with the ellipse

$$\frac{x^2}{9} + \frac{y^2}{25} = 1.$$

3. The width of a parabola is 16 in. at a distance of 6 in. along the axis from the vertex. How wide is it at the focus?

4. A parabolic arch has the dimensions shown in Figure 2.45. Find the equation of the parabola with respect to the axes as shown. Compute the values of y at $x = 2$, $x = 4$, $x = 8$, and $x = 16$.

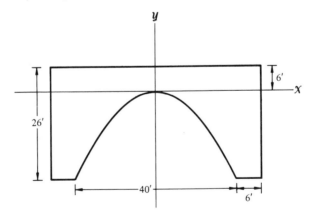

FIGURE 2.45

5. A bridge is 2000 feet long and is supported by a suspension cable attached to a tower at each end. The towers are 100 feet high and the cable is 20 feet from the bridge at its closest point P. (a) Give the equation of the cable if it forms a parabola with the point P as the origin. (b) If a second cable connects the bridge to the suspension cable at a point 50 feet from a tower, how long is it?

6. The chord through the focus of a parabola that is perpendicular to the axis of the parabola is called the *latus rectum*. Determine a general formula for the length of the latus rectum of a parabola.

2.6 LIMITS AND ASYMPTOTES

We shall now consider two important topics that will aid us further in graphing and interpreting functions. These are the topics of limits and asymptotes.

Limits

The limit notion is fundamental in the study of calculus and we shall only state intuitive definitions and some of the resulting theorems. In order to prove theorems involving limits one must have rigorous definitions that are beyond the scope of this text.

Example: Define $f(x) = 1/x$. Some corresponding values of x and $f(x)$ are listed in the following table:

x	$f(x)$
$\frac{1}{2}$	2
1	1
$\frac{3}{2}$	$\frac{2}{3}$
2	$\frac{1}{2}$
3	$\frac{1}{3}$
4	$\frac{1}{4}$
100	$\frac{1}{100}$
$10,000$	$\frac{1}{10,000}$

Notice that as the value of the domain variable x increases, the corresponding functional values $f(x)$ become nearer to zero. Thus, as x grows

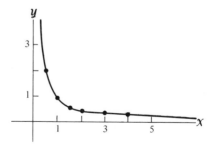

FIGURE 2.46

extremely large (symbolized by "$x \to \infty$," read "x goes to infinity"), the functional value $f(x)$ gets extremely close to 0 (symbolized by "$f(x) \to 0$," read "$f(x)$ goes to zero"). (See Figure 2.46.)

Example: Let us again look at $f(x) = 1/x$. We now want to know what happens to the functional values of f as we take values for x that are very close to 2 (but not equal to 2).

x	$f(x)$
1	1
$\frac{3}{2}$	$\frac{2}{3}$
$\frac{7}{4}$	$\frac{4}{7}$
$\frac{31}{16}$	$\frac{16}{31}$
$\frac{33}{16}$	$\frac{16}{33}$
$\frac{9}{4}$	$\frac{4}{9}$

We see from the table that if x gets close to 2, then $f(x)$ gets close to $\frac{1}{2}$. (As $x \to 2$, $f(x) \to \frac{1}{2}$.)

Example: Let $g(x) = (x^2 - 1)/x^2 = 1 - (1/x^2)$. As $x \to \infty$, what happens to $g(x)$? It appears that $g(x) \to 1$. Also note that as $x \to 1$, $g(x) \to 0$.

We now state an "intuitive definition" of the limit concept.

2.6-1 **Definition:** Let a and b be real numbers and $f : R \to R$.
   i. The symbol
$$\text{"}\lim_{x \to a} f(x) = b\text{"}$$
   means that if x is sufficiently close to a, then $f(x)$ is close to b. (Note that "close" and "sufficiently close" have no precise meaning here, and thus our apology for not being rigorous.)
   ii. The symbol
$$\text{"}\lim_{x \to \infty} f(x) = b\text{"}$$
   means that if x is very large, then $f(x)$ is very near b.
   iii. The symbol
$$\text{"}\lim_{x \to a} f(x) = \infty\text{"}$$
   means that $f(x)$ can be made larger than any given number by taking x sufficiently near a.

Remark: Similar definitions hold for $-\infty$.

Example: If $f(x) = 1 - (1/x^2)$, then $\lim_{x\to\infty} f(x) = 1$, $\lim_{x\to1} f(x) = 0$, and $\lim_{x\to2} f(x) = \frac{3}{4}$.

Example: If $g(x) = 2/(1 - x^2)$, then $\lim_{x\to0} g(x) = 2$, $\lim_{x\to1} g(x) = \infty$, and $\lim_{x\to\infty} g(x) = 0$.

It is also useful to discuss limits in which the domain values are close to the number a, but are restricted to values only to the right or only to the left of a.

Example: If $f(x) = 1/x$, then $\lim_{x \to 0^+} f(x) = \infty$ (this means that $f(x)$ gets very large as x approaches 0 *from the right*). Also, $\lim_{x \to 0^-} f(x) = -\infty$ ($f(x)$ gets very large in the negative direction as x approaches 0 *from the left*). Thus, as x approaches 0 from the right, $f(x)$ takes on large positive values, but as x goes to 0 from the left, $f(x)$ takes on negative values that are large in absolute value.

Example: If $f(x) = 1/(1 - x)$, then

$$\lim_{x \to 1^+} f(x) = -\infty \quad \text{and} \quad \lim_{x \to 1^-} f(x) = \infty \, .$$

But $\lim_{x \to 1} f(x)$ does not exist, since merely taking x near 1 does not guarantee that the values of f are large (or small).

The process of finding limits is sometimes very difficult and to do more than scratch the surface would require precise definitions. However, for the simple cases with which we shall deal, a simple intuitive feel for numbers and functions along with the following limit facts should suffice.

2.6-2 Theorem: (The limit theorem). Suppose that $f : R \to R$, $g : R \to R$, and

$$\lim_{x \to a} f(x) = b \quad \text{and} \quad \lim_{x \to a} g(x) = d,$$

then

i. $\lim_{x \to a} (f(x) + g(x)) = \lim_{x \to a} f(x) + \lim_{x \to a} g(x) = b + d;$

ii. $\lim_{x \to a} f(x)g(x) = (\lim_{x \to a} f(x))(\lim_{x \to a} g(x)) = bd;$

iii. for every $c \in R$,

$$\lim_{x \to a} cf(x) = c \lim_{x \to a} f(x) = cb;$$

iv. if $d \neq 0$, then

$$\lim_{x \to a} \frac{f(x)}{g(x)} = \frac{\lim_{x \to a} f(x)}{\lim_{x \to a} g(x)} = \frac{b}{d}.$$

Example: Let

$$f(x) = \frac{2x^3 + 2x^2 - 1}{x^3 + 1}.$$

Then

$$\lim_{x \to 1} f(x) = \tfrac{3}{2} \quad \text{and} \quad \lim_{x \to \infty} f(x) = 2.$$

You may question this assertion. Note, however, that on dividing numerator and denominator by x^3 we have

$$f(x) = \frac{2 + (2/x) - (1/x^3)}{1 + (1/x^3)}$$

for nonzero x. Since

$$\lim_{x \to \infty} \left(\frac{2}{x}\right) = 0 \quad \text{and} \quad \lim_{x \to \infty} \left(\frac{1}{x^3}\right) = 0,$$

it follows from the limit theorem that

$$\lim_{x \to \infty} f(x) = 2.$$

Asymptotes

It is interesting and useful to see how certain limits can be interpreted graphically. Suppose, for example, that f is a function such that $\lim_{x \to \infty} f(x) = 5$. Then we know that for sufficiently large x, the function must behave essentially as the constant function 5. Knowing this is a great help in graphing f, since we need not worry about finding ordered pairs and plotting f for large values of x in such a case. Suppose it is also known that $\lim_{x \to -\infty} f(x) = 0$ (that is, $f(x)$ is close to zero for x sufficiently far to the left). Then in order to graph f, we need only check its behavior for x values relatively close to the origin.

Example: Consider the function $g(x) = 2^x$. Note that $\lim_{x \to -\infty} 2^x = 0$, since taking 2 to very large negative powers results in numbers close to zero. Thus we know that the graph of g approaches the x-axis for x far to the left (see Figure 2.47). Noting that $\lim_{x \to \infty} 2^x = \infty$ informs us that for

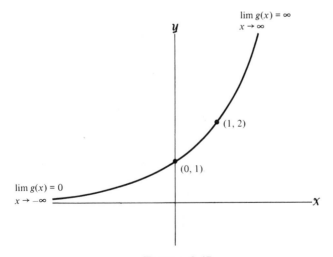

FIGURE 2.47

positive x values, the graph trails up into the first quadrant. The graph is completed very easily by finding a few ordered pairs such as $(0, 1)$ and $(1, 2)$ (that is, $2^0 = 1$ and $2^1 = 2$).

2.6-3   Definition: If $\lim_{x \to \infty} f(x) = a$, then the line $y = a$ is called a *horizontal asymptote* of f in the *positive direction*. If $\lim_{x \to -\infty} f(x) = b$, then $y = b$ is called a *horizontal asymptote* of f in the *negative direction*.

It is also possible that the graph of a function approaches a vertical line for x values near *one* side of some point a.

2.6-4   Definition: The line $x = a$ is called a *vertical asymptote* of f if any one of the following limit conditions holds:

$$\lim_{x \to a^-} f(x) = \infty , \qquad \lim_{x \to a^-} f(x) = -\infty ,$$

$$\lim_{x \to a^+} f(x) = \infty , \qquad \lim_{x \to a^+} f(x) = -\infty .$$

Example: Consider again $y = h(x) = 1/x$. In this case, we have

$$\lim_{x \to \infty} h(x) = 0 \qquad \text{and} \qquad \lim_{x \to -\infty} h(x) = 0,$$

so that the x-axis is a horizontal asymptote in both directions. Also,

$$\lim_{x \to 0^+} h(x) = \infty \qquad \text{and} \qquad \lim_{x \to 0^-} h(x) = -\infty ,$$

so f has a vertical asymptote $x = 0$ as x approaches 0 from the right, and also as x approaches 0 from the left. This knowledge of asymptotes

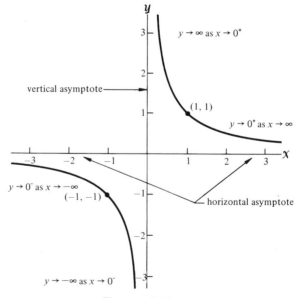

FIGURE 2.48

informs us a great deal about the graph of $h(x) = 1/x$. The graph is very easily completed by checking a few ordered pairs such as $(1, 1)$ and $(-1, -1)$, observing that $1/x$ is never zero, and noting the symmetries of $h(x) = 1/x$. (See Figure 2.48.)

Question: There are two kinds of symmetries here; what are they?

Remark: Limit statements such as "$\lim_{x \to a} f(x) = b$" are often written in the form "$f(x) \to b$ as $x \to a$." This notation is used in Figure 2.48.

The idea of vertical and horizontal asymptotes is easily generalized. First of all, we might be willing to relax the condition that an asymptote be a vertical or horizontal line. Thus we consider *oblique asymptotes* as well as horizontal and vertical ones. In addition, it seems rather strict to insist that the graphs in question always approach lines. We might be willing to take asymptotes to be familiar curves of various kinds, in addition to straight lines.

Example: Consider the function $f(x) = x - (1/x)$. Note that $\lim_{x \to 0^+} f(x) = -\infty$, and also that $f(x) \to +\infty$ as $x \to 0^-$. Thus, we know the behavior of the graph of $f(x)$ near the origin. In order to determine the function's behavior "in the large" (that is, for x values far from the origin), we compute $\lim_{x \to \infty} f(x) = \infty$, and $\lim_{x \to -\infty} f(x) = -\infty$. Unfortunately, this tells us very little about f in quadrants I and III. A close inspection reveals that as $x \to \infty$, f becomes essentially the function x (that is, the line $y = x$), since $1/x \to 0$. Similarly, for negative values of x we have $f(x) \to x$. Thus it appears that the line $y = x$ is an oblique asymptote. (See Figure 2.49.)

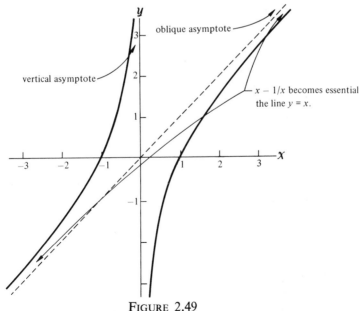

oblique asymptote

vertical asymptote

$x - 1/x$ becomes essential the line $y = x$.

FIGURE 2.49

Example: Consider the function described by $g(x) = 2^x + x^{-2} = 2^x + (1/x^2)$. Note that $g(x) \to \infty$ as $x \to 0$; thus, the line $x = 0$ is a vertical asymptote. Note that g becomes essentially the function 2^x for very large values of $|x|$. That is, $g(x) \to 2^x$ as $x \to \infty$, and $g(x) \to 2^x$ as $x \to -\infty$. By noting that $g(x) \geqslant 2^x$ for all x in its domain and plotting some well-selected points, we obtain the graph shown in Figure 2.50.

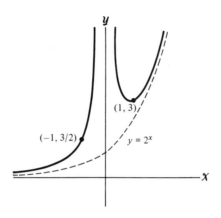

FIGURE 2.50

Example: Graph $f(x) = y = x^2 + (1/x)$. Note first that

$$\lim_{x \to \infty} f(x) = \infty, \qquad \lim_{x \to -\infty} f(x) = \infty,$$

$$\lim_{x \to 0^+} f(x) = \infty, \qquad \text{and} \qquad \lim_{x \to 0^-} f(x) = -\infty.$$

Thus, $f(x)$ has the y-axis as a vertical asymptote, downward on the left and upward on the right. Also, if x values are taken far to the right or left, $f(x)$ values are very large. However, we can be more definite about $f(x)$ in the large by noticing that as $x \to \pm\infty$, $x^2 + (1/x) \to x^2$. Thus, we can view the parabola $y = x^2$ as an asymptote for large values of $|x|$. By computing some additional points in the graph, such as $(\frac{1}{2}, \frac{9}{4})$, $(1, 2)$, $(2, \frac{9}{2})$, $(-\frac{1}{2}, -\frac{7}{4})$, $(-1, 0)$, and $(-2, -\frac{7}{2})$, we have the graph in Figure 2.51.

EXERCISES 2.6

1. Find the following limits.

a. $\displaystyle \lim_{x \to \infty} \frac{5 - 2x}{3 + x}$.

b. $\displaystyle \lim_{x \to \infty} \frac{4x^2 - 5x + 2}{2x^2 + 3x - 4}$.

c. $\displaystyle \lim_{x \to -\infty} \frac{x + 1}{x^2 + 1}$.

d. $\displaystyle \lim_{x \to -\infty} \frac{x^3 + 3x}{x^4 + 1}$.

e. $\displaystyle \lim_{x \to 3^-} \frac{9}{x^2 - 9}$.

f. $\displaystyle \lim_{x \to 3^+} \frac{9}{x^2 - 9}$.

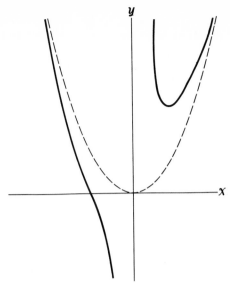

FIGURE 2.51

g. $\lim\limits_{x \to 1^+} \dfrac{x+1}{x^2-1}$.

h. $\lim\limits_{x \to 2^-} \dfrac{x+9}{x^2+3x-10}$.

i. $\lim\limits_{x \to 2} \dfrac{9x^2-36}{x-2}$.

j. $\lim\limits_{x \to 3} \dfrac{x^2+x-6}{x^2-4}$.

k. $\lim\limits_{x \to 4} (x+1)^3$.

l. $\lim\limits_{x \to \pi} \pi x^2$.

2. For each of the following, find the vertical and horizontal asymptotes, if any, and graph the function.

a. $y = \dfrac{x-1}{x^2+1}$.

b. $y = \dfrac{1}{2x^2-3x+1}$.

c. $y = \dfrac{x^2}{x^2-9}$.

d. $y = \dfrac{1}{x-3} + \dfrac{1}{x+1}$.

3. Graph the following curves using asymptotes and by making comparisons with familiar curves.

a. $y = \dfrac{x-1}{x^2-2x-3}$.

b. $y = \dfrac{x^2+x-2}{2x^2+1}$.

c. $y = \dfrac{x^2+2}{x+2}$.

d. $y = \dfrac{x-1}{x^3+x^2}$.

e. $y = 2^x + \dfrac{1}{x^3}$.

f. $y = 2^x - \dfrac{1}{x}$.

2.7 HYPERBOLAS WITH CENTERS AT THE ORIGIN

In an earlier section we defined an ellipse to be the set of all points having the same total distance from two fixed focal points. We now look at sets of points in which the difference (in absolute value) of the distances from two focal points is constant.

2.7-1 Definition: A set of points $\mathcal{K}$ is a *hyperbola* iff there are two points $F_1 = (a_1, b_1)$ and $F_2 = (a_2, b_2)$ and a positive constant k such that for every point $A \in \mathcal{K}$,

$$|d(A, F_1) - d(A, F_2)| = k.$$

The points F_1 and F_2 are called the *foci* of $\mathcal{K}$ and $C = ((a_1 + a_2)/2, (b_1 + b_2)/2)$ is called the *center* of $\mathcal{K}$. The line through F_1 and F_2 is called the *major axis* and the line through C perpendicular to the major axis is called the *minor axis*. (See Figure 2.52.)

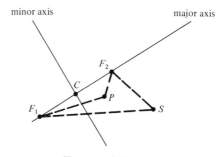

FIGURE 2.52

Major Axis the X-Axis

Suppose we consider a case in which the center of the hyperbola is the point $O = (0, 0)$, the major axis is the x-axis, and k is the fixed positive distance. Thus, the foci are of the form $(c, 0)$ and $(-c, 0)$; $c > 0$. (See Figure 2.53.)

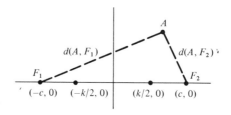

FIGURE 2.53

Notice that

$$2c + d(A, F_1) > d(A, F_2).$$

(Why?) Therefore

$$2c > d(A, F_2) - d(A, F_1).$$

Similarly

$$2c > d(A, F_1) - d(A, F_2).$$

Thus

$$2c > |d(A, F_1) - d(A, F_2)| = k,$$

which yields $c > k/2 > 0$.

Let us now find a constraining equation for the coordinates x and y of a point in $\mathfrak{IC}$. If we have $A = (x, y) \in \mathfrak{IC}$, then

$$k = |d(A, F_1) - d(A, F_2)| = |\sqrt{(x - c)^2 + y^2} - \sqrt{(x + c)^2 + y^2}|.$$

Squaring both sides we have

$$k^2 = (x - c)^2 + y^2 - 2\sqrt{(x - c)^2 + y^2}\,\sqrt{(x + c)^2 + y^2} + (x + c)^2 + y^2$$
$$= 2x^2 + 2c^2 + 2y^2 - 2\sqrt{(x - c)^2 + y^2}\,\sqrt{(x + c)^2 + y^2}.$$

Before we continue, let us note that $(k/2, 0) \in \mathfrak{IC}$, since

$$2\left(\frac{k}{2}\right)^2 + 2c^2 - 2\sqrt{\left(\frac{k}{2} - c\right)^2}\sqrt{\left(\frac{k}{2} + c\right)^2}$$

$$= \frac{k^2}{2} + 2c^2 - 2\left|\frac{k}{2} - c\right|\left|\frac{k}{2} + c\right| = \frac{k^2}{2} + 2c^2 - 2\left(c - \frac{k}{2}\right)\left(\frac{k}{2} + c\right)$$

(recall that $c > k/2 > 0$)

$$= \frac{k^2}{2} + 2c^2 - 2c^2 - kc + kc + \frac{k^2}{2} = k^2.$$

Similarly, $(-k/2, 0) \in \mathfrak{IC}$. Thus, $\mathfrak{IC}$ intersects the major axis, in this case the x-axis. The figure $\mathfrak{IC}$ does not intersect the y-axis; for if it did, say at $(0, y)$, we would have

$$k^2 = 2c^2 + 2y^2 - 2\sqrt{c^2 + y^2}\,\sqrt{c^2 + y^2} = 2c^2 + 2y^2 - 2(c^2 + y^2) = 0.$$

But $k > 0$, thus $\mathfrak{IC}$ does not intersect its minor axis.

2.7-2   **Definition:** The points of intersection of a hyperbola with its major axis are called the *vertices* of the hyperbola. The segment between the vertices is called the *transverse diameter*, and has length k. For simplification of the algebraic expressions that will appear, it is convenient to let $a = \dfrac{k}{2}$. In this case, the transverse diameter has length $2a$. (See Figure 2.54.)

Let us now complete the problem of finding a constraining equation for the hyperbola $\mathfrak{IC}$. So far, we have (after substituting $2a$ for k)

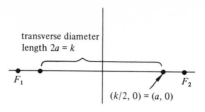

transverse diameter
length $2a = k$

F_1 F_2

$(k/2, 0) = (a, 0)$

FIGURE 2.54

$$4a^2 = 2x^2 + 2y^2 + 2c^2 - 2\sqrt{(x-c)^2 + y^2}\ \sqrt{(x+c)^2 + y^2},$$

which yields

$$\sqrt{(x-c)^2 + y^2}\ \sqrt{(x+c)^2 + y^2} = x^2 + y^2 + c^2 - 2a^2.$$

Squaring and simplifying, we get

$$(c^2 - a^2)x^2 - a^2y^2 = a^2(c^2 - a^2).$$

Above, we saw that $c > k/2 = a > 0$. Thus, $c^2 - a^2 > 0$. Let $b = \sqrt{c^2 - a^2}$ (note the different relationship here between a, b, and c from that for the ellipse). Therefore, the constraining equation becomes $b^2x^2 - a^2y^2 = a^2b^2$, which can be written in the form

$$\frac{x^2}{a^2} - \frac{y^2}{b^2} = 1.$$

This is the *standard form* of the equation of a hyperbola whose focal points lie on the x axis.

If $(x, y) \in \mathcal{K}$, then $(-x, y)$, $(-x, -y)$, and $(x, -y)$ are also in $\mathcal{K}$. Therefore $\mathcal{K}$ is symmetric with respect to the y-axis, the origin, and the x-axis. Let us observe in particular how $\mathcal{K}$ appears in the first quadrant. From the equation $(x^2/a^2) - (y^2/b^2) = 1$, assuming that $y \geqslant 0$ and $x \geqslant 0$, we can solve for y as follows:

$$y = \sqrt{\frac{b^2x^2}{a^2} - b^2} = \frac{b}{a}\sqrt{x^2 - a^2} = \frac{bx}{a}\sqrt{1 - \frac{a^2}{x^2}}.$$

Since

$$\lim_{x \to \infty}\sqrt{1 - \frac{a^2}{x^2}} = 1,$$

we see that

$$y = \frac{bx}{a}\sqrt{1 - \frac{a^2}{x^2}}$$

approaches bx/a as $x \to \infty$. Thus, in the first quadrant the hyperbola $\mathcal{K}$ is approximated by $(b/a)x$ for large x. Recall that in this case $(b/a)x$ is called an oblique asymptote of $\mathcal{H}$. The graph of $\mathcal{H}$ in the first quadrant is shown in Figure 2.55.

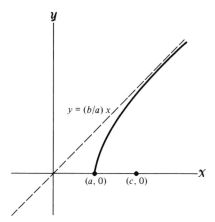

FIGURE 2.55

Using the fact that $\mathcal{H}$ is symmetric with respect to the y-axis, the origin, and the x-axis, the graph of $\mathcal{H}$ is as shown in Figure 2.56.

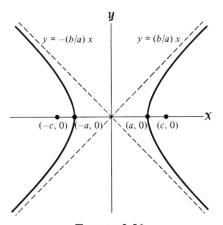

FIGURE 2.56

Major Axis the Y-Axis

If the hyperbola $\mathcal{H}$ above is reflected about the line $x = y$, we get a hyperbola whose constraining equation is

$$\frac{y^2}{a^2} - \frac{x^2}{b^2} = 1$$

and whose graph is shown in Figure 2.57.

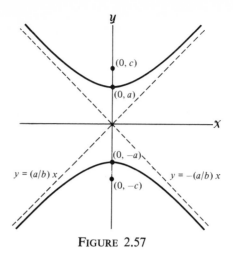

FIGURE 2.57

Summary

It is possible to derive the equation for a hyperbola with foci $(0, c)$ and $(0, -c)$, where $c^2 = a^2 + b^2$, in the same manner used to obtain the equation for a hyperbola with foci on the x axis. It is useful to note in each case that the slopes of the asymptotes may be found by taking $\pm\beta/\alpha$, where $1/\beta^2$ is the coefficient of the y^2 term and $1/\alpha^2$ is the coefficient of the x^2 term. In order to tell from the equation whether a hyperbola opens to the left and right or up and down, one needs only to look at the position of the minus sign in the standard form of the equation; that is, the foci lie on the axis which displays a plus sign in the standard form.

Example: Find a constraining equation for, and the graph of, a hyperbola whose foci are $(2, 0)$ and $(-2, 0)$ and whose asymptotes are $y = \frac{1}{2}x$ and $y = -\frac{1}{2}x$.

Solution: Since the foci are on the x axis, the desired equation is of the form $(x^2/a^2) - (y^2/b^2) = 1$. When we have this type of hyperbola, the equations of its asymptotes are $y = (b/a)x$ and $y = -(b/a)x$. Thus, $b/a = \frac{1}{2}$, and $c = 2$. Using the fact that for a hyperbola we have $c^2 = a^2 + b^2$, we know that $4 = a^2 + b^2$. Solving the equations simultaneously, we get $a = 4\sqrt{5}/5$ and $b = 2\sqrt{5}/5$. The constraining equation in standard form is thus

$$\frac{x^2}{\frac{16}{5}} - \frac{y^2}{\frac{4}{5}} = 1.$$

The graph is shown in Figure 2.58.

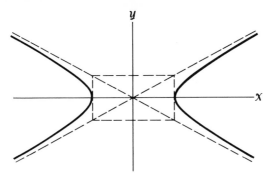

FIGURE 2.58

The Auxiliary Rectangle

You will notice in Figure 2.58 that a rectangle was constructed whose center is the origin and whose sides have length $2a$ and $2b$. The extensions of its diagonals are the asymptotes of the hyperbola. This rectangle is sometimes referred to as the *auxiliary rectangle*.

Example: Find the equation and sketch a graph of the hyperbola that has a transverse diameter 8 units long and the y-axis as the major axis, and one asymptote as $y = -(\frac{3}{2})x$.

Solution: Since the y-axis is the major axis, the foci are of the form $(0, c)$ and $(0, -c)$ while the vertices are of the form $(0, a)$ and $(0, -a)$. The transverse diameter is the segment between the vertices, thus $a = 4$. The asymptotes are of the form $y = (b/a)x$ and $y = -(b/a)x$, and hence we have $-b/4 = -\frac{3}{2}$, from which $b = 6$. The foci are $(0, 2\sqrt{13})$ and $(0, -2\sqrt{13})$, since $c^2 = b^2 + a^2$. A constraining equation for the hyperbola is thus

$$\frac{y^2}{16} - \frac{x^2}{36} = 1.$$

The graph is shown in Figure 2.59.

In a later chapter, we consider the more general problem in which the foci do not necessarily lie on one of the coordinate axes.

Conjugate Hyperbolas

It is interesting to consider the graphs given by the pair of equations

$$\frac{x^2}{a^2} - \frac{y^2}{b^2} = 1 \quad \text{and} \quad \frac{y^2}{b^2} - \frac{x^2}{a^2} = 1.$$

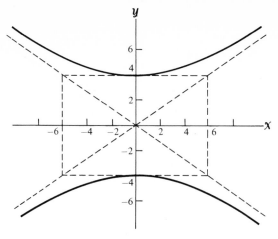

FIGURE 2.59

From the previous discussion, the asymptotes in each case have slopes b/a and $-b/a$. Both have foci at a distance $c = \sqrt{a^2 + b^2}$ from the origin. The first opens to the left and right, and the second up and down. Hyperbolas of such a pair are called *conjugate hyperbolas*.

2.7-3   Definition: If $\mathcal{H}$ and $\mathcal{K}$ are two hyperbolas with constraining equations

$$\frac{x^2}{a^2} - \frac{y^2}{b^2} = 1 \qquad \text{and} \qquad \frac{y^2}{b^2} - \frac{x^2}{a^2} = 1,$$

then $\mathcal{H}$ and $\mathcal{K}$ are called *conjugate hyperbolas* (see Figure 2.60).

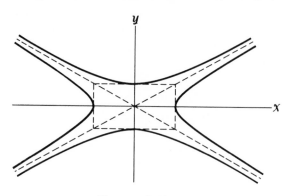

FIGURE 2.60

EXERCISES 2.7

1. Find the vertices, foci, auxiliary rectangle, and asymptotes of the following hyperbolas. Sketch each figure.

a. $\dfrac{x^2}{3} - \dfrac{y^2}{9} = 1.$ b. $\dfrac{y^2}{4} - \dfrac{x^2}{25} = 1.$

c. $\dfrac{x^2}{16} - \dfrac{y^2}{25} = -1.$ d. $14x^2 - 21y^2 + 7 = 0.$

2. Sketch each of the following and find the foci.
   a. $3x^2 - 12y^2 - 4 = 0.$ b. $25x^2 - 36y^2 + 8 = 0.$
   c. $36x^2 - 42y^2 = 252.$ d. $49x^2 - y^2 = 1.$

3. Sketch the conjugate of each hyperbola in Exercise 2, and determine its equation.

4. Find a constraining equation of the hyperbola whose center is the origin, and whose vertices and foci are the foci and vertices respectively of the ellipse $9x^2 + 36y^2 - 4 = 0.$

5. Find an equation of the hyperbola whose asymptotes are $2x + y = 0$ and $2x - y = 0$ and whose vertices are $(0, 4)$ and $(0, -4).$

6. Find an equation of the hyperbola that has as asymptotes $3x - 4y = 0$ and $3x + 4y = 0$ and that passes through the point $(8, 3).$

7. Find an equation of the hyperbola whose asymptotes are $2x - y = 0$ and $2x + y = 0$ and whose foci are $(10, 0)$ and $(-10, 0).$

8. Find an equation of the hyperbola whose major axis is the y axis, whose center is the origin, whose foci are 3 units from the center, and whose vertices are 2 units from the center.

9. The segment cut by a hyperbola from a line that contains a focus and is perpendicular to the major axis is called a *latus rectum* of the hyperbola.
   a. If the equation of the hyperbola is $(x^2/a^2) - (y^2/b^2) = 1$, show that the length of a latus rectum is $2b^2/a.$
   b. Find the length of the latus rectum of $9x^2 - 4y^2 = 36.$

10. Derive the standard equation of a hyperbola having center at the origin and foci on the y axis. You may wish to follow our derivation for the hyperbola with foci on the x axis.

2.8   PERIODIC FUNCTIONS AND TRANSLATIONS

An additional type of "symmetry" that a function or relation can have involves invariance under certain translations rather than reflections of some sort. We call this property *periodicity*. In this section we discuss periodic functions, and the closely related idea of translations. Later we shall discuss some very important examples of periodic functions, the trigonometric functions.

Periodic Functions

Let us now define the very important class of functions known as *periodic functions*. These functions "periodically" take on the same values again and again as one evaluates the function at domain values along the real line.

2.8-1 **Definition:** A function $f : R \rightarrow R$ is *periodic* iff for some $p, f(x + p) = f(x)$ for all x.

Example: Consider the function f graphed in Figure 2.61, which has the property that $f(x + 2) = f(x)$ for any x. Note also that for all x, $f(x + 4) = f(x)$ and $f(x + 6) = f(x)$.

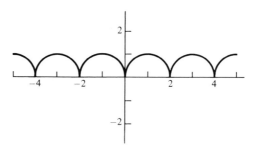

FIGURE 2.61

2.8-2 **Definition:** If f is a periodic function, the *smallest* $p > 0$ such that for all $x, f(x + p) = f(x)$ is called the *period* of f.

Remark: A periodic function may not have a period! Notice that our definitions have allowed the constant functions (functions of the form $f(x) = c$) to be periodic, although they have no period.

Question: Why does a constant function have no period?

Example: The function f graphed in Figure 2.61 is periodic with period 2.

A well-known fact about **R** is that every real number α either is an integer or lies between two consecutive integers (that is, $n \leqslant \alpha < n + 1$ for some unique $n \in Z$). An important function is based on this fact.

2.8-3 **Definition:** The *greatest integer function* is a mapping $[\ \ ] : \mathbf{R} \rightarrow \mathbf{R}$ such that for all $x \in \mathbf{R}$,

$$[x] = n,$$

where n is the unique integer such that $n \leqslant x < n + 1$.

A sketch of the graph of the greatest integer function is shown in Figure 2.62. This is not a periodic function as is clearly seen, but the associated function f, described by "for all $x, f(x) = x - [x]$," called the *fractional part* of x, is periodic. (See Figure 2.63.)

Other Translational Invariances

Note that by "translating" the graph of a periodic function right or left by one period p, we obtain the same graph. That is, for all $x, f(x - p) =$

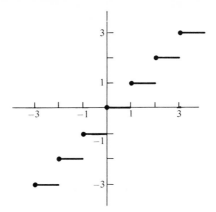

FIGURE 2.62

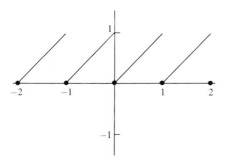

FIGURE 2.63

$f(x + p) = f(x)$. The idea of *translational invariance* need not be restricted to functions and translations along the *x*-axis, but can be generalized to relations in general and to translations along any line. Let us first consider the relation $\mathcal{S}$, which is graphed in Figure 2.64. It should be clear from the figure, that for any point $(a, b) \in \mathcal{S}$, there also is the point $(a, b + 4) \in \mathcal{S}$. For example $(1, -3) \in \mathcal{S}$, and it follows due to this translational invariance that $(1, 1) \in \mathcal{S}$.

Consider now the relation $\mathcal{F}$, shown in Figure 2.65. We see in this case that we have invariance if we "slide" the curve an appropriate distance along the dotted line. This translation can be described in terms of horizontal and vertical components. That is, if $(a, b) \in \mathcal{F}$, then $(a + 2, b + 1) \in \mathcal{F}$. The relation $\mathcal{F}$ is invariant under a two-unit translation to the right (left) followed by a one unit translation upward (downward).

EXERCISES 2.8

1. Suppose a function f has the property that for all $x, f(x + 4) = f(x)$. Why can one not deduce that f has a period of 4?

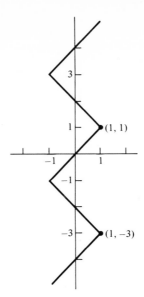

FIGURE 2.64

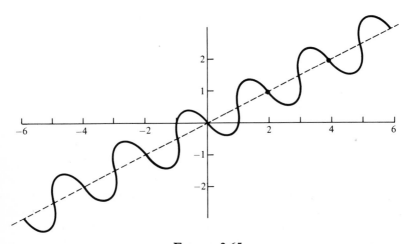

FIGURE 2.65

2. a. Suppose that f is periodic with period p. Show that for any $n \in Z$, $f(x + np) = f(x)$ for all x.
    b. If for all x, $f(x + m) = f(x)$, then we know, since p is the period of f, that $m \geqslant p$. Show that $m = np$ for some $p \in Z$.

3. The greatest integer function is not periodic. Does it have any translational invariance? Explain.

4. Graph $[y] - y = x$ (that is, the set $\{(x, y) : [y] - y = x\}$). Does this graph have a translational invariance of any sort?

5. a. Describe the graphs of constant functions.

b. Is the composition of constant functions a constant function?

6. a. Suppose f and g are periodic. Show that $g \circ f$ is periodic.

b. Do you suppose that f and g's being periodic implies that $f + g$ is periodic?

7. Let

$$f(x) = \begin{cases} 1, \text{ if } x \in [2n, 2n+1) \text{ for some } n \in Z, \\ -1, \text{ otherwise.} \end{cases}$$

a. Sketch a graph of f.

b. Show that f is periodic and find its period.

8. Sketch a graph representing (or argue that no such relation exists):

a. A periodic function that is symmetric with respect to the origin, but not with respect to the y axis.

b. A periodic 1–1 function.

c. A periodic function that is symmetric with respect to the y-axis, but not with respect to the origin.

d. A periodic function that is symmetric with respect to the origin and the y-axis.

9. Graph each of the following and decide whether they are periodic or have any translational invariance. If they are periodic, find the period (if it exists).

a. $f(x) = 3(x - [x]) + 2.$ b. $g(x) = x - [x] + 2.$

c. $k(x) = (x - [x])^2.$

10. Prove or disprove: Any periodic function without a period is a constant function.

11. Graph the relation $\mathfrak{I}$ that contains

$$\mathcal{S} = \{(x, y) : |x| + |y| = 1\}$$

and has the property that

$$(x, y) \in \mathfrak{I} \Leftrightarrow (x + 2, y + 3) \in \mathfrak{I}.$$

12. Graph the relation $\mathfrak{I}$ that contains

$$\mathcal{S} = \{(x, y) : y = 4x^2\}$$

and has the property that

$$(x, y) \in \mathfrak{I} \Leftrightarrow (x + 3, y + 1) \in \mathfrak{I}.$$

2.9 THE TRIGONOMETRIC FUNCTIONS

We now review three important periodic functions that are fundamental in the study of trigonometry and essential for our work with vectors. These functions—sine, cosine, and tangent—are important and useful in almost every branch of mathematics and science. A complete course in trigonometry would introduce many related functions and applications. However, we shall find it sufficient to review only the basic facts about the functions mentioned above.

Sine and Cosine

Let us consider the set $\mathcal{C}$ of points in the plane called the *unit circle* (with respect to some Cartesian coordinate system—see Figure 2.66). This is the circle with center at the origin having radius 1. Thus,

$$\mathcal{C} = \{(x, y) : x^2 + y^2 = 1\}.$$

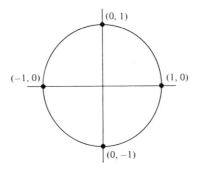

FIGURE 2.66

Consider a point (x, y) on the circle whose distance (measured in the units of the particular coordinatization) from the point $(1, 0)$, measured counterclockwise along the circle, is t units ($t \geqslant 0$). If $t < 0$, we measure clockwise along $\mathcal{C}$, $-t = |t|$ units. (See Figure 2.67.)

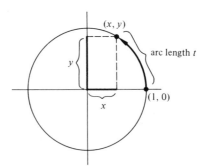

FIGURE 2.67

Remark: A definition of *arc length* cannot be given here since it requires the use of limit notions beyond the scope of this text.

Note that for each $t \in R$ there is a point in $\mathcal{C}$ uniquely determined in this manner. One can view this process as "wrapping" the real line around the unit circle somewhat like thread on a spool. The 0 on the real line is placed at the point $(1, 0)$ on the unit circle and then the positive part of the real line is wrapped counterclockwise and the negative part is wrapped clockwise (Figure 2.68).

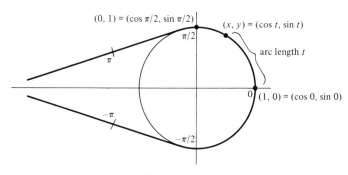

FIGURE 2.68

We wish to define two functions from **R** to **R** by separating the two components of the coordinate (x, y) of the point determined on the circle for a given length t.

2.9-1 Definition: Let t be a nonnegative real number and let (x, y) be the point on the unit circle ℮ that is t units from $(1, 0)$ measured counterclockwise along ℮. Then, define

$$\cos t = x \qquad \text{and} \qquad \sin t = y.$$

For a negative real number t, measure $|t|$ clockwise from $(1, 0)$ to (x, y), and again define $\cos t = x$ and $\sin t = y$.

Example: Let $t = \pi/2$. The circumference of ℮ is 2π, thus $\pi/2$ is one-quarter of the way around ℮ and hence the point $(0, 1)$ on ℮ is determined. Thus $\cos \pi/2 = 0$ and $\sin \pi/2 = 1$.

Example: Suppose $t = \pi/4$. Then the point (x, y) lies one-eighth of the way around the circle. For this case, $x = y$, and since $x^2 + y^2 = 1$, we have $x = y = \sqrt{\frac{1}{2}} = \sqrt{2}/2$. Thus $\cos \pi/4 = \sqrt{2}/2$ and $\sin \pi/4 = \sqrt{2}/2$. If $t = -\pi/4$, we have $x = -y$ and $x > 0$. Hence, $\cos(-\pi/4) = \sqrt{2}/2$ and $\sin(-\pi/4) = -\sqrt{2}/2$. (See Figure 2.69.)

We now define two functions: cosine $= \{(t, x) : x = \cos t\}$ and sine $= \{(t, y) : y = \sin t\}$. Since the unit circle has circumference 2π, it is clear that the values of these two functions will repeat for t values ranging over any interval of length 2π; that is, the sine and cosine functions are periodic functions from **R** into **R**.

The sine and cosine values for arbitrary values of t are fairly difficult to find, but we can use the following construction to determine the values for $t = \pi/6$ and $t = \pi/3$. (See Figure 2.70.)

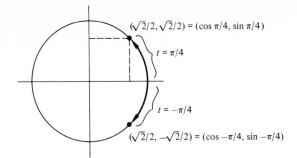

FIGURE 2.69

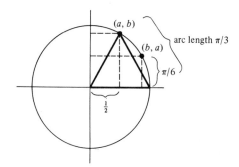

FIGURE 2.70

The point (a, b) is two-thirds of the distance (measured around the arc of the circle) from the point $(1, 0)$ toward the point $(0, 1)$. Also, (b, a) is the point on the circle which is one-third of the same distance (explain). Since the triangle formed by the origin $(0, 0)$, (a, b), and, $(1, 0)$ is equilateral, it follows that $a = \frac{1}{2}$. Since $a^2 + b^2 = 1$, then $b = \sqrt{3}/2$, and hence we have the following: $\cos \pi/3 = \frac{1}{2}$, $\sin \pi/3 = \sqrt{3}/2$, and $\cos \pi/6 = \sqrt{3}/2$, $\sin \pi/6 = \frac{1}{2}$.

For approximate values of sine and cosine on the interval $[0, \pi/2]$ see the Appendix. For approximate values in other quadrants, one uses periodicity and the facts that (a) $\sin(-t) = -\sin t$ and $\cos(-t) = \cos t$ (Figure 2.71), and (b) $\sin(t + \pi/2) = \cos t$ (see Figure 2.72).

Remark: One can also show that $\cos(t - \pi/2) = \sin t$, and that

$$\sin(t + \pi) = -\sin t \quad \text{and} \quad \cos(t + \pi) = -\cos t.$$

The Tangent Function

The tangent function is defined in terms of the sine and cosine functions.

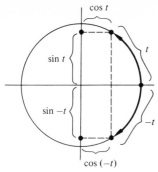
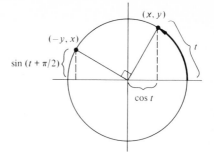

FIGURE 2.71   FIGURE 2.72

2.9-2   **Definition:** For each t such that $\cos t \neq 0$, define

$$\tan t = \frac{\sin t}{\cos t}.$$

This function is called the *tangent function*. The domain of tangent is the set of all real numbers except odd multiples of $\pi/2$, since for such values of t, $\cos t = 0$ and the ratio $\sin t/\cos t$ is undefined.

Remark: Note that the tangent at t can be regarded as the ratio of the length of the vertical leg to the length of the horizontal leg of the right triangle formed by the points $(0, 0)$, $(\cos t, 0)$, and $(\cos t, \sin t)$. (See Figure 2.73.)

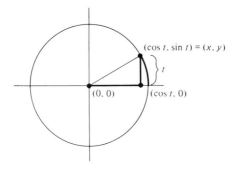

FIGURE 2.73

From the known values of sine and cosine for $t = 0$, $\pi/3$, $\pi/4$, and so on, we can compute corresponding values of the tangent function for these preimages.

Example: $\tan 0 = 0$, $\tan \pi/4 = 1$, $\tan \pi/3 = 3$, but $\tan \pi/2$ does not exist!

Graphs of Sine, Cosine, and Tangent

We would now like to graph in a Cartesian coordinate system, the sine, cosine, and tangent functions. We use horizontal axes to indicate the real number t at which the values are taken. Here, we are not viewing the real line as wrapped about $\mathcal{C}$, but we are simply graphing the values the functions take at various real number values of t. By carefully following the horizontal and vertical components of a point as it moves counterclockwise around the circle, we see that the sine and cosine between 0 and 2π are as shown in Figure 2.74.

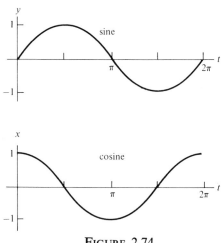

FIGURE 2.74

Whereas the sine and cosine functions are periodic with period 2π, it turns out that the tangent function is periodic with period π. We show that tangent repeats at least this often as follows:

$$\tan(t + \pi) = \frac{\sin(t + \pi)}{\cos(t + \pi)} = \frac{-\sin t}{-\cos t} = \tan t.$$

By considering the ratio $\sin t/\cos t$ as t traverses the interval $(-\pi/2, \pi/2)$, and noting that

$$\lim_{t \to (\pi/2^-)} \frac{\sin t}{\cos t} = \infty \quad \text{and} \quad \lim_{t \to -(\pi/2^+)} \frac{\sin t}{\cos t} = -\infty,$$

one obtains the graph for a full period of the tangent function shown in Figure 2.75.

By considering the values taken on these three functions over one period and allowing for the periodicity, we have the graphs as shown in Figure 2.76.

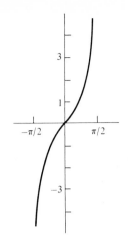

FIGURE 2.75

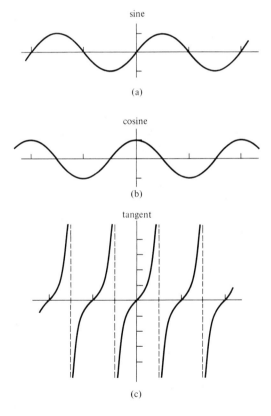

sine

(a)

cosine

(b)

tangent

(c)

FIGURE 2.76

The Inverse Tangent

A function of particular importance is the function obtained by interchanging the components of the ordered pairs of the tangent function when it is restricted to the interval $(-\pi/2, \pi/2)$ (one period).

2.9-3   Definition:

$$\text{Tan}^{-1} = \{(s, \theta) : s = \tan \theta \text{ and } \theta \in (-\pi/2, \pi/2)\} \, .$$

This function is graphed in Figure 2.77, and is called the *principle inverse tangent*. Note that Tan^{-1} has domain R and range $(-\pi/2, \pi/2)$.

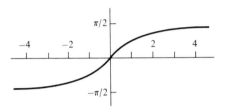

FIGURE 2.77

Example: Let (x, y) be a point in the plane, and let θ measure the arc length of the unit circle (counterclockwise) from the x-axis to the line segment from $(0, 0)$ to (x, y). (See Figure 2.78.)

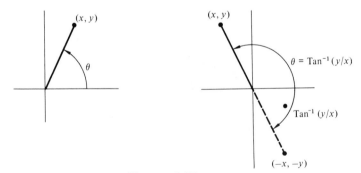

FIGURE 2.78

Since $\tan \theta = y/x$, it follows that $\theta = \text{Tan}^{-1}(y/x)$ if (x, y) is in quadrants I or IV and $\theta = \pi + \text{Tan}^{-1}(y/x)$ if (x, y) is in quadrants II or III.

We must end our brief review of trigonometry here. Later we will introduce some applications related to other subject matter.

EXERCISES 2.9

1. Complete the following table:

t	0	$\pi/6$	$\pi/4$	$\pi/3$	$\pi/2$	$2\pi/3$	$3\pi/4$	$5\pi/6$	π	$7\pi/6$	$5\pi/4$
cos t											
sin t											
tan t											

t	$4\pi/3$	$3\pi/2$	$5\pi/3$	$7\pi/4$	$11\pi/6$	2π
cos t						
sin t						
tan t						

2. Determine
  a. $\cos(-13\pi/6)$.   b. $\sin(-3\pi/4)$.
  c. $\cos(-7\pi/6)$.   d. $\sin(-7\pi/6)$.
  e. $\cos(-19\pi)$.   f. $\tan(17\pi/6)$.

3. Argue that
  a. $\cos(t - \pi/2) = \sin t$;   b. $\sin(t + \pi) = -\sin t$;
  c. $\cos(t + \pi) = -\cos t$.
  What about $\cos(t - \pi)$ and $\sin(t - \pi)$?

4. With your eyes shut, graph sine, cosine, and tangent.

5. What are the domains and ranges of sine, cosine, tangent, and Tan^{-1}?

6. Determine all vertical asymptotes of the tangent function.

7. Sketch the inverses of each of the relations, sine, cosine, and tangent.

8. a. Cos^{-1} is the function obtained by restricting cosine^{-1} to range values in $[0, \pi]$. Graph Cos^{-1}, called the *principle inverse cosine*. What are the domain and range of Cos^{-1}?
  b. Sin^{-1} is the function obtained by restricting sine^{-1} to range values in $[-\pi/2, \pi/2]$. Graph Sin^{-1}, called the *principle inverse sine*. What are the domain and range of Sin^{-1}?

9. Define three functions—cotangent, secant, and cosecant—as follows: $\cot t = 1/\tan t$, $\sec t = 1/\cos t$, $\csc t = 1/\sin t$. Graph these functions.

10. Use the identity $\sin^2 t + \cos^2 t = 1$ and the definitions in Exercise 9 to show that (a) $1 + \cot^2 t = \csc^2 t$; (b) $\tan^2 t + 1 = \sec^2 t$.

2.10 INTRODUCTION TO POLAR COORDINATES

Angles and Trigonometric Functions

The functions, sine, cosine, and tangent are known as trigonometric functions (triangular functions) as a result of many simple relationships they bear to triangles. In fact, these functions originated from such relationships although today their applications are considerably more varied.

The notion of an angle is of fundamental importance. Let us make the following definition of an angle and describe a method for assigning measures to angles.

2.10-1 **Definition:** Let α and $\mathcal{B}$ be two half-lines (see Definition 2.2-5) having a common initial point P. The configuration $\alpha \cup \mathcal{B}$ is called an *angle*. (See Figure 2.79.) The point P is called the vertex of the angle.

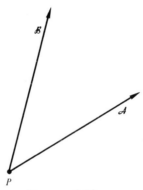

FIGURE 2.79

2.10-2 **Definition:** Let Θ be an angle with vertex P, and let $\mathcal{C}$ be a circle with radius 1 and center at P. If θ is the length of the shortest arc on $\mathcal{C}$ from the intersection with $\mathcal{C}$ of one half-line of Θ to the intersection with $\mathcal{C}$ of the other half-line, then θ is called the *radian measure* of Θ. (See Figure 2.80.) The angle Θ is often (although incorrectly) called simply θ.

Remark: This definition must by necessity be somewhat vague. Recall that we are working without a definition for arc length.

2.10-3 **Theorem:** (The right triangle theorem). Given a right triangle with vertex angle θ (that is, whose radian measure is θ), whose sides have lengths as shown in Figure 2.81, then,

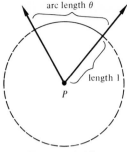

FIGURE 2.80

i. $\cos \theta = \dfrac{a}{c} = \dfrac{\text{length of side adjacent to } \theta}{\text{length of hypotenuse}}$;

ii. $\sin \theta = \dfrac{b}{c} = \dfrac{\text{length of side opposite } \theta}{\text{length of hypotenuse}}$;

iii. $\tan \theta = \dfrac{b}{a} = \dfrac{\text{length of side opposite } \theta}{\text{length of side adjacent to } \theta}$.

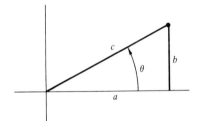

FIGURE 2.81

PROOF: Orient the triangle with the vertex of θ at $(0, 0)$ and the side of length a along the positive real axis. Strike an arc of unit length that crosses the line containing the hypotenuse at the point $P = (x, y)$. (See Figure 2.82.) Observe that the right triangle whose hypotenuse has length 1 and whose legs have length x and y is similar to the original triangle.

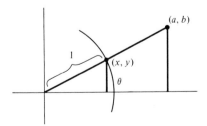

FIGURE 2.82

By definition, $x = \cos \theta$ and $y = \sin \theta$, so by considering ratios of sides of similar triangles, we see that

$$\frac{b}{c} = \frac{y}{1} = \sin \theta,$$

and

$$\frac{a}{c} = \frac{x}{1} = \cos \theta.$$

It follows immediately that $\tan \theta = \sin \theta / \cos \theta = b/a$.

Remark: Notice that a line with equation $y = mx + b$ intersects the x-axis at an angle θ where $\tan \theta = m$ (Figure 2.83).

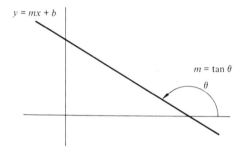

$y = mx + b$

$m = \tan \theta$

θ

FIGURE 2.83

Polar Coordinates

We will now coordinatize the plane in a manner quite different from the Cartesian and other rectangular and skewed coordinatizations previously discussed. We will establish a one–one correspondence between the points of the plane and the set of ordered pairs $(0, \infty) \times [0, 2\pi) \cup \{(0, 0)\}$. Let us begin by assuming that a Cartesian coordinatization of the plane has already been given. We will call the nonnegative half of the x-axis the *polar axis*. The point corresponding to the number zero on the polar axis we call the *pole*, and assign to it the ordered pair $(0, 0)$. (See Figure 2.84.) Now, any

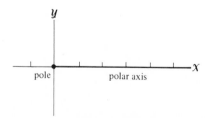

y

pole   polar axis x

FIGURE 2.84

point P in the plane other than the pole is some unique positive distance r from the pole. Further, there is some unique number θ in $[0, 2\pi)$ such that θ measures the angle (measured counterclockwise) between the polar axis and the line segment connecting P and the pole (see Figure 2.85). We call the

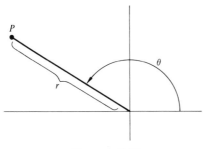

FIGURE 2.85

ordered pair (r, θ) the *polar coordinate* of the point P. We have thus established a one–one correspondence between points in the plane and the set of ordered pairs

$$(0, \infty) \times [0, 2\pi) \cup \{(0, 0)\} .$$

This correspondence is a coordinatization of the plane.

Example: The point whose Cartesian coordinate is $(\sqrt{2}/2, \sqrt{2}/2)$ has polar coordinate $(1, \pi/4)$. The point whose Cartesian coordinate is $(0, 1)$ has polar coordinate $(1, \pi/2)$. The point with polar coordinate $(2, \pi)$ has Cartesian coordinate $(-2, 0)$.

We made the assignment of polar coordinates based on an already given Cartesian system. The trigonometric functions may be used to establish a connection between these two different coordinatizations. If a point P has polar coordinate (r, θ) and Cartesian coordinate (x, y), then from the definitions of the trigonometric functions and the right triangle theorem,

$$x = r \cos \theta \quad \text{and} \quad y = r \sin \theta .$$

Example: The point P with polar coordinate $(2, 3\pi/4)$ has Cartesian coordinate (x, y), where

$$x = 2 \cos (3\pi/4) = 2(-\sqrt{2}/2)$$

and

$$y = 2 \sin (3\pi/4) = 2(\sqrt{2}/2).$$

That is, P has Cartesian coordinate $(-\sqrt{2}, \sqrt{2})$.

We would now like to extend the notion of polar coordinates so that any pair of real numbers (r, θ) determines a point in the plane. In making this extension, we must give up the property that each point has a unique coordinate, but this loss is more than offset by certain advantages we gain in so doing.

2.10-4 **Definition:** If a point P has Cartesian coordinate (x, y), then any pair (r, θ) such that $x = r \cos \theta$ and $y = r \sin \theta$ will be called a *polar coordinate* of P.

Clearly, any point can have an infinite number of polar coordinates. If a point P has polar coordinate (r, θ), then for any integer n, $(r, \theta + 2n\pi)$ will also be a polar coordinate of P. Further, if (r, θ) is a polar coordinate for a point, then $(-r, \theta + \pi)$ is also a polar coordinate for the point since both $\cos(\theta + \pi) = -\cos\theta$ and $\sin(\theta + \pi) = -\sin\theta$. That is, if $x = r \cos \theta$ and $y = r \sin \theta$, then it follows that $x = (-r)\cos(\theta + \pi)$ and $y = (-r)\sin(\theta + \pi)$.

Remark: Note that the origin $((0, 0)$ in Cartesian coordinates) corresponds to any polar coordinate of the form $(0, \theta)$, for any θ.

Example: Let P be the point with Cartesian coordinate $(x, y) = (\frac{3}{2}, 3\sqrt{3}/2)$. That is, $x = 3 \cos \pi/3$ and $y = 3 \sin \pi/3$. (See Figure 2.86.) This same

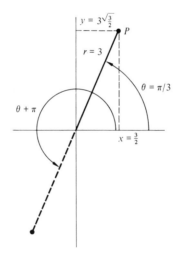

FIGURE 2.86

point has a polar coordinate $(-3, \pi/3 + \pi)$. That is, by measuring off an angle of $\pi/3 + \pi$, and interpreting the minus sign as a reflection back through the pole, we obtain the same point P.

Let us now determine a method for finding a polar coordinate (r, θ) for a point if the Cartesian coordinate (x, y) is given. We consider three cases, $x > 0$, $x < 0$, and $x = 0$. In any case, the distance from P to the origin is given by $\sqrt{x^2 + y^2}$. Further, if $x \neq 0$, then by the definition of the tangent function

$$\tan \theta = \frac{\sin \theta}{\cos \theta} = \frac{y}{x}.$$

It should follow then that $\theta = \text{Tan}^{-1} y/x$. However, the Tangent^{-1} takes values only in the interval $(-\pi/2, \pi/2)$. That is, $\text{Tan}^{-1}y/x$ would yield the same value for the point (x, y) as it would for the point $(-x, -y)$. We note, however, that θ is in the interval $(-\pi/2, \pi/2)$ when $x > 0$, and that the point $(-x, -y)$ is just a reflection through the origin of the point (x, y). We therefore have the following.

2.10-5   Theorem: If (x, y) is the Cartesian coordinate of a point P, then a polar coordinate for P is

$$\left(\sqrt{x^2 + y^2}, \text{Tan}^{-1} \frac{y}{x}\right) \qquad \text{if } x > 0,$$

and

$$\left(-\sqrt{x^2 + y^2}, \text{Tan}^{-1} \frac{y}{x}\right) \qquad \text{if } x < 0,$$

and

$$\left(y, \frac{\pi}{2}\right) \qquad \text{if } x = 0.$$

Graphing with Polar Coordinates

Many geometric figures can be described very easily by indicating a constraint on the polar coordinates of the points in the figure. Consider for example, all points having a polar coordinate (r, θ) satisfying the conditions

$$r = \theta \qquad \text{and} \qquad \theta \geqslant 0.$$

This is the spiral as shown in Figure 2.87. It would be considerably more difficult to describe the same figure in terms of Cartesian coordinates.

Example: Graph the curve whose polar coordinates satisfy the equation

$$r = \cos \theta.$$

Here, the radius r never exceeds 1; in fact, as θ traverses the interval $[-\pi/2, \pi/2]$, r goes from 0 to 1 and back to 0. In $[\pi/2, 3\pi/2]$, r goes from 0 to -1 and back to 0, which merely duplicates (by reflecting through the pole) the curve for $\theta \in [-\pi/2, \pi/2]$. Since the cosine function is periodic, the curve obtained for $\theta \in [-\pi/2, \pi/2]$ is traced repeatedly as θ varies over R. Thus, we obtain the curve shown in Figure 2.88.

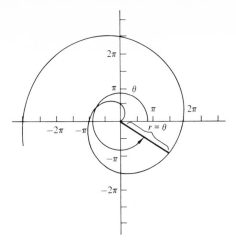

FIGURE 2.87

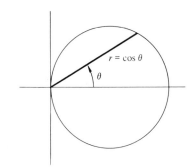

FIGURE 2.88

EXERCISES 2.10

1. Graph the point whose polar coordinate (r, θ) is:
   a. (2, 1.5).   b. (16, 2.4).
   c. (3, 3).   d. (5, 3.14).
   e. (1, 0).   f. (3, π).

2. Which points in the plane have polar coordinates (r, θ) equal to their Cartesian coordinate (x, y)?

3. Determine a polar coordinate for each of the following points whose Cartesian coordinate is given. Graph the point.
   a. (0, 1).   b. (0, −1).
   c. (0, 3).   d. (4, 4).
   e. (−4, −4).   f. (2, −2).
   g. $(\frac{1}{2}, \sqrt{3}/2)$.   h. $(\sqrt{3}/2, \frac{1}{2})$.
   i. $(2\sqrt{3}, 2)$.   j. $(-2, -2\sqrt{3})$.

4. Write a set description for all points on the unit circle (center at the pole and radius 1) using polar coordinates.

5. Graph each of the following sets. A point in the plane is to be identified with its polar coordinate.
   a. $\{(r, \theta) : r = 2 \cos \theta\}$.
   b. $\{(r, \theta) : \theta = 1\}$.
   c. $\{(r, \theta) : r = 2\}$.
   d. $\{(r, \theta) : r \sin \theta = 2\}$.

6. Graph the set of points whose Cartesian coordinates satisfy the conditions given. Then determine an equation in r and θ that determines the same set of points with polar coordinates (r, θ).
   a. $x^2 + y^2 = 25$.
   b. $x = 4$.
   c. $y = -6$.
   d. $x^2 - 4y^2 = 4$.
   e. $x = y$.
   f. $x + y = 1$.

7. Graph the set of points whose polar coordinates satisfy the conditions given. Then determine an equation in x and y that determines the same set of points with Cartesian coordinates (x, y).
   a. $r = 7$.
   b. $r = 9 \sin \theta$.
   c. $r = 4 \cos \theta$.
   d. $r(1 - \cos \theta) = 2$.

8. Discuss the graph of the spiral $r = \theta$ if the constraint $\theta \geqslant 0$ is omitted.

9. Graph the sets whose polar coordinates satisfy the given condition.
   a. $r = 2$.
   b. $r\theta = 1$.
   c. $r = 1 + \cos \theta$.
   d. $r = 1 - \sin \theta$.
   e. $r^2 = \sin \theta$.
   f. $r^2 = \cos \theta$.

10. Graph (in polar coordinates).
   a. $r = \sin 2\theta$.
   b. $r = \sin 3\theta$.
   c. $r = \cos 2\theta$.
   d. $r = \cos 3\theta$.
   e. $r = 1 + 2 \cos \theta$.
   f. $r = 2 - \cos \theta$.

VECTORS

INTRODUCTION

Our work in this chapter is aimed chiefly at introducing and investigating properties of a new type of object, called a *vector*. We shall see how the notion of vector grows naturally from geometric notions regarding points in the Euclidean plane and coordinate ordered pairs in $\mathbf{R}^2 = \mathbf{R} \times \mathbf{R}$. After some geometrically motivated work with vectors, we shall isolate the abstract properties of a vector space. This in turn suggests a host of interesting mathematical questions concerning new operations on vectors and vector spaces. You may find it surprising that these rather abstract considerations give rise to new insight and understanding of many familiar tasks, such as solving systems of equations and graphing certain relations. Thus, we see once again that the power of abstraction provides us with new ways to understand and solve old problems, as well as providing a framework in which to formulate and solve new problems.

3.1 POSITION VECTORS

Points and Vectors

Suppose x and y are the Cartesian coordinates of a point in the plane (i.e., $(x, y) \in \mathbf{R}^2$). The point may also be described with respect to its polar coordinate (r, θ). (See Figure 3.1.)

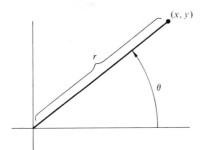

FIGURE 3.1

If *r* is positive, we know that the point is located by measuring out from the origin (pole) *r* units at an angle *θ*. It seems that we are locating a point by specifying an "arrow" with a certain length and direction with respect to the given origin. For this reason, it is often convenient to regard each position (location of a point with respect to a fixed origin *O*) as being an arrow with tail at the origin and head at the given point. We call such an arrow a *position vector*. Each such position vector can be denoted by an ordered pair of points in which the first component is the fixed origin *O*.

3.1-1 Definition: Let *O* be a fixed point in the plane (called the origin). If *A* is some point in the plane, then the ordered pair (*O*, *A*) is called a *position vector* (with respect to the origin *O*). The point *A* is called the *head* and the point *O* is called the *tail*. The line segment between *O* and *A* is called the *shaft*.

In any discussion involving position vectors, it will be assumed that the origin *O* has been specified, and hence we make the following convention.

3.1-2 Notation convention: If the origin *O* for an affine coordinate system has been chosen, and *A* is a point of the plane, then by **A**, we mean the position vector with *head* at *A* and *tail* at the origin *O*. That is

$$\mathbf{A} = (O, A).$$

If the point *A* has coordinate (x, y), then $(\mathbf{x}, \mathbf{y})$ means the position vector **A**. (See Figure 3.2.)

Remark: A position vector is different from a point in that a point is independent of any given coordinatization whereas a position vector is associated with the origin of a given coordinate system. However, once the origin has been established, a point *A* and the position vector **A** may be viewed as being essentially identical.

Operations on Position Vectors

Each point in the plane is identified with an ordered pair of numbers (x, y) in $\mathbf{R}^2$, provided some affine coordinatization is given (or understood). We

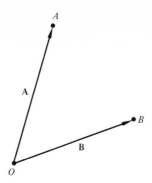

FIGURE 3.2

intend to introduce an algebraic structure on our position vectors. In order to do this, we will define the operations via the coordinates of the points involved. In spite of the fact that the operations on these position vectors are defined in terms of a given coordinatization, it is possible to show that the results would be the same for any affine coordinate system (having the same origin).

3.1-3   Definition: The *sum* of two position vectors (x, y) and (u, v) is the vector $(x + u, y + v)$. This may be denoted by

$$(x, y) + (u, v) = (x + u, y + v).$$

Vector addition is both *commutative and associative* (see Exercise 8).

Example: $(1, 2) + (-4, 2) = (-3, 4)$. Notice in Figure 3.3, that $A + B$ represents the diagonal of the parallelogram having adjacent sides given by **A** and **B**.

Example: Suppose $A = (3, 3)$ and $B = (-3, -3)$. Then

$$A + B = (0, 0) = 0.$$

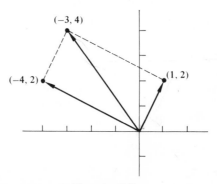

FIGURE 3.3

Before we proceed, let us give a geometric argument to show that addition of position vectors is truly independent of the particular affine coordinatization of the plane. Consider two points A and B in the plane, and an arbitrary affine coordinatization having origin O. Let A have coordinate (a_1, a_2) and B have coordinate (b_1, b_2). (See Figure 3.4.) Consider now, the location of the

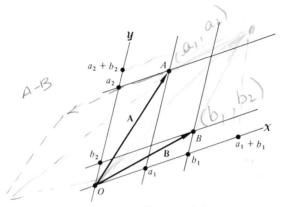

FIGURE 3.4

point $C = (a_1 + b_1, a_2 + b_2)$, which is the head of the position vector $\mathbf{C} = (\mathbf{a}_1 + \mathbf{b}_1, \mathbf{a}_2 + \mathbf{b}_2)$. (See Figure 3.5.) We see from the diagram that the resultant vector $\mathbf{A} + \mathbf{B}$ forms the diagonal of the parallelogram whose adjacent sides are determined by $\mathbf{A}$ and $\mathbf{B}$. This geometric result is independent of the particular affine coordinatization used. Thus, in spite of the fact that we compute the addition of position vectors $\mathbf{A}$ and $\mathbf{B}$ by using the coordinates

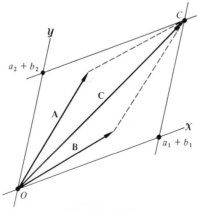

FIGURE 3.5

of the points A and B, the resultant vector $\mathbf{A} + \mathbf{B}$ is independent of any particular affine coordinatization used (except that we assume a common origin O).

Suppose $\mathbf{U} = (\mathbf{x}, \mathbf{y})$. Then

$$\mathbf{U} + \mathbf{U} = (\mathbf{x}, \mathbf{y}) + (\mathbf{x}, \mathbf{y}) = (\mathbf{x} + \mathbf{x}, \mathbf{y} + \mathbf{y}) = (2\mathbf{x}, 2\mathbf{y}).$$

It seems reasonable to define a multiplication operation for numbers times vectors such that $\mathbf{U} + \mathbf{U} = 2\mathbf{U}$. That is, we find $2(\mathbf{x}, \mathbf{y}) = (2\mathbf{x}, 2\mathbf{y})$, $3(\mathbf{x}, \mathbf{y}) = (3\mathbf{x}, 3\mathbf{y})$, and so on, to be a useful algebraic maneuver for our treatment of vectors. We now establish a second operation on vectors, *scalar multiplication*. This is an operation that allows us to form a vector that is some "scalar" (in our case, a real number) times a given vector. In what follows, the word *scalar* means *number*, in our case, *real number*. As with vector addition, we define scalar multiplication in terms of coordinates.

3.1-4   **Definition:** The *product* of a *scalar* (real number) α and a *vector* $(\mathbf{x}, \mathbf{y})$ is the *vector* $(\alpha\mathbf{x}, \alpha\mathbf{y})$. This is denoted by

$$\alpha(\mathbf{x}, \mathbf{y}) = (\alpha\mathbf{x}, \alpha\mathbf{y}).$$

Example: $2(1, -1) = (2, -2)$ (see Figure 3.6).

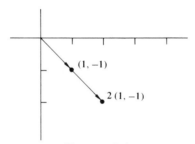

FIGURE 3.6

Remark: If a position vector $\mathbf{A}$ is given, then the set $\{\alpha\mathbf{A} : \alpha \in \mathbf{R}\}$ of all scalar multiples of $\mathbf{A}$ (actually the heads of $\alpha\mathbf{A}$) forms a line passing through the origin and the point A (see Exercise 9).

We also define negation and subtraction of vectors.

3.1-5   **Definition:** Let $\mathbf{A}$ and $\mathbf{B}$ be vectors, then

$$-\mathbf{B} = (-1)\mathbf{B} \quad \text{and} \quad \mathbf{A} - \mathbf{B} = \mathbf{A} + (-\mathbf{B}).$$

It is natural at this point to wonder whether a distributive law holds for a scalar times a sum of vectors; or perhaps for a sum of scalars times a vector. Let us consider an example of each situation before stating and proving a theorem about these distributive laws.

Example: $2((-1, 3) + (5, 4)) = 2(4, 7) = (8, 14)$. On the other hand, we also have $2(-1, 3) + 2(5, 4) = (-2, 6) + 10, 8) = (8, 14)$.

Example: $(4 + 7)(2, -1) = 11(2, -1) = (22, -11)$. Also, $4(2, -1) + 7(2, -1) = (8, -4) + (14, -7) = (22, -11)$.

3.1-6 Theorem: Suppose that (x, y) and (u, v) are vectors and let α, β be real numbers. Then

$$\text{(i)}\quad (\alpha + \beta)(x, y) = \alpha(x, y) + \beta(x, y),$$

and

$$\text{(ii)}\quad \alpha((x, y) + (u, v)) = \alpha(x, y) + \alpha(u, v).$$

PROOF: We shall prove only the first part, leaving the second as an exercise. Note that by definition

$$(\alpha + \beta)(x, y) = ((\alpha + \beta)x, (\alpha + \beta)y) = (\alpha x + \beta x, \alpha y + \beta y)$$
$$= (\alpha x, \alpha y) + (\beta x, \beta y) = \alpha(x, y) + \beta(x, y).$$

For a given coordinatization of the plane, we wish to specify and name two vectors that have a special significance with regard to that coordinatization.

3.1-7 Definition: Let $(1, 0) = I$, and $(0, 1) = J$. (Thus, $(1, 0) = \mathbf{I}$, and $(0, 1) = \mathbf{J}$.)

This definition along with the following theorem allows us to identify vectors without using the ordered pair notation.

3.1-8 Theorem: If (a, b) is a position vector, then $(a, b) = a\mathbf{I} + b\mathbf{J}$.

PROOF: $a\mathbf{I} + b\mathbf{J} = a(1, 0) + b(0, 1) = (a, 0) + (0, b) = (a, b)$.

Length of a Vector

If we assume that a Cartesian coordinate system is being used, then the distance the point (a, b) is from the origin is given by $\sqrt{a^2 + b^2}$. Thus, we speak of the *length* of a vector as follows.

3.1-9 Definition: The *length* of the vector $a\mathbf{I} + b\mathbf{J}$ is given by

$$|a\mathbf{I} + b\mathbf{J}| = \sqrt{a^2 + b^2}.$$

This length, unlike addition and multiplication of vectors, is *not* independent of the particular coordinate system used to match points with ordered pairs of numbers.

Remark: If A and B are points of the plane, then the distance between A and B is given by $|\mathbf{A} - \mathbf{B}|$. (See Figure 3.7.)

We have seen that $|\mathbf{A} + \mathbf{B}|$ is the length of one diagonal of the parallelo-

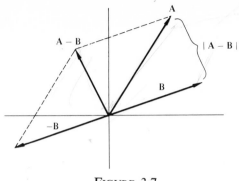

FIGURE 3.7

gram having adjacent sides **A** and **B**. Notice that the other diagonal has length $|\mathbf{A} - \mathbf{B}|$. (See Figure 3.8.)

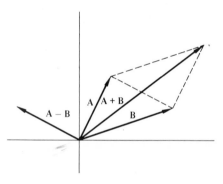

FIGURE 3.8

Direction Numbers

It is often helpful to be able to specify a direction for position vectors. This must be done in terms of a given coordinatization.

3.1-10   Definition: If $x\mathbf{I} + y\mathbf{J}$ is a position vector and α is a *positive* real number, then the numbers αx and αy are called *direction numbers* for the vector $x\mathbf{I} + y\mathbf{J} = (\mathbf{x}, \mathbf{y})$.

A vector has many direction numbers. We find one particular pair of direction numbers to be more important than the others. If a Cartesian coordinate system is being used (and this is almost always the case), and if

$\mathbf{N} = (\mathbf{a}, \mathbf{b}) = a\mathbf{I} + b\mathbf{J}$ is a *unit vector* ($|\mathbf{N}| = 1$), then $a = \cos \alpha$ and $b = \cos \beta$, where α and β measure the angles as shown in Figure 3.9. In general,

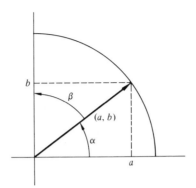

FIGURE 3.9

$$\frac{1}{|(\mathbf{x}, \mathbf{y})|}(\mathbf{x}, \mathbf{y}) = \frac{1}{\sqrt{x^2 + y^2}}(\mathbf{x}, \mathbf{y}) = \frac{x}{\sqrt{x^2 + y^2}}\mathbf{I} + \frac{y}{\sqrt{x^2 + y^2}}\mathbf{J}$$

is a unit vector, provided that $(x, y) \neq (0, 0)$, and so we have the following definition.

3.1-11 Definition: The numbers $x/\sqrt{x^2 + y^2}$ and $y/\sqrt{x^2 + y^2}$ are called the *direction cosines* of the nonzero position vector $(\mathbf{x}, \mathbf{y}) = x\mathbf{I} + y\mathbf{J}$.

Example: The vector $(\mathbf{2}, \mathbf{3})$ has direction cosines $2/\sqrt{13}$ and $3/\sqrt{13}$. (See Figure 3.10.)

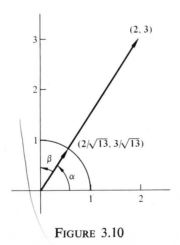

FIGURE 3.10

Notice that if a vector has direction cosines a and b, then $a^2 + b^2 = 1$
That is, $\cos^2 \alpha + \cos^2 \beta = 1$. (Explain!)

1. Let $A = 2I + 3J$. Locate and graph the vectors 2A, 3A, $-2A$. Find the direction cosines of A, 2A, 3A and $-2A$.

2. Using a Cartesian coordinate system, graph A, B, and $A + B$, where
   a. $A = (1, 3)$, $B = (2, 3)$. b. $A = (6, -1)$, $B = (7, 2)$.
   c. $A = (1, 3)$, $B = (-4, 2)$.

3. Graph and find the length of the given vectors. Also find the direction cosines.
   a. $(1, 4)$. b. $(7, -4)$.
   c. $(-3, 0)$. d. $(-2, -3)$.
   e. $(-6, -2)$. f. $(-5, 2)$.

4. Find the distance between the heads of the given vectors.
   a. $(1, 3), (2, 7)$. b. $(-1, 7), (-3, -2)$.
   c. $(2, 3), (-2, -3)$. d. $(5, 6), (-3, -1)$.

5. Graph $\{\alpha A : \alpha \in R\}$ where
   a. $A = (1, 3)$. b. $A = (-3, 4)$.
   c. $A = (-4, -1)$. d. $A = (6, -2)$.

6. Prove the second part of Theorem 3.1-6.

7. State a conclusion and prove it: $(a + b)(A + B) = $ _____. (HINT: Use Theorem 3.1-6.)

8. a. Show that $U + V = V + U$ (Commutative property of vector addition).
   b. Show that $(U + V) + W = U + (V + W)$ (Associative property of vector addition).

9. Show that $\{\alpha(a, b) : \alpha \in R\}$ forms a line in the plane that contains the origin.

10. a. Interpret $-U$ geometrically in terms of U.
    b. Show that

    $$U + V = U - V \Rightarrow V = O, \text{ (where O means the vector } (0, 0).)$$

    c. Interpret $U - V$ geometrically.
    d. Suppose $U = (x, y)$. Then $-U = $ _____.
    e. Show that $U - U = 0$.
    f. Show that $a(U - V) = aU - aV$.

11. Now would you define Ua?

12. Show that $a(bU) = (ab)U$.

13. Show that $0U = O$, and $aO = O$.

14. Show graphically that the result of a scalar times a vector is independent of the particular coordinatization used.

15. Show that all vectors on the half-line with initial point gotten by taking positive scalar multiples of some nonzero vector have the same direction cosines.

16. a. Graph $A = (3, 2)$ and $B = (1, 3)$.
    b. Graph $A + B$, and $B - A$.
    c. Draw the parallelogram having adjacent sides $A + B$ and $B - A$.
    d. What vectors represent the diagonals of this parallelogram?

3.2   INTRODUCTION TO VECTOR SPACES

Mathematicians often designate certain algebraic structures such as groups, rings, and fields and study their properties abstractly. By doing this, they can save a great deal of time when studying different examples of such structures. For example, **Q** and **R** are both fields, and as a result, have the same elementary algebraic properties. Using this information, one avoids building a completely new list of equation-solving rules for **R** once they have been established for the field Q. One merely uses any of the field properties that are used to solve equations in **Q**.

We wish now to designate two simple abstract structures motivated by the work of the previous section. The first of these is a structure with a single operation, called a *group*.

Groups

3.2-1   Definition: A *commutative group* is a set $\mathcal{G}$ along with a binary operation $+$ on $\mathcal{G}$ with the following properties:

1. For all $X, Y, Z \in \mathcal{G}$, $(X + Y) + Z = X + (Y + Z)$.   (Associative law)

2. For all $X, Y \in \mathcal{G}$, $X + Y = Y + X$.   (Commutative law)

3. There is a $0 \in \mathcal{G}$ such that for all $X \in \mathcal{G}$, $X + 0 = X$. (0 is called the *identity element*.)   (Identity law)

4. For each $X \in \mathcal{G}$, there is some $(-X) \in \mathcal{G}$ such that $X + (-X) = 0$. ($-X$ is called the *inverse* of X.)   (Law of inverses)

You are familiar with the fact that the rational numbers **Q**, and the real numbers **R** are groups under the operation of addition. You are in fact familiar with many simple group results, such as uniqueness of the identity element and the inverse of a given element.

Example: Consider $\mathcal{G} = \{(\mathbf{x}, \mathbf{y}) : x, y \in R\}$ (that is, $\mathcal{G}$ is the collection of position vectors discussed in the last section). Define $(\mathbf{x}, \mathbf{y}) + (\mathbf{a}, \mathbf{b}) = (\mathbf{x} + \mathbf{a}, \mathbf{y} + \mathbf{b})$ (addition by components). We have already seen that these vectors, under this addition operation, satisfy the properties of a commutative group. The zero vector **O** is the identity element, and the inverse of a vector **A** is $-\mathbf{A}$.

Example: The set Z of integers forms a group under addition.

Question: Does Z form a group under subtraction? Under multiplication?

We have previously discussed **R** $\times$ **R**, the set of ordered pairs of real numbers. It is also useful to introduce an *ordered triple* of real numbers. An *ordered triple* is a mathematical object (x, y, z) with the property that

$$(x, y, z) = (u, v, w) \qquad \text{iff} \qquad x = u, y = v, \text{and } z = w.$$

(See Exercise 12.)

3.2-2   Definition: $\mathbf{R}^3 = \mathbf{R} \times \mathbf{R} \times \mathbf{R} = \{(x, y, z) : x, y, z \in \mathbf{R}\}$.

Example: If we define addition in $\mathbf{R}^3$ by components, then it is easy to see that we have a group. (You should show this now!)

Vector Spaces

We shall now define vectors from an abstract point of view. We define a *vector space* to be a class of objects with operations satisfying the addition and scalar multiplication properties we have already noted. A *vector* is simply any member of this class. A vector space (also sometimes called a *linear space*) involves two kinds of algebraic structures, a field and a group, along with an operation (scalar multiplication) connecting them in a certain fashion.

3.2-3   Definition: A *vector space* consists of a group $\mathcal{U}$ and a field F along with an operation $\cdot : F \times \mathcal{U} \to \mathcal{U}$ (called *scalar multiplication*) such that:

1. For all $X \in \mathcal{U}$, $1 \cdot X = X$ (1 is the multiplicative identity element in F).
2. For all $a \in F$, and for all $X, Y, \in \mathcal{U}$, $a \cdot (X + Y) = a \cdot X + a \cdot Y$.
3. For all $a, b \in F$, and for all $X \in \mathcal{U}$, $(a + b) \cdot X = a \cdot X + b \cdot X$.
4. For all $a, b \in F$, and for all $X \in \mathcal{U}$, $(ab) \cdot X = a \cdot (b \cdot X)$.

Note the various kinds of addition and multiplication in this definition. The elements of $\mathcal{U}$ are called *vectors*, and the elements of F are called *scalars*. We say that $\mathcal{U}$ is a vector space over the scalar field F, and denote it by $\langle \mathcal{U}, F \rangle$.

Although we have four distinct operations defined on a single vector space, we usually use only two symbols to denote them, leaving it for the context to make it clear which is intended. That is, we use the same method (usually juxtaposition) to denote both the multiplicative operation in F and scalar multiplication. We use the same sign, $+$, to denote both the additive operation on F and the group operation in $\mathcal{U}$.

Example: Consider $\mathcal{U} = \mathbf{R} \times \mathbf{R}$ using component-wise addition:

$$(x, y) + (u, v) = (x + u, y + v).$$

Let $\mathbf{R}$ be the set of scalars, where scalar multiplication is defined by the statement: For all $a \in \mathbf{R}$, and for all $(x, y) \in \mathbf{R} \times \mathbf{R}$, $a(x, y) = (ax, ay)$.

Exercise: Verify that $\langle \mathcal{U}, F \rangle = \langle \mathbf{R} \times \mathbf{R}, \mathbf{R} \rangle$ satisfies the properties of a vector space.

Example: Let $\mathcal{U} = \mathbf{R} \times \mathbf{R} \times \mathbf{R}$ and define addition and scalar multiplication by $(x, y, z) + (a, b, c) = (x + a, y + b, z + c)$, and for all $\alpha \in \mathbf{R}$, $\alpha(x, y, z) = (\alpha x, \alpha y, \alpha z)$. Then $\langle \mathcal{U}, \mathbf{R} \rangle = \langle \mathbf{R} \times \mathbf{R} \times \mathbf{R}, \mathbf{R} \rangle$ is a vector space.

We have noted two special examples of vector spaces; $\langle \mathbf{R} \times \mathbf{R}, \mathbf{R} \rangle$ and $\langle \mathbf{R} \times \mathbf{R} \times \mathbf{R}, \mathbf{R} \rangle$. These vector spaces of coordinate 2-tuples and 3-tuples are analytic objects with no geometry involved. You should have noticed, however, that after a coordinatization of the plane has been established, then the vector space of *position vectors* and the vector space $\langle \mathbf{R} \times \mathbf{R}, \mathbf{R} \rangle$ are algebraically identical. Although we do not wish to formalize this notion, we point out that in such a case one says the two structures are *isomorphic.*

Linear Combinations

One of the basic ideas concerning vector spaces is the concept of combining vectors. In a vector space we have the ability to add two vectors or to multiply one vector by a scalar. We can of course extend this to the addition of several vectors which themselves may have been the result of a scalar multiplication.

Example: Let $\mathcal{U} = \mathbf{R} \times \mathbf{R}$ and $F = \mathbf{R}$. Let $A = (1, 4)$, $B = (6, 3)$, $a = 3$, and $b = 2$. We have here that $A, B \in \mathcal{U}$ are vectors and $a, b \in R$ are scalars. If $C = aA + bB = 3(1, 4) + 2(6, 3) = (3, 12) + (12, 6) = (15, 18)$, then C is a *linear combination* of A and B.

3.2-4 Definition: Let $\mathcal{U}$ be a vector space over the field F. If

$$Z = \sum_{i=1}^{n} a_i X_i = a_1 X_1 + a_2 X_2 + \cdots + a_n X_n,$$

then we say that Z is a *linear combination* of the vectors $X_1, X_2, \ldots, X_n$.

In this chapter and later ones, we shall do considerable work with the vector spaces $\mathbf{R} \times \mathbf{R} = \mathbf{R}^2$, and $\mathbf{R} \times \mathbf{R} \times \mathbf{R} = \mathbf{R}^3$. In more advanced courses, one deals with the more general case $\mathbf{R}^n$. We often find it useful to denote the n-tuples in such spaces by a vertical notation as well as the horizontal. For example, we sometimes denote the coordinate vector $(2, 4)$ by $\begin{bmatrix} 2 \\ 4 \end{bmatrix}$ and the coordinate vector $(4, 1, 7)$ by $\begin{bmatrix} 4 \\ 1 \\ 7 \end{bmatrix}$.

Example: Let

$$X = \begin{bmatrix} 2 \\ 1 \\ 4 \end{bmatrix} \quad \text{and} \quad Y = \begin{bmatrix} 3 \\ 1 \\ 3 \end{bmatrix}.$$

Let $a = 4$ and $b = 2$. Then

$$aX + bY = 4\begin{bmatrix} 2 \\ 1 \\ 4 \end{bmatrix} + 2\begin{bmatrix} 3 \\ 1 \\ 3 \end{bmatrix} = \begin{bmatrix} 8 \\ 4 \\ 16 \end{bmatrix} + \begin{bmatrix} 6 \\ 2 \\ 6 \end{bmatrix} = \begin{bmatrix} 14 \\ 6 \\ 22 \end{bmatrix}.$$

Notice that any vector $\begin{bmatrix} a \\ b \end{bmatrix}$ in the space $\langle R^2, R \rangle$ can be expressed as a linear combination of the vectors $\begin{bmatrix} 1 \\ 0 \end{bmatrix}$ and $\begin{bmatrix} 0 \\ 1 \end{bmatrix}$. That is,

$$\begin{bmatrix} a \\ b \end{bmatrix} = a\begin{bmatrix} 1 \\ 0 \end{bmatrix} + b\begin{bmatrix} 0 \\ 1 \end{bmatrix}.$$

Although it is not so obvious, any vector

$$\begin{bmatrix} a \\ b \end{bmatrix}$$

can also be expressed as a linear combination of

$$\begin{bmatrix} 1 \\ 1 \end{bmatrix} \quad \text{and} \quad \begin{bmatrix} -1 \\ 0 \end{bmatrix};$$

that is,

$$\begin{bmatrix} a \\ b \end{bmatrix} = b\begin{bmatrix} 1 \\ 1 \end{bmatrix} + (b - a)\begin{bmatrix} -1 \\ 0 \end{bmatrix}.$$

Thus, we note that in some cases, certain vectors can be used to *generate* the space. That is, any vector in the vector space υ can be obtained by selecting proper scalars and forming the corresponding linear combination thus formed. We shall later return to the problem of generating vector spaces, but wish now to introduce a related notion.

Linear Independence

Let us consider the pair of vectors

$$\mathbf{I} = \begin{bmatrix} 1 \\ 0 \\ 0 \end{bmatrix} \quad \text{and} \quad \mathbf{J} = \begin{bmatrix} 0 \\ 1 \\ 0 \end{bmatrix}$$

in $\langle \mathbf{R}^3, \mathbf{R} \rangle$. Notice that the vector $\begin{bmatrix} 2 \\ 3 \\ 0 \end{bmatrix}$ can be gotten by a certain linear combination of $\mathbf{I}$ and $\mathbf{J}$; $2\mathbf{I} + 3\mathbf{J}$. The vector $\begin{bmatrix} 0 \\ 0 \\ 2 \end{bmatrix}$, however, can never be gotten by taking linear combinations of $\mathbf{I}$ and $\mathbf{J}$. In this sense, $\begin{bmatrix} 0 \\ 0 \\ 2 \end{bmatrix}$ is independent of $\mathbf{I}$ and $\mathbf{J}$, while $\begin{bmatrix} 2 \\ 3 \\ 0 \end{bmatrix}$ is not. Thus, we make the following definition.

3.2-5   **Definition:** A given collection of vectors $A_1, A_2, \ldots, A_n$, is said to be *linearly dependent* if it is possible to find scalars $a_1, a_2, \ldots, a_n$, not all zero, such that

$$a_1 A_1 + a_2 A_2 + \cdots + a_n A_n = 0 \quad \text{(the zero vector)}.$$

Otherwise, the collection is said to be *linearly independent*.

Example: The vectors

$$\mathbf{I} = \begin{bmatrix} 1 \\ 0 \end{bmatrix} \quad \text{and} \quad \mathbf{J} = \begin{bmatrix} 0 \\ 1 \end{bmatrix}$$

are independent since it is impossible to find nonzero scalars a and b such that $a\mathbf{I} + b\mathbf{J} = 0 = \begin{bmatrix} 0 \\ 0 \end{bmatrix}$.

Example: The vectors

$$\begin{bmatrix} 2 \\ 1 \\ 0 \end{bmatrix}, \quad \begin{bmatrix} 1 \\ 1 \\ 1 \end{bmatrix}, \quad \text{and} \quad \begin{bmatrix} 7 \\ 5 \\ 3 \end{bmatrix}$$

are dependent since

$$2\begin{bmatrix} 2 \\ 1 \\ 0 \end{bmatrix} + 3\begin{bmatrix} 1 \\ 1 \\ 1 \end{bmatrix} = \begin{bmatrix} 7 \\ 5 \\ 3 \end{bmatrix}$$

from which

$$2\begin{bmatrix} 2 \\ 1 \\ 0 \end{bmatrix} + 3\begin{bmatrix} 1 \\ 1 \\ 1 \end{bmatrix} + (-1)\begin{bmatrix} 7 \\ 5 \\ 3 \end{bmatrix} = \begin{bmatrix} 0 \\ 0 \\ 0 \end{bmatrix}.$$

Subspaces

In general, a substructure of a given algebraic structure (such as a group, field, or vector space) is defined to be a similar structure in which the set of objects under consideration is a subset of the original structure and the operations remain the same as in the original. Moreover, the operation must be closed on the given subset.

Example: Consider the field of real numbers. Under the same operations (ordinary addition and multiplication), the set $\mathbf{Q}$ of rational numbers forms a subfield of $\mathbf{R}$.

3.2-6   **Definition:** If $\langle \mathcal{U}, F \rangle$ is a vector space, then $\mathcal{W}$ is said to be a *subspace* of $\mathcal{U}$, provided that

(a) $\mathcal{W} \subset \mathcal{V}$

and

(b) $\langle \mathcal{W}, F \rangle$

forms a vector space using the same operations as $\langle \mathcal{V}, F \rangle$ (restricted to $\mathcal{W}$).

Example: Let $\mathcal{W} = \{(x, 0) : x \in \mathbf{R}\}$. Then $\langle \mathcal{W}, \mathbf{R} \rangle$ is a subspace of $\langle \mathbf{R}^2, \mathbf{R} \rangle$. In order to prove this assertion, we must show that (a) $\mathcal{W} \subset \mathbf{R}^2$, and (b) $\mathcal{W}$ forms a vector space under the same operations as those on $\mathbf{R}^2$. (Note that we assume the same scalar field $\mathbf{R}$ for both of these vector spaces.) Part (a) is obvious. In order to verify Part (b), we need to check each of the properties of a vector space. We leave the details for the reader. Note that $\mathcal{W}$ is closed under addition, since $(a, 0) + (b, 0) = (a + b, 0)$, which is a member of $\mathcal{W}$. The commutative and associative laws for addition, and the laws for scalar multiplication follow directly from the fact that $\langle \mathbf{R}^2, \mathbf{R} \rangle$ is a vector space. (Explain!) It is important to notice that $(0, 0)$ is in $\mathcal{W}$ and serves as the zero vector. Further, $(a, 0) + (-a, 0) = (0, 0)$, and hence any element in $\mathcal{W}$ has an inverse in $\mathcal{W}$.

We now show that any subset formed by taking all multiples of a given vector in $\mathcal{V}$ forms a subspace of $\mathcal{V}$.

3.2-7   Theorem: Suppose $X \in \mathcal{V}$. Then $\langle \mathcal{W}, F \rangle$ where

$$\mathcal{W} = \{\alpha X : \alpha \in F\}$$

is a subspace of $\langle \mathcal{V}, F \rangle$.

PROOF: $\mathcal{W}$ is a commutative group under (vector) addition, since (1) the sum $aX + bX$ of two elements of $\mathcal{W}$ is $(a + b)X$, an element of $\mathcal{W}$; (2) $0 = 0X$ is in $\mathcal{W}$; (3) $aX + (-a)X = 0$, and $(-a)X$ is in $\mathcal{W}$. The remaining conditions are certainly satisfied because $\mathcal{W} \subset \mathcal{V}$.

Example: When coordinate vectors in $\langle \mathbf{R}^2, \mathbf{R} \rangle$ are identified with position vectors in the plane, multiples of a given vector fall along a line through the origin. Thus, subspaces of position vectors must consist either of the single vector $\mathbf{O}$ (origin) or vectors in a line through the origin; or the whole space, since the whole space also satisfies the conditions to qualify for a subspace of itself.

EXERCISES 3.2

1. Let $\mathcal{V} = \mathbf{R} \times \mathbf{R}$, $F = \mathbf{R}$. Let

$$X = \begin{bmatrix} 2 \\ 1 \end{bmatrix}, \ Y = \begin{bmatrix} 3 \\ 3 \end{bmatrix}, \text{ and } Z = \begin{bmatrix} 1 \\ 4 \end{bmatrix}.$$

Find:

a. $X + Y$.   b. $Y + Z$.
c. $2X + Y$.   d. $3X + -2Y$.
e. $2X + 3Y + -1Z$.   f. $3X + 4Z$.

2. Write a definition for *subtraction of vectors*.

3. Let $\mho = \mathbf{R} \times \mathbf{R} \times \mathbf{R}$, $F = \mathbf{R}$. Let

$$X = \begin{bmatrix} 2 \\ 1 \\ 9 \end{bmatrix}, \quad Y = \begin{bmatrix} 3 \\ 4 \\ 1 \end{bmatrix}, \quad Z = \begin{bmatrix} 1 \\ 1 \\ 2 \end{bmatrix}.$$

Find:

a. $2X + Y$. b. $7X - 4Y + Z$.
c. $X + 2Z$. d. $2X + 3Y + 2Z$.
e. $a, b \in \mathbf{R}$ such that $aX + bY = Z$.
f. $a, b \in \mathbf{R}$ such that $aX + bZ = Y$.

4. Let $\mho = \mathbf{R} \times \mathbf{R} \times \mathbf{R}$, $F = \mathbf{R}$. Let

$$I = \begin{bmatrix} 1 \\ 0 \\ 0 \end{bmatrix}, \quad J = \begin{bmatrix} 0 \\ 1 \\ 0 \end{bmatrix}, \quad K = \begin{bmatrix} 0 \\ 0 \\ 1 \end{bmatrix}.$$

If possible find
a. $a, b, c \in R$ such that

$$aI + bJ + cK = \begin{bmatrix} 4 \\ 1 \\ 2 \end{bmatrix}.$$

b. $a, b, c \in R$ such that

$$aI + bJ + cK = \begin{bmatrix} 1 \\ -2 \\ 4 \end{bmatrix}.$$

c. $a, b \in R$ such that $aI + bJ = K$.
Show that if $X \in \mathbf{R} \times \mathbf{R} \times \mathbf{R}$, then there exist $a, b, c \in \mathbf{R}$, where

$$aI + bJ + cK = X.$$

5. Show that the set of all linear functions on $\mathbf{R}$ (functions that can be expressed by $f(x) = mx + b$) is a linear space over $\mathbf{R}$.

6. Show that

$$\mathcal{W} = \left\{ \begin{bmatrix} x \\ y \\ 0 \end{bmatrix} : x, y \in \mathbf{R} \right\}$$

is a subspace of $\mathbf{R} \times \mathbf{R} \times \mathbf{R}$.

7. a. List some of the elements in the set $\mho = \left\{ \begin{bmatrix} x \\ y \end{bmatrix} : y = 3x \right\}$.

b. Show that if $A, B \in \mho$ and $a, b \in \mathbf{R}$, then $aA + bB \in \mho$.
c. Can you find some collection of objects in $\mho$ that can be combined linearly (that is, multiplied by scalars and then added together) that give as a result

$$\begin{bmatrix} 4 \\ 1 \end{bmatrix} ?$$

8. Investigate (prove or disprove):
a. Any two vectors in $\mathbf{R} \times \mathbf{R}$ can be expressed as a linear combination of

$$\begin{bmatrix} 1 \\ 1 \end{bmatrix} \quad \text{and} \quad \begin{bmatrix} 1 \\ -1 \end{bmatrix}.$$

b. Any two vectors in $\mathbf{R} \times \mathbf{R}$ can be expressed as a linear combination of

$$\begin{bmatrix} 1 \\ 1 \end{bmatrix} \quad \text{and} \quad \begin{bmatrix} -1 \\ -1 \end{bmatrix}.$$

c. If $\mathbf{X}$ and $\mathbf{Y}$ are two position vectors that do not lie on the same straight line passing through the origin, then any position vector $\mathbf{Z}$ can be expressed as $\mathbf{Z} = a\mathbf{X} + b\mathbf{Y}$, for some $a, b \in \mathbf{R}$.

9. Investigate (prove or disprove). Let $\mathcal{U} = \mathbf{R} \times \mathbf{R} \times \mathbf{R}$, using the real field for scalars.

a. If $X \in \mathcal{U}$, then X is a linear combination of

$$\begin{bmatrix} 1 \\ 0 \\ 0 \end{bmatrix}, \begin{bmatrix} 0 \\ 1 \\ 0 \end{bmatrix}, \quad \text{and} \quad \begin{bmatrix} 0 \\ 0 \\ 1 \end{bmatrix}.$$

b. If $X \in \mathcal{U}$, then X is some linear combination of

$$\begin{bmatrix} 2 \\ 1 \\ 1 \end{bmatrix}, \begin{bmatrix} 1 \\ 2 \\ 1 \end{bmatrix}, \quad \text{and} \quad \begin{bmatrix} 1 \\ 1 \\ 2 \end{bmatrix}.$$

c. If $X \in \mathcal{U}$, then for some $a, b, c \in \mathbf{R}$

$$X = a\begin{bmatrix} 1 \\ 1 \\ 1 \end{bmatrix} + b\begin{bmatrix} 1 \\ -1 \\ 1 \end{bmatrix} + c\begin{bmatrix} 1 \\ 0 \\ 1 \end{bmatrix}.$$

10. a. Show that these vectors are linearly dependent:

$$\begin{bmatrix} 1 \\ 1 \\ 2 \end{bmatrix}, \begin{bmatrix} 1 \\ 0 \\ 1 \end{bmatrix}, \quad \text{and} \quad \begin{bmatrix} 4 \\ 2 \\ 6 \end{bmatrix}.$$

b. Show that these vectors are linearly independent:

$$\begin{bmatrix} 1 \\ 1 \end{bmatrix} \quad \text{and} \quad \begin{bmatrix} -1 \\ 1 \end{bmatrix}.$$

11. Determine whether or not the given vectors are linearly independent.

a.
$$\begin{bmatrix} 1 \\ 1 \\ 2 \end{bmatrix}, \begin{bmatrix} -1 \\ -1 \\ -2 \end{bmatrix}, \begin{bmatrix} 0 \\ 3 \\ 1 \end{bmatrix}.$$

b.
$$\begin{bmatrix} 2 \\ 2 \\ 3 \end{bmatrix}, \begin{bmatrix} 1 \\ 1 \\ 0 \end{bmatrix}.$$

c.
$$\begin{bmatrix} 2 \\ 1 \\ 3 \end{bmatrix}, \begin{bmatrix} 1 \\ 1 \\ 0 \end{bmatrix}, \begin{bmatrix} 2 \\ 1 \\ -1 \end{bmatrix}.$$

12. Define an *ordered triple* (a, b, c) of elements from a set S to be a function f, $f : \{1, 2, 3\} \rightarrow S$, where $f(1) = a$, $f(2) = b$, and $f(3) = c$. That is,

$$(a, b, c) = \{(1, a), (2, b), (3, c)\}.$$

Show that $(u, v, w) = (x, y, z)$ iff $u = x$, $v = y$, and $w = z$.

3.3   THE LAW OF COSINES AND THE DOT PRODUCT

We shall now relate and apply vector notions to certain geometric and trigonometric ideas.

The trigonometric functions sine and cosine are special functions that can be used to locate points (x, y) on the unit circle in terms of distances measured on the circumference of the circle. (See Figure 3.11.) That is, if (x, y) is on the

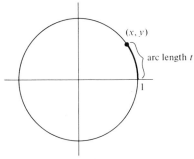

FIGURE 3.11

unit circle, then $x = \cos t$ and $y = \sin t$, where t is the length (measured counterclockwise) along the circumference from the point $(1, 0)$. If we view the point (x, y) as the corresponding position vector with respect to the origin $(0, 0)$, then we have $x\mathbf{I} + y\mathbf{J} = \cos t\mathbf{I} + \sin t\mathbf{J}$. (See Figure 3.12.)

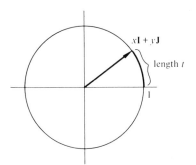

FIGURE 3.12

Let us now consider the effect of multiplying a position vector $\mathbf{A}$ on the unit circle ($|\mathbf{A}| = 1$) by a scalar a. If $\mathbf{A} = x\mathbf{I} + y\mathbf{J}$, then $a\mathbf{A} = ax\mathbf{I} + ay\mathbf{J}$. Thus, both the horizontal and vertical components are multiplied by a. This has the effect of putting $a\mathbf{A}$ on the same line through the origin as $\mathbf{A}$, since $y/x = ay/ax$. (See Figure 3.13.) If $a > 1$, then $a\mathbf{A}$ lies outside the circle in

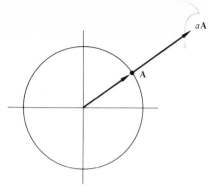

FIGURE 3.13

the same direction as the vector **A**. If $0 < a < 1$, then a**A** lies inside the circle in the same direction as **A**. What happens if $a < 0$? See Exercise 1.

Notice that any vector **B** can be written as r**A**, where $r = |\mathbf{B}|$ and **A** = $\dfrac{1}{|\mathbf{B}|}$ **B**. That is, **B** = r**A**, where r is the length of **B**, and **A** is a vector on the unit circle. Thus, if θ is the measure of the angle between the "shaft" of **B** and the x-axis (counterclockwise) and r is the length of **B**, then **B** = $r(\cos \theta \mathbf{I} + \sin \theta \mathbf{J})$. In this case, we have given **B** in terms of a polar coordinate (r, θ).

Remark: If

$$\mathbf{B} = r(\cos \theta \mathbf{I} + \sin \theta \mathbf{J}),$$

then also

$$\mathbf{B} = r(\cos (\theta + 2n\pi)\mathbf{I} + \sin (\theta + 2n\pi)\mathbf{J})$$

for any $n \in Z$. Also

$$\mathbf{B} = -r(\cos (\theta + (2n + 1)\pi)\mathbf{I} + \sin (\theta + (2n + 1)\pi)\mathbf{J})$$

for any $n \in Z$. (Explain!)

The Law of Cosines

We now establish the famous geometric result known as the law of cosines.

3.3-1 Theorem: *The law of cosines.* If a triangle has adjacent sides of length a and b that meet to form an angle of measure θ, then the length c of the third side is given by

$$c^2 = a^2 + b^2 - 2ab \cos \theta.$$

(See Figure 3.14.)

PROOF: Coordinatize the plane with Cartesian coordinates so that the vertex of the triangle is at the origin, and the side b (actually the side with

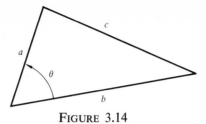

FIGURE 3.14

length b) lies along the x-axis. The sides of the triangle with lengths a and b can be viewed as vectors **A** and **B** respectively, as shown in Figure 3.15. We now have

$$\mathbf{A} = a \cos \theta \mathbf{I} + a \sin \theta \mathbf{J} \qquad \text{and} \qquad \mathbf{B} = b\mathbf{I}.$$

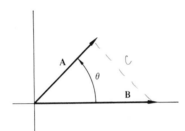

FIGURE 3.15

The length c is the distance between the points A and B, which are the heads of the vectors **A** and **B**, so

$$
\begin{aligned}
c &= |\mathbf{A} - \mathbf{B}| = |a \cos \theta \mathbf{I} + a \sin \theta \mathbf{J} - b\mathbf{I}| \\
&= |(a \cos \theta - b)\mathbf{I} + a \sin \theta \mathbf{J}| \\
&= \sqrt{(a \cos \theta - b)^2 + (a \sin \theta)^2}.
\end{aligned}
$$

Therefore

$$c^2 = a^2 \cos^2 \theta - 2ab \cos \theta + b^2 + a^2 \sin^2 \theta.$$

Since $\cos^2 \theta + \sin^2 \theta = 1$, the result follows.

The Dot Product

We shall introduce and discuss a third operation on the vector space of position vectors, and give a geometric interpretation of this operation. This will enable us (among other things) to determine the length of a vector in a way that is consistent with our previous definition and that can be used in later courses to generalize the notion of length.

3.3-2   Definition: The *dot product* of two vectors $\mathbf{V} = (v_1, v_2)$ and $\mathbf{W} = (w_1, w_2)$ is the scalar (number) $\mathbf{V} \cdot \mathbf{W} = v_1 w_1 + v_2 w_2$.

Remark: The dot product maps a pair of vectors to a scalar (that is, $\cdot : \mho \times \mho \to \mathbf{R}$). The dot product is sometimes called the *inner product* or *scalar product*.

Example: $(1, 5) \cdot (-2, 0) = -2$ and $(3, 4) \cdot (-1, 2) = -3 + 8 = 5$.

3.3-3   Theorem: The dot product operation is commutative.

PROOF: $(\mathbf{a}, \mathbf{b}) \cdot (\mathbf{c}, \mathbf{d}) = ac + bd = ca + db = (\mathbf{c}, \mathbf{d}) \cdot (\mathbf{a}, \mathbf{b})$.

We are naturally interested in connections between the dot product and the other operations on scalars and vectors. It is easy to show that the dot product distributes over vector addition.

3.3-4   Theorem: The dot product distributes over vector addition; that is, for vectors $\mathbf{U}$, $\mathbf{V}$, and $\mathbf{W}$,

$$\mathbf{U} \cdot (\mathbf{V} + \mathbf{W}) = (\mathbf{U} \cdot \mathbf{V}) + (\mathbf{U} \cdot \mathbf{W}).$$

The proof is left as an exercise.

3.3-5   Theorem: The length of a vector $\mathbf{U}$ is given by $\sqrt{\mathbf{U} \cdot \mathbf{U}}$.

PROOF: Let $\mathbf{U} = (u, v)$. By definition,

$$|\mathbf{U}| = \sqrt{u^2 + v^2}.$$

But

$$\mathbf{U} \cdot \mathbf{U} = u^2 + v^2,$$

so the result follows.

Remark: Recall that the distance between points U and V is the length of the vector $\mathbf{U} - \mathbf{V}$. It follows that the square of the distance between points $\mathbf{U}$ and $\mathbf{V}$ is given by

$$(\mathbf{U} - \mathbf{V}) \cdot (\mathbf{U} - \mathbf{V}) = \mathbf{U} \cdot \mathbf{U} - 2\mathbf{V} \cdot \mathbf{U} + \mathbf{V} \cdot \mathbf{V}.$$

Multiplying a position vector by a scalar has the effect of multiplying the length of the vector by the absolute value of that scalar. This is easily proved.

3.3-6   Theorem: If $\mathbf{U}$ is a vector and α a real number, then $|\alpha \mathbf{U}| = |\alpha|\,|\mathbf{U}|$.

PROOF: Suppose $\mathbf{U} = (u, v)$, so that

$$|\alpha \mathbf{U}| = |(\alpha u, \alpha v)| = \sqrt{\alpha^2 u^2 + \alpha^2 v^2} = |\alpha|\sqrt{u^2 + v^2} = |\alpha|\,|\mathbf{U}|.$$

In the exercises you are asked to show that

$$a(\mathbf{U} \cdot \mathbf{V}) = (a\mathbf{U}) \cdot \mathbf{V} = \mathbf{U} \cdot (a\mathbf{V}).$$

This shows that one may write $a\mathbf{U} \cdot \mathbf{V}$ using no grouping symbols without causing confusion.

The dot product has an interesting geometric interpretation that could have provided us with a definition for the *angle between two vectors*.

3.3-7   Derivation: Suppose **U** and **V** are vectors, as shown in Figure 3.16, and suppose the angle from **U** to **V** in the positive (counterclockwise) direction has measure θ. (We assume that $\mathbf{U} \neq 0$ and $\mathbf{V} \neq 0$.)

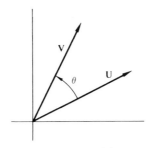

FIGURE 3.16

By the law of cosines,

$$|\mathbf{V} - \mathbf{U}|^2 = |\mathbf{U}|^2 + |\mathbf{V}|^2 - 2|\mathbf{U}|\,|\mathbf{V}|\cos\theta.$$

Also

$$|\mathbf{V} - \mathbf{U}|^2 = (\mathbf{V} - \mathbf{U}) \cdot (\mathbf{V} - \mathbf{U}) = \mathbf{V} \cdot \mathbf{V} - 2\mathbf{U} \cdot \mathbf{V} + \mathbf{U} \cdot \mathbf{U}$$
$$= |\mathbf{V}|^2 - 2\mathbf{U} \cdot \mathbf{V} + |\mathbf{U}|^2.$$

Hence, by equating and simplifying, we have the important result that if **U** and **V** are two nonzero-position vectors that form an angle of measure θ, then

$$\mathbf{U} \cdot \mathbf{V} = |\mathbf{U}|\,|\mathbf{V}|\cos\theta.$$

Remark: Note that it does not matter how θ is measured, clockwise or counterclockwise, since cosine is an even function, and we obtain $\cos(-\theta) = \cos\theta$. This is equivalent to the observation that $\mathbf{U} \cdot \mathbf{V} = \mathbf{V} \cdot \mathbf{U}$.

Example:

$$\mathbf{U} \cdot \mathbf{U} = |\mathbf{U}|\,|\mathbf{U}|\cos 0 = |\mathbf{U}|^2.$$

It follows that two nonzero vectors are perpendicular iff their dot product is zero. This gives us the ability to define the notion of perpendicularity in terms of vector operations.

3.3-8   Definition: Vectors **U** and **V** are *perpendicular* iff $\mathbf{U} \cdot \mathbf{V} = 0$.

Remark: The zero vector **O** is thus perpendicular to every vector.

Example: The set of vectors perpendicular to the vector $(2, 3)$ is the set of all vectors (x, y) satisfying the equation $(2, 3) \cdot (x, y) = 0$, that is, all vectors whose coordinates satisfy the equation $2x + 3y = 0$.

1. Explain the location of the vector $a\mathbf{A}$ as compared with $\mathbf{A}$, if (a) $a < -1$; (b) $a = -1$; (c) $-1 < a < 0$.

2. Find and graph the set of vectors perpendicular to the vector (a) $(-2, 4)$; (b) $(1, -3)$; (c) $(4, 1)$; (d) $(-3, -2)$.

3. Let $a \in R$, and $\mathbf{U}$ and $\mathbf{V}$ be vectors. Show that

$$a(\mathbf{U} \cdot \mathbf{V}) = (a\mathbf{U}) \cdot \mathbf{V} = \mathbf{U} \cdot (a\mathbf{V}).$$

4. Show that

$$2\mathbf{U} \cdot \mathbf{V} = |\mathbf{U} + \mathbf{V}|^2 - |\mathbf{U}|^2 - |\mathbf{V}|^2.$$

5. Show that

$$\mathbf{U} \cdot (\mathbf{V} + \mathbf{W}) = \mathbf{U} \cdot \mathbf{V} + \mathbf{U} \cdot \mathbf{W}.$$

(HINT: Expand both sides of the equation in the ordered pair notation and compute.)

6. Use dot products to show that if $\mathbf{U}$, $\mathbf{V}$, and $\mathbf{W}$ are nonzero vectors and $\mathbf{U}$ is perpendicular to $\mathbf{V}$ and $\mathbf{W}$ is perpendicular to $\mathbf{V}$, then $\mathbf{U}$ is a scalar multiple of $\mathbf{W}$.

7. Show that $|\mathbf{V}| = 0$ iff $\mathbf{V} = \mathbf{O}$.

8. A *unit vector* is a vector with length 1. Show that for any nonzero vector $\mathbf{V}$, $\dfrac{1}{|\mathbf{V}|} \mathbf{V}$ is a unit vector.

9. Find a position vector perpendicular to $(2, 7)$ with head (x, y) lying on the line $y = 2x + 4$.

10. Let $\mathbf{A} = 3\mathbf{I} + \mathbf{J}$. Let $\mathbf{B}$ be the unit vector that is perpendicular to $\mathbf{A}$ and has positive component along $\mathbf{I}$. Let $\mathbf{C} = -\mathbf{I} + 2\mathbf{J}$. Find a and b such that $\mathbf{C} = a\mathbf{A} + b\mathbf{B}$.

11. Let $\mathbf{S}$ be a position vector with head at the point with coordinate (x, y) and let $\mathbf{A} = 2\mathbf{I} + 3\mathbf{J}$. Graph the set of all vector heads such that
    a. $\mathbf{S} \cdot \mathbf{A} = 6$.   b. $|\mathbf{S}| + |\mathbf{A}| = 6$.
    c. $|\mathbf{S} + \mathbf{A}| = 6$.   d. $2\mathbf{S} \cdot \mathbf{A} = |\mathbf{S}| \, |\mathbf{A}|$.

12. Suppose a coordinate system with x'-axis and y'-axis is obtained from a given Cartesian system by rotating the x-axis and y-axis through an angle of θ. Show that unit vectors $\mathbf{I}'$ and $\mathbf{J}'$ along the x'-axis and y'-axis can be written as

$$\mathbf{I}' = \cos \theta \, \mathbf{I} + \sin \theta \, \mathbf{J}$$

and

$$\mathbf{J}' = -\sin \theta \, \mathbf{I} + \cos \theta \, \mathbf{J}.$$

Assume a point P has x-y coordinate (x, y) and x'-y' coordinate (x', y'). Use these equations to express the position vector $x'\mathbf{I}' + y'\mathbf{J}'$ for P in terms of $\mathbf{I}$ and $\mathbf{J}$. Now equate this expression to the position vector $x\mathbf{I} + y\mathbf{J}$ of the same point P, thereby obtaining the equations

$$x = x' \cos \theta - y' \sin \theta,$$
$$y = x' \sin \theta + y' \cos \theta.$$

(HINT: Use the linear independence of $\mathbf{I}$ and $\mathbf{J}$.)

3.4 INTRODUCTION TO FIXED VECTORS AND FREE VECTORS

Let us now consider a vector space that is algebraically identical to the space of position vectors, but that allows us some liberty with regard to physical applications not available there. The vectors we wish to consider appear in the form of "arrows" lying in the plane; however, we wish to regard any arrow with a given length and given direction equivalent with any other having the same length and direction. This will give us the ability to view vectors as entities that are independent of any particular chosen origin.

Fixed Vectors

We begin by considering the notion of a *fixed vector*. We hesitate to use the word "vector" since there is no useful general way to add fixed vectors and produce a vector space. We overcome this handicap by grouping them into equivalence classes, and adding the classes.

3.4-1 Definition: A *fixed vector* is an ordered pair of points in the plane. The first component is called the *tail* or *initial point*, and the second component is called the *head* or *terminal point*.

Example: $((1, 2), (3, 3))$ is a fixed vector with tail at $(1, 2)$ and head at $(3, 3)$. We mean, of course, the fixed vector (A, B) where A has coordinate $(1, 2)$, and B has coordinate $(3, 3)$. (See Figure 3.17.)

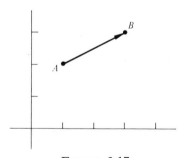

FIGURE 3.17

Example: A fixed vector with initial point $(0, 0)$ and terminal point (x, y) has already been designated as a position vector $(\mathbf{x}, \mathbf{y})$.

Example: The fixed vectors $((0, 0), (1, 3))$ and $((2, -1), (3, 2))$ are graphed in Figure 3.18. Note that these fixed vectors differ only in their location

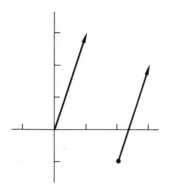

FIGURE 3.18

in the plane. That is, they have the same length and direction relative to their respective initial points.

Free Vectors

Many physical quantities seem to involve only two of the three attributes of fixed vectors, namely, direction and length. Acceleration and velocity are such quantities. This motivates us to consider an equivalence relation (see Section 1.5) on the class of all fixed vectors such that fixed vectors with the same length and direction are in a common equivalence class. The equivalence classes will be called *free vectors*.

Notice that a fixed vector $((a, b), (x, y))$ has a particular relationship to the position vector

$$(\mathbf{x, y}) - (\mathbf{a, b}) = (\mathbf{x - a, y - b}).$$

Both vectors point the same direction and have the same length. (See Figure 3.19.) Thus, we have the following definition.

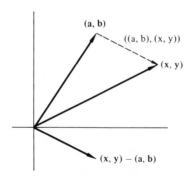

FIGURE 3.19

3.4-2   **Definition:** Let $((a, b), (c, d))$ and $((x, y), (v, w))$ be fixed vectors. Then define a relation $\sim$ by

$$((a, b), (c, d)) \sim ((x, y), (v, w))$$

iff

$$(\mathbf{c, d}) - (\mathbf{a, b}) = (\mathbf{v, w}) - (\mathbf{x, y}),$$

that is, provided

$$(\mathbf{c} - \mathbf{a}, \mathbf{d} - \mathbf{b}) = (\mathbf{v} - \mathbf{x}, \mathbf{w} - \mathbf{y})$$

or equivalently,

$$c - a = v - x \quad \text{and} \quad d - b = w - y.$$

Example:

$$((1, 2), (4, 3)) \sim ((-1, 0), (2, 1))$$

since

$$(\mathbf{4, 3}) - (\mathbf{1, 2}) = (\mathbf{3, 1})$$

and

$$(\mathbf{2, 1}) - (\mathbf{-1, 0}) = (\mathbf{3, 1}).$$

(See Figure 3.20.)

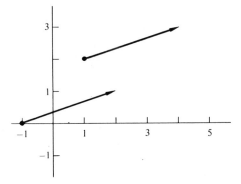

FIGURE 3.20

Question: What are some other fixed vectors in the same class as $((1, 2), (4, 3))$?

3.4-3   **Theorem:** The relation $\sim$ is an equivalence relation, and hence partitions the set of all fixed vectors into disjoint nonempty equivalence classes. Further, each equivalence class contains exactly one fixed vector with tail at $(0, 0)$ (that is, one position vector).

Proof: We must first show that $\sim$ is reflexive, symmetric, and transitive.

REFLEXIVE: Obviously any fixed vector is equivalent to itself under the above definition.

SYMMETRIC: If
$$((a, b), (c, d)) \sim ((x, y), (v, w)),$$
then
$$(\mathbf{c} - \mathbf{a}, \mathbf{d} - \mathbf{b}) = (\mathbf{v} - \mathbf{x}, \mathbf{w} - \mathbf{y}),$$
and since equality is reflexive, we have
$$(\mathbf{v} - \mathbf{x}, \mathbf{w} - \mathbf{y}) = (\mathbf{c} - \mathbf{a}, \mathbf{d} - \mathbf{b}).$$
It follows that
$$((x, y), (v, w)) \sim ((a, b), (c, d)).$$

TRANSITIVE: If
$$((a, b), (c, d)) \sim ((x, y), (v, w))$$
and
$$((x, y), (v, w)) \sim ((\alpha, \beta), (\gamma, \delta)),$$
then
$$(\mathbf{c} - \mathbf{a}, \mathbf{d} - \mathbf{b}) = (\mathbf{v} - \mathbf{x}, \mathbf{w} - \mathbf{y})$$
and
$$(\mathbf{v} - \mathbf{x}, \mathbf{w} - \mathbf{y}) = (\boldsymbol{\gamma} - \boldsymbol{\alpha}, \boldsymbol{\delta} - \boldsymbol{\beta}).$$
It follows that
$$(\mathbf{c} - \mathbf{a}, \mathbf{d} - \mathbf{b}) = (\boldsymbol{\gamma} - \boldsymbol{\alpha}, \boldsymbol{\delta} - \boldsymbol{\beta})$$
from which
$$((a, b), (c, d)) \sim ((\alpha, \beta), (\gamma, \delta)).$$

We leave it as an exercise to show that each class contains exactly one fixed vector of the form $((0, 0), (x, y))$.

As discussed in Section 1.5, this equivalence relation induces a partition of the fixed vectors into equivalence classes. A convenient way to name one of these equivalence classes is to use some fixed vector it contains. Thus, we have the following notation convention.

3.4-4 Definition: If $((a, b), (c, d))$ is a fixed vector, then $((\mathbf{a, b}), (\mathbf{c, d}))$ denotes the entire class of fixed vectors equivalent with $((a, b), (c, d))$. That is,

$$((\mathbf{a, b}), (\mathbf{c, d})) = \{((x, y), (u, v)) : ((x, y), (u, v)) \sim ((a, b), (c, d))\}.$$

Each such class of fixed vectors is called a *free vector*.

Example: $((2, 3), (1, 1)) \sim ((2, 1), (1, -1))$. Thus

$$((\mathbf{2, 3}), (\mathbf{1, 1})) = ((\mathbf{2, 1}), (\mathbf{1, -1})).$$

Since each equivalence class contains exactly one position vector, we can use it to characterize or identify the entire class. Thus, the free vector $((\mathbf{a, b}), (\mathbf{x, y}))$ is the same as $((\mathbf{0, 0}), (\mathbf{x - a, y - b}))$. Although it is possible to name the equivalence classes using only symbols of the form $((\mathbf{0, 0}), (\mathbf{x, y}))$, we find it convenient to choose a simpler label.

3.4-5   Definition: A free vector $[\mathbf{x}, \mathbf{y}]$ is the equivalence class of fixed vectors $((0, 0), (\mathbf{x}, \mathbf{y}))$. Numbers αx and $\alpha y (\alpha > 0)$ are called *direction numbers* of the vector. The direction numbers

$$\frac{x}{\sqrt{x^2 + y^2}} \quad \text{and} \quad \frac{y}{\sqrt{x^2 + y^2}}$$

are called *direction cosines*.

It should be clear that a free vector is a mathematical object that has the attributes of length and direction. Moreover, by the way in which we have defined free vectors, it is possible (and convenient) to consider them without reference to a coordinate system.

Graphically, we can interpret a free vector as an arrow that is "free" to slide in the plane to any location as long as the sliding maintains a vector of constant length and direction. (See Figure 3.21.)

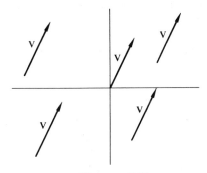

FIGURE 3.21

We should now like to mention a particular application of free vectors that shows the need to have both position vectors and free vectors. In physics, one finds it useful to examine the action of a moving body by associating its position and its velocity. One can view the velocity of the body as a particular vector having magnitude and direction. However, since the body is moving, these vectors must be viewed as being independent of the location of the body. Thus, one uses a position vector to locate the body and a free vector to indicate the velocity. (See Figure 3.22.)

Operations on Free Vectors

We now define operations on free vectors. Suppose, for example, the two vectors **F** and **G** in Figure 3.23 represent forces acting upon a point. The geometric interpretation of the forces **F**, **G**, and **F** + **G** suggests that **F** + **G** is a diagonal (oriented in the proper direction) of a parallelogram with sides

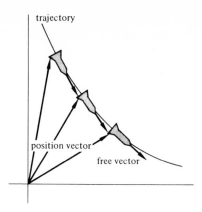

FIGURE 3.22

formed by **F** and **G**. For this reason, the addition operation is sometimes referred to as "the parallelogram rule of vector addition." We see in Figure 3.23 that **F** + **G** may be viewed as the third (directed) side of a triangle with sides **F** and **G**. The addition operation we are describing is exactly like the

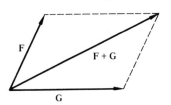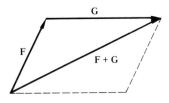

FIGURE 3.23

coordinate-wise sum described earlier in reference to position vectors. Since each fixed vector is equivalent to exactly one position vector, we can develop the algebraic properties in terms of position vector representations and at the same time interpret the arrow as being movable in the plane. We have, then, the following algebraic structure on the set of free vectors.

3.4-6 Definition: If $A = ((0, 0), (a, b))$ and $B = ((0, 0), (c, d))$, then $A + B = ((0, 0), (a + c, b + d))$. That is,

$$[a, b] + [c, d] = [a + c, b + d].$$

Example: Add the free vectors $((2, 1), (1, 3))$ and $((5, -1), (2, -3))$. Since

$$((2, 1), (1, 3)) = ((0, 0), (-1, 2)) = [-1, 2]$$

and

$$((5, -1), (2, -3)) = ((0, 0), (-3, -2)) = [-3, -2],$$

the sum is $[-4, 0]$. If one wishes to view this vector as having tail at the point $(2, 2)$, then he simply notices that $[-4, 0] = ((2, 2), (-2, 2))$.

Similarly, we define *scalar multiplication*.

3.4-7 Definition: Let α be a real number, and $[\mathbf{x}, \mathbf{y}]$ be a free vector. Then $\alpha[\mathbf{x}, \mathbf{y}] = [\alpha\mathbf{x}, \alpha\mathbf{y}]$.

Clearly, the class of free vectors has an algebraic structure exactly like the position vectors. When adding free vectors, or multiplying by a scalar, one simply looks at their particular representatives with tail at the origin (the representative position vector).

Since the algebra on the class of free vectors is defined in terms of representative position vectors, it is possible to extend the notion of length of a vector and the dot product to free vectors. These values are computed in terms of representative fixed vectors with tail at $(0, 0)$. The geometric interpretation is the same as before, and can often be applied more usefully since one need not think in terms of any fixed origin.

3.4-8 Definition: If $[\mathbf{a}, \mathbf{b}]$ and $[\mathbf{c}, \mathbf{d}]$ are free vectors, then the *dot product* is given by

$$[\mathbf{a}, \mathbf{b}] \cdot [\mathbf{c}, \mathbf{d}] = ac + bd.$$

The *length* of $[\mathbf{a}, \mathbf{b}]$ is given by

$$|[\mathbf{a}, \mathbf{b}]| = \sqrt{a^2 + b^2} = \sqrt{[\mathbf{a}, \mathbf{b}] \cdot [\mathbf{a}, \mathbf{b}]}.$$

The *angle θ between vectors* $\mathbf{A}$ and $\mathbf{B}$ is defined by

$$|\mathbf{A}| \, |\mathbf{B}| \cos \theta = \mathbf{A} \cdot \mathbf{B}.$$

Example: Determine the cosine of the angle θ between the fixed vectors $A = ((2, 3), (3, 4))$ and $B = ((2, 3), (4, 2))$ (see Figure 3.24).

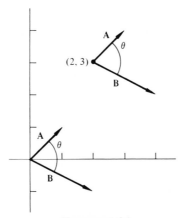

FIGURE 3.24

The angle θ is the same whether viewed in terms of the given fixed vectors or in terms of representative position vectors. Hence, we compute

$$((2, 3), (3, 4)) \cdot ((2, 3), (4, 2)) = [1, 1] \cdot [2, -1] = 1.$$

Also, $|\mathbf{A}| = \sqrt{2}$ and $|\mathbf{B}| = \sqrt{5}$. Thus,

$$|\mathbf{A}|\,|\mathbf{B}|\cos\theta = \mathbf{A} \cdot \mathbf{B} = 1.$$

Thus,

$$\cos\theta = \frac{1}{\sqrt{2}\,\sqrt{5}} = \frac{\sqrt{10}}{10}.$$

The commutative and distributive laws for the dot product of free vectors follow from the fact that computation is done in terms of representative position vectors. Also, it is true that $|\mathbf{A}|^2 = \mathbf{A} \cdot \mathbf{A}$ for a free vector $\mathbf{A}$.

Parallel and Perpendicular Vectors

There are many applications of vectors in which it is useful to consider simultaneously free vectors, fixed vectors, and position vectors. Note that two free vectors are parallel if their position vector representatives lie on the same line. That is, free vectors are parallel provided they are scalar multiples of each other. Formally, we make the following definition.

3.4-9 Definition: Two free vectors $\mathbf{U}$ and $\mathbf{V}$ are *parallel* iff there is some scalar t such that $\mathbf{U} = t\mathbf{V}$ or $\mathbf{V} = t\mathbf{U}$. (For position vectors, replace the word "parallel" with "collinear.")

Example: $((1, 2), (3, -1)) = [2, -3]$ and $((5, 1), (1, 7)) = [-4, 6]$ are parallel since $[-4, 6] = -2[2, -3]$. (See Figure 3.25.)

By taking multiples of a vector $\mathbf{U}$, say $t\mathbf{U}$, we obtain vectors parallel to $\mathbf{U}$ but of varying length and sense of direction as t varies. If $t < 0$, $t\mathbf{U}$ has direction opposite that of $\mathbf{U}$.

As with position vectors, free vectors are perpendicular if their dot product is zero.

3.4-10 Definition: Free vectors $\mathbf{A}$ and $\mathbf{B}$ are *perpendicular* iff $\mathbf{A} \cdot \mathbf{B} = 0$. Fixed vectors are perpendicular iff the free vectors they represent are perpendicular.

Applications

One of the most useful facts involving points, position vectors, fixed vectors, and free vectors is the following.

3.4-11 Theorem: If A and B are points in the plane, and $\mathbf{A}$ and $\mathbf{B}$ are position vectors with heads at A and B respectively, then the fixed

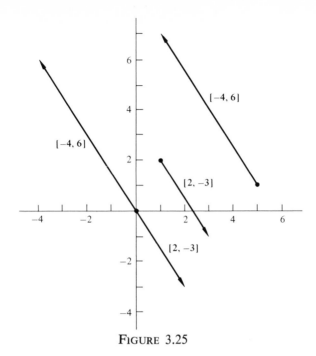

FIGURE 3.25

vector (A, B) is in the same equivalence class as the position vector
B − **A**.

PROOF: This follows directly from the definitions and is left as an exercise.

This theorem can be used in many ways. Notice in particular, if a triangle
has two sides given by vectors **A** and **B** (with tails at a common vertex), then
the third side is represented by the vector **B** − **A** having head at the head of
B and tail at the head of **A** (see Figure 3.26). Since **A** + **B** can be interpreted

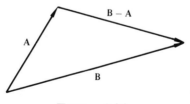

FIGURE 3.26

by the parallelogram law of addition, it follows that **A** + **B** and **B** − **A** can
be viewed as forming the two diagonals of a parallelogram, as shown in
Figure 3.27.

Example: Show that the diagonals of a rhombus are perpendicular.

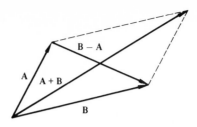

FIGURE 3.27

Solution: The rhombus can be viewed as having **U** and **V** for adjacent sides (Figure 3.28). We assume that **U** and **V** are not parallel, and that

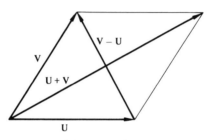

FIGURE 3.28

$|\mathbf{U}| = |\mathbf{V}|$ (so the parallelogram is a rhombus). We need only show that $(\mathbf{V} - \mathbf{U}) \cdot (\mathbf{V} + \mathbf{U}) = 0$. This is easily seen as follows:

$$(\mathbf{V} - \mathbf{U}) \cdot (\mathbf{V} + \mathbf{U}) = \mathbf{V} \cdot \mathbf{V} - \mathbf{U} \cdot \mathbf{V} + \mathbf{V} \cdot \mathbf{U} - \mathbf{U} \cdot \mathbf{U}$$
$$= |\mathbf{V}|^2 - |\mathbf{U}|^2 = 0.$$

3.4-12 Definition: The line containing distinct points A and B is said to be *determined* by the fixed vector (A, B). Lines are *perpendicular* iff vectors determining the lines are perpendicular.

Example: Show that the line containing the points $(-2, 0)$ and $(0, 1)$ is perpendicular to the line containing the points $(2, 2)$ and $(0, 6)$.

Solution: The lines are determined by the vectors $((0, 1), (-2, 0))$ and $((2, 2), (0, 6))$. These vectors are perpendicular since

$$((0, 1), (-2, 0)) \cdot ((2, 2), (0, 6)) = [-2, -1] \cdot [-2, 4] = 4 - 4 = 0.$$

Thus, the lines are perpendicular. (See Figure 3.29.)

In the next section, we illustrate many additional simple geometric applications of vectors. We conclude this section by remarking that it is very common not to mention specifically the type of vector (position, fixed, or

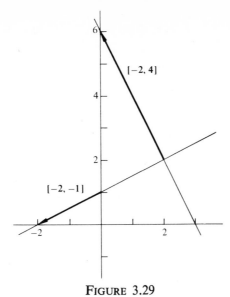

FIGURE 3.29

free) one has in mind in a given discussion, but to assume that the context makes it clear.

EXERCISES 3.4

1. Graph each of the following fixed vectors.
   a. $((0, 1), (2, 4))$.   b. $((-1, -3), (-1, 7))$.
   c. $((1, -2), (-6, -2))$.   d. $((2, 3), (6, -1))$.

2. Given the fixed vector $((2, 3), (-1, 7))$, find an equivalent fixed vector with tail at the given point. Graph the vector.
   a. $(1, 1)$.   b. $(-1, 2)$.   c. $(-3, 6)$.   d. $(0, 0)$.

3. Express each of the following free vectors, using a representative with tail at the origin. Graph.
   a. $((2, 4), (7, 7))$.   b. $((-1, 3), (6, -2))$.
   c. $((3, 4), (-3, -4))$.   d. $((2, 3), (-4, -6))$.

4. Express each pair of vectors using the $[x, y]$ notation, and then add the vectors. Draw a diagram that indicates the two vectors and the result.
   a. $((2, 1), (-1, 3)), ((-1, 6), (0, -4))$.
   b. $((-3, 7), (5, 5)), ((4, 0), (1, -3))$.
   c. $((0, 0), (6, 7)), ((-1, -4), (-1, 7))$.

5. Express each vector in terms of a representative having tail at the point given.
   a. $[4, 3], (1, 7)$.   b. $[-6, -1], (2, -1)$.
   c. $[-2, 3], (4, 1)$.   d. $[1, -2], (-2, 6)$.

6. Graph the line passing through the points A and B and the line passing through the points C and D, and show that they are perpendicular.

  a. $A = (0, 1)$, $B = (1, 3)$, $C = (0, -1)$, $D = (2, 0)$.
  b. $A = (2, 1)$, $B = (-4, 1)$, $C = (4, 3)$, $D = (4, 7)$.
  c. $A = (2, -1)$, $B = (5, 2)$, $C = (4, 7)$, $D = (5, 6)$.
  d. $A = (-1, 3)$, $B = (2, 4)$, $C = (2, 7)$, $D = (3, 4)$.

7. Show that if the diagonals of a parallelogram are perpendicular, then the parallelogram is a rhombus.

8. Show that the points A, B, and C are the vertices of a right triangle.
   a. $A = (1, 4)$, $B = (2, 1)$, $C = (5, 2)$.
   b. $A = (3, -1)$, $B = (4, 7)$, $C = (-8, 1)$.
   c. $A = (5, 2)$, $B = (-3, -2)$, $C = (-5, 10)$.

9. Find the constraining equation of all points (x, y) such that (x, y), $(4, 7)$, and $(9, 20)$ are the vertices of a right triangle where $(4, 7)$ is the vertex of the right angle.

10. Draw a free vector diagram that illustrates the associative law of vector addition.

11. Draw a sketch and interpret geometrically the following inequalities.
    a. $|A + B| \leqslant |A| + |B|$.   b. $|A - B| \leqslant |A| + |B|$.
    c. $|A - B| \geqslant |A| - |B|$.

3.5   APPLICATIONS OF VECTOR METHODS

The uses of coordinate free vectors are many and varied. In this section we examine some applications.

Using our knowledge of vector addition for free vectors, we can see plainly that if several vectors are represented in the plane such that the head of the first coincides with the tail of the second, the head of the second coincides with the tail of the third, and so on, the sum of the vectors is represented by the vector with tail at the tail of the first vector and head at the head of the last vector. (See Figure 3.30.) Let us apply this to a problem.

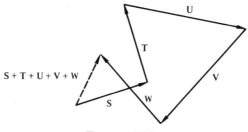

FIGURE 3.30

Example: Two adjoining sides of a regular hexagon are represented by vectors **U** and **V** (Figure 3.31). What are the vectors forming the other sides?

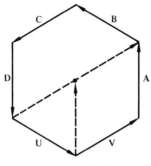

FIGURE 3.31

Solution: Let us label the remaining four vectors as **A**, **B**, **C**, and **D**, as shown. It is clear that

$$\mathbf{A} + \mathbf{B} + \mathbf{C} + \mathbf{D} + \mathbf{U} + \mathbf{V} = \mathbf{0}.$$

By symmetry, we can see that $\mathbf{C} = -\mathbf{V}$, $\mathbf{B} = -\mathbf{U}$, and $\mathbf{A} = -\mathbf{D}$. We need then only to find **A**. Using the fact that the diameter shown in the figure is parallel to **V** and is twice its length (look at the equilateral triangles), we have $\mathbf{U} + \mathbf{V} + \mathbf{A} = 2\mathbf{V}$, so that $\mathbf{A} = \mathbf{V} - \mathbf{U}$.

Example: Show that the diagonals of a parallelogram bisect one another.

Solution: Suppose that **U** and **V** form two adjacent sides of the parallelogram in Figure 3.32. We also assume that the parallelogram is nondegener-

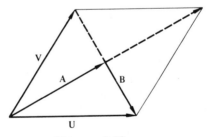

FIGURE 3.32

ate, that is, that **U** and **V** are nonzero and not parallel. The diagonals are represented by $\mathbf{U} + \mathbf{V}$ and $\mathbf{U} - \mathbf{V}$, so that $\mathbf{A} = \alpha(\mathbf{U} + \mathbf{V})$ and $\mathbf{B} = \beta(\mathbf{U} - \mathbf{V})$ for some scalars α and β. We wish to show that $\alpha = \beta = \frac{1}{2}$.

Note that $\mathbf{U} = \mathbf{A} + \mathbf{B}$. That is,

$$\mathbf{U} = \alpha(\mathbf{U} + \mathbf{V}) + \beta(\mathbf{U} - \mathbf{V}) = (\alpha + \beta)\mathbf{U} + (\alpha - \beta)\mathbf{V},$$

so that

$$(1 - \alpha - \beta)\mathbf{U} = (\alpha - \beta)\mathbf{V}.$$

But this equation must be of the form $0U = 0V$, since **U** and **V** are assumed nonparallel and nonzero. (Explain!) Thus,

$$1 - \alpha - \beta = 0 \quad \text{and} \quad \alpha - \beta = 0,$$

from which $\alpha = \beta = \frac{1}{2}$.

Example: A plane is headed due north at air speed 600 mph in a cross wind of 80 mph from the southwest (represented by a vector with direction numbers $(1, 1)$). (See Figure 3.33.)

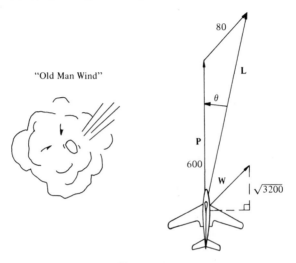

FIGURE 3.33

What is the true direction and speed of the plane relative to the ground?

Solution: The "resultant vector" is shown in the figure, under the assumption that the plane vector **P** and the wind vector **W** add to form the ground vector **L**. We must find the angle θ and the ground speed $|\mathbf{L}|$. We see that

$\mathbf{P} = [0, 600]$ and $\mathbf{W} = \alpha[1, 1]$ for some α. Since
$$80 = |\mathbf{W}| = |\alpha| \, |[1, 1]| = |\alpha| \sqrt{2},$$

we have $\alpha = 40\sqrt{2}$. Thus, $\mathbf{W} = [40\sqrt{2}, 40\sqrt{2}]$. Now

$$
\begin{aligned}
|\mathbf{L}| = |\mathbf{P} + \mathbf{W}| &= |[40\sqrt{2}, 600 + 40\sqrt{2}]| \\
&= \sqrt{3200 + 360000 + 48000\sqrt{2} + 3200} \\
&= 10\sqrt{3664 + 480\sqrt{2}} = 20\sqrt{916 + 120\sqrt{2}} \\
&\cong 659.
\end{aligned}
$$

Applying properties of the dot product, we have

$$\mathbf{P} \cdot \mathbf{L} = \mathbf{P} \cdot (\mathbf{P} + \mathbf{W}) = \mathbf{P} \cdot \mathbf{P} + \mathbf{P} \cdot \mathbf{W}$$
$$= [0, 600] \cdot [0, 600] + [0, 600] \cdot [40\sqrt{2}, 40\sqrt{2}]$$
$$= 360000 + 24000\sqrt{2} \cong 393840.$$

Also, $\mathbf{P} \cdot \mathbf{L} = |\mathbf{P}| \, |\mathbf{L}| \cos \theta = 600 \times 659 \cos \theta$, from which

$$\cos \theta = \frac{393840}{395400} \cong 0.996.$$

Thus, $\theta \cong 0.089$ radians (see table). Thus, the ground speed of the plane is approximately 659 mph and the direction is approximately 0.089 radians east of due north.

Example: Two forces are acting on a body as shown in Figure 3.34. The vector $\mathbf{F}$ has length 50 and is directed 30 deg ($\pi/6$ radians) above

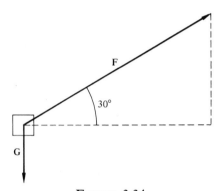

FIGURE 3.34

the horizontal. The vector $\mathbf{G}$ has length 25 and is directed vertically downward. Find the resultant force on the body. That is, add the two force vectors.

Solution:

$$\mathbf{F} = |\mathbf{F}|[\cos \pi/6, \sin \pi/6] = 50[\sqrt{3}/2, 1/2] = [25\sqrt{3}, 25],$$

and $\mathbf{G} = [0, -25]$. Hence, $\mathbf{F} + \mathbf{G} = [25\sqrt{3}, 0]$, indicating that the resultant force is horizontal to the right and has magnitude $25\sqrt{3}$.

Example: Use vector methods to show that the three medians of a triangle intersect in a common point two-thirds of the way from a vertex to the midpoint of the opposite side.

Solution: Let the triangle have vertices O (the origin), A, and B (see Figure 3.35), thus having sides represented by $\mathbf{A}$, $\mathbf{B}$, and $\mathbf{B} - \mathbf{A}$. The medians shown intersect at P and can be represented by $\mathbf{M}_1 = \mathbf{A} + \frac{1}{2}(\mathbf{B} - \mathbf{A})$ and

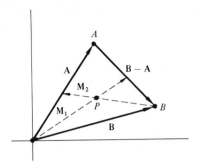

FIGURE 3.35

$M_2 = -B + \frac{1}{2}A$. Notice also that for some α and β, $B = \alpha M_1 + \beta(-M_2)$ (see Figure 3.36). Thus

$$B = \alpha \left(A + \frac{1}{2}B - \frac{1}{2}A \right) - \beta \left(-B + \frac{1}{2}A \right) = \frac{\alpha}{2}A + \frac{\alpha}{2}B + \beta B - \frac{\beta}{2}A .$$

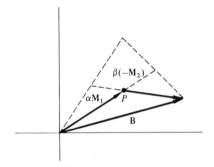

FIGURE 3.36

This is equivalent to

$$\frac{1}{2}(\alpha - \beta)A + \left(\frac{\alpha}{2} + \beta - 1 \right) B = 0 .$$

Since **A** and **B** are noncollinear, (linearly independent) it follows that

$$\frac{1}{2}(\alpha - \beta) = 0 \quad \text{and} \quad \left(\frac{\alpha}{2} + \beta - 1 \right) = 0,$$

from which $\alpha = \beta = \frac{2}{3}$. Thus, the medians intersect at a point two-thirds of the way along each, measured from the vertex at which it has initial point. Since we can make the same argument for any pair of medians, it follows that all three meet at a common point that trisects the length of each.

Projection of a Vector on Another Vector

We close this section with a definition for the projection of one vector onto another. We wish to determine a vector that essentially has its attribute of length determined by one vector and its direction by another. Since we are dealing with free vectors, there is no loss of generality in working with vectors with tail at O. Let X and Y be vectors, as shown in Figure 3.37.

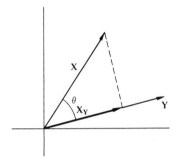

FIGURE 3.37

By the *projection* of X onto Y, (denoted by X_Y), we mean a vector along Y having the length of a "shadow" cast from X by a source perpendicular to Y. Since this length is given by the scalar $\alpha = |X| \cos \theta$, the vector we wish is given by α times the unit vector $(1/|Y|)Y$. If $\theta \in [0, \pi/2)$, then $\alpha > 0$, but if $\theta \in (\pi/2, \pi]$, then $\alpha < 0$ and our projection points in the opposite sense as Y does. (See Figure 3.38.)

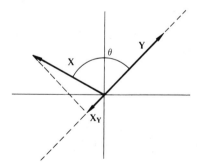

FIGURE 3.38

Thus far, we have

$$X_Y = |X| \cos \theta \, \frac{Y}{|Y|},$$

which can also be written as $\left(\dfrac{|X|\,|Y|\,\cos\theta}{|Y|\,|Y|}\right)$ **Y**, which suggests the use of the dot product.

3.5-1 Definition: Let **X** and **Y** be free vectors (**Y** $\neq$ **0**), then the *projection* of **X** onto **Y** is the vector

$$X_Y = \left(\frac{X \cdot Y}{Y \cdot Y}\right) Y \,.$$

Example: Let us determine the projection of **X** = ((2, 2), (3, 6)) onto **Y** = ((1, 1), (5, 2)). Notice that **X** = [**1, 4**] and **Y** = [**4, 1**]. (See Figure 3.39.) We have then

$$X_Y = \left(\frac{[1,\,4] \cdot [4,\,1]}{[4,\,1] \cdot [4,\,1]}\right)[4,\,1] = \frac{8}{17}[4,\,1] = \left[\frac{32}{17},\frac{8}{17}\right].$$

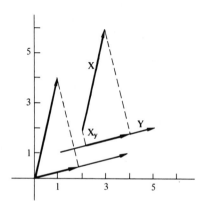

FIGURE 3.39

This can of course, be represented with tail at the location (a, b) by $((a, b), (a + \frac{32}{17}, b + \frac{8}{17}))$.

EXERCISES 3.5

1. Suppose that a triangle has vertices at the points U, V, and W. Use vector methods to show that the medians of the triangle meet at the head of the position vector $\frac{1}{3}(U + V + W)$.

2. Suppose that a parallelogram has adjacent sides represented by the fixed vectors ((1, 2), (4, 4)) and ((1, 2), (2, 6)). Find the fixed vectors that represent the other sides and the diagonals.

3. Suppose that line segments are formed joining a vertex of a parallelogram to the midpoints of the opposite side. Show that these lines trisect a diagonal of the parallelogram.

4. Suppose that points A, B, C, and D are the vertices of a parallelogram (in rotation) and P is the midpoint of the segment BC. Show that the segments AP and BD meet in a point that trisects the length of both.

5. Show that if the diagonals of a quadrilateral bisect each other, then the quadrilateral is a parallelogram.

6. Show that the segments joining the midpoints of opposite sides of any quadrilateral bisect each other.

7. Consider a triangle with vertices at the origin and the points A and B. Show that the head of the vector $\frac{1}{2}(A + B)$ lies at the midpoint of the line segment from A to B.

8. Find and graph the projection of X onto Y where
   a. $X = [2, 1]$, $Y = [7, -1]$.   b. $X = [-1, 3]$, $Y = [5, 1]$.
   c. $X = [2, 4]$, $Y = [-4, -1]$.   d. $X = [-4, -1]$, $Y = [-1, -5]$.

9. When will the projection of X onto Y be the zero vector?

10. Find and graph the projection of X onto Y, represented with tail at the point P.
   a. $X = [1, 7]$, $Y = [3, 4]$, $P = (2, 1)$.
   b. $X = ((2, 2), (7, 6))$, $Y = ((3, 1), (6, 7))$, $P = (3, -1)$.
   c. $X = ((1, -2), (6, 4))$, $Y = ((2, 1), (-3, 1))$, $P = (2, 1)$.

3.6   VECTOR METHODS AND LINES IN THE PLANE

We now look at ways in which vectors and dot products can be used to analyze lines.

Lines a Certain Distances from the Origin

Consider a unit position vector N (that is, $|N| = 1$) and a vector X. These vectors form an angle θ, as shown in Figure 3.40.
Since

$$N \cdot X = |N| \, |X| \cos \theta = |X| \cos \theta,$$

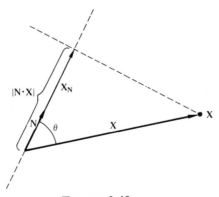

FIGURE 3.40

it follows that $|\mathbf{N} \cdot \mathbf{X}|$ measures the length of the projection of X onto $\mathbf{N}$.

Consider the line $\mathcal{L}$ that passes through the point X and is perpendicular to $\mathbf{N}$. This line also passes through the head of $\mathbf{X_N}$. Notice in particular that any position vector $\mathbf{Y}$ with head Y on the line $\mathcal{L}$ will have the same projection onto $\mathbf{N}$ (for each X and Y in $\mathcal{L}$, $\mathbf{X_N} = \mathbf{Y_N}$). (See Figure 3.41.)

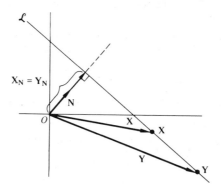

FIGURE 3.41

This projection is a fixed scalar multiple of $\mathbf{N}$. That is, $\mathbf{X_N} = \alpha\mathbf{N}$, where $\alpha = \mathbf{X} \cdot \mathbf{N}$. Since $|\mathbf{N}| = 1$, it follows that $|\alpha|$ is the distance (perpendicular) of the line $\mathcal{L}$ from the origin. Thus, for any unit vector $\mathbf{N}$ and any number α, the equation

$$\mathbf{N} \cdot \mathbf{X} = \alpha$$

describes a line perpendicular to $\mathbf{N}$ and a distance $|\alpha|$ from the origin. We thus have the following.

3.6-1 Theorem: Let $(\mathbf{a}, \mathbf{b})$ be a position vector. Let α be a real number. Then the equation

$$(\mathbf{a}, \mathbf{b}) \cdot (\mathbf{x}, \mathbf{y}) = \alpha\sqrt{a^2 + b^2},$$

or equivalently

$$ax + by = \alpha\sqrt{a^2 + b^2}$$

describes a line that is perpendicular to $(\mathbf{a}, \mathbf{b})$ and that is a distance $|\alpha|$ from O. (Any vector perpendicular to a certain line is called a *normal* to that line.)

Question: What two distinct situations occur depending on whether $\alpha > 0$ or $\alpha < 0$?

Example: Let us find an equation of the line perpendicular to $(2, 1)$ which has positive intercepts and lies 3 units from the origin. This line has equation

$$(\mathbf{2}, \mathbf{1}) \cdot (\mathbf{x}, \mathbf{y}) = 3\sqrt{4 + 1}$$

or equivalently

$$2x + y = 3\sqrt{5}.$$

If we had taken $\alpha = -3$, we would have had a line with negative intercepts. (See Figure 3.42.)

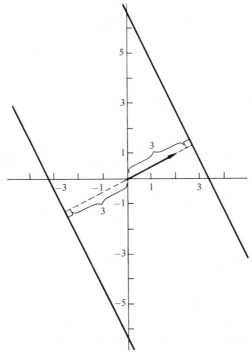

FIGURE 3.42

Lines through a Point Having a Given Normal

We now introduce another useful theorem regarding vector methods and lines in the plane.

3.6-2 Theorem: If $\mathbf{A}$ is a free vector with direction numbers a and b (that is, $\mathbf{A} = [\mathbf{a}, \mathbf{b}]$), then the equation of the line passing through the point $P = (p, q)$, which is perpendicular to $\mathbf{A}$, is given by the equation

$$[\mathbf{a}, \mathbf{b}] \cdot [\mathbf{x} - \mathbf{p}, \mathbf{y} - \mathbf{q}] = 0,$$

or equivalently

$$a(x - p) + b(y - q) = 0.$$

PROOF: Let $P = (p, q)$ be given and consider a representative of $\mathbf{A}$ with tail at P (Figure 3.43). The point (x, y) will lie on the line through P and

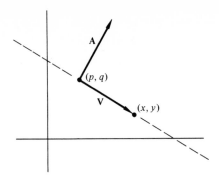

FIGURE 3.43

be perpendicular to **A** iff the vector $\mathbf{V} = [\mathbf{x} - \mathbf{p}, \mathbf{y} - \mathbf{q}]$ is perpendicular to **A**. However, **A** and **V** are perpendicular if and only if $\mathbf{A} \cdot \mathbf{V} = 0$.

Example: Find the equation of a line $\mathcal{L}$ passing through $(2, 3)$ and perpendicular to the vector $\mathbf{A} = [\mathbf{2}, -\mathbf{2}]$.

Solution: If (x, y) represents an arbitrary point on the line, then

$$[\mathbf{x} - \mathbf{2}, \mathbf{y} - \mathbf{3}] \cdot [\mathbf{2}, -\mathbf{2}] = 0.$$

Hence, $2(x - 2) - 2(y - 3) = 0$, or equivalently,

$$2x - 2y = -2$$

is the equation of the line $\mathcal{L}$. (See Figure 3.44.)

Example: Find the equation of the line passing through the point $(1, 1)$ and perpendicular to the fixed vector with tail at $(1, 1)$ and head at $(2, 5)$.

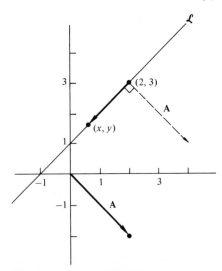

FIGURE 3.44

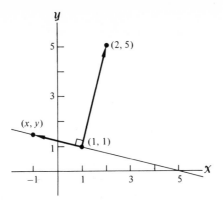

FIGURE 3.45

(See Figure 3.45.) The fixed vector $((1, 1), (2, 5))$ is in the equivalence class $[\mathbf{1, 4}]$, and the fixed vector $((1, 1), (x, y))$ is in the class $[\mathbf{x - 1, y - 1}]$. Hence for these vectors to be perpendicular, we must have

$$[\mathbf{1, 4}] \cdot [\mathbf{x - 1, y - 1}] = 0.$$

Thus, $(x - 1) + 4(y - 1) = 0$, or equivalently,

$$x + 4y = 5$$

is the desired equation.

Example: Find the equation of the line $\mathcal{K}$ that is perpendicular to the line $y = 3x + 1$ and intersecting it at $(-1, -2)$.

Solution: We note that $(0, 1)$ is also a point on the line $y = 3x + 1$, and hence the fixed vector $((-1, -2), (0, 1))$ should be perpendicular to each fixed vector $((-1, -2), (x, y))$. (See Figure 3.46.) The equation of $\mathcal{K}$ is thus given by

$$[\mathbf{1, 3}] \cdot [\mathbf{x + 1, y + 2}] = 0$$

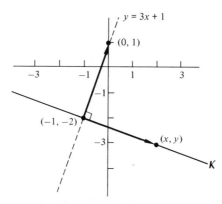

FIGURE 3.46

or equivalently

$$1(x + 1) + 3(y + 2) = 0,$$

which simplifies to

$$x + 3y = -7.$$

Parametric Equations

Any fixed vector (with nonzero length) determines a particular line in the plane. We shall describe this line by making use of vector addition and the fact that any given fixed vector is equivalent to a particular position vector. Recall that the fixed vector (A, B) with tail at A and head at B has the same length and points the same direction as the position vector $\mathbf{B} - \mathbf{A}$. (See

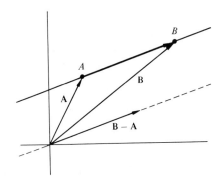

FIGURE 3.47

Figure 3.47.) We wish to describe all position vectors having head on the line $\mathcal{K}$ determined by the fixed vector (A, B). The collection

$$\mathcal{L} = \{t(\mathbf{B} - \mathbf{A}) : t \in R\}$$

of all scalar multiples of $\mathbf{B} - \mathbf{A}$ is a line passing through the origin parallel to the desired line. Now, if we add to each point of $\mathcal{L}$ the vector $\mathbf{A}$ (or any other vector on $\mathcal{K}$), we obtain the line $\mathcal{K}$. (See Figure 3.48.) That is, for any $t \in R$, the head of the position vector

$$t(\mathbf{B} - \mathbf{A}) + \mathbf{A}$$

is a point on the line determined by the fixed vector (A, B). If we let $\mathbf{A} = (a_1, a_2)$ and $\mathbf{B} = (b_1, b_2)$, then any point $X = (x, y)$ on the line is given by

$$\mathbf{X} = t(\mathbf{B} - \mathbf{A}) + \mathbf{A} = t((b_1, b_2) - (a_1, a_2)) + (a_1, a_2),$$

or

$$(\mathbf{x}, \mathbf{y}) = (t(b_1 - a_1) + a_1, t(b_2 - a_2) + a_2),$$

from which the components of $\mathbf{X}$ are given by

$$x = t(b_1 - a_1) + a_1 \qquad \text{and} \qquad y = t(b_2 - a_2) + a_2.$$

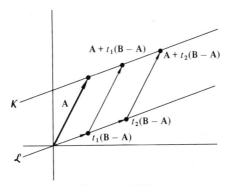

FIGURE 3.48

These equations are called the *parametric equations* of the line containing the points (a_1, a_2) and (b_1, b_2).

Example: Describe by using a parameter t, the line containing the two points $(2, 3)$ and $(4, 1)$. That is, give parametric equations for the line determined by the fixed vector $V = ((2, 3), (4, 1))$.

Solution: $(4, 1) - (2, 3) = (2, -2)$ is a position vector with the same length and direction as V, and hence the line $\mathcal{L} = \{t(2, -2) : t \in \mathbf{R}\}$ is parallel to the position vector on the desired line. (See Figure 3.49.) Adding some

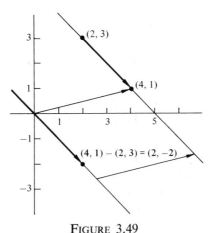

FIGURE 3.49

vector on the desired line to each member of $\mathcal{L}$ gives us the set of points we wish to determine. Thus,

$$\mathcal{K} = \{t(2, -2) + (4, 1) : t \in \mathbf{R}\}$$

is a parametric vector description of the line determined by the fixed vector

$((2, 3), (4, 1))$. That is, any vector $\mathbf{X} = (\mathbf{x}, \mathbf{y})$ with head on the line is given by

$$(\mathbf{x}, \mathbf{y}) = ((4, 1) - (2, 3))t + (4, 1) = (2, -2)t + (4, 1)$$
$$= (2t + 4, -2t + 1), \qquad \text{for some } t.$$

Hence, parametric equations for $\mathcal{K}$ are

$$x = 2t + 4 \qquad \text{and} \qquad y = -2t + 1.$$

Eliminating the Parameter

Consider the line $\mathcal{L}$ shown in Figure 3.50. Suppose that $\mathbf{U}$ and $\mathbf{V}$ are position vectors with heads U and V on the line as shown. We wish to describe the line $\mathcal{L}$ both in terms of vectors using a parameter, and in terms of the two components. First, note that a fixed vector (U, V) is in the same free class as

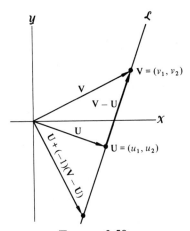

FIGURE 3.50

the position vector $\mathbf{V} - \mathbf{U}$. Thus, a position vector with head on the line will be of the form $\mathbf{U} + \alpha(\mathbf{V} - \mathbf{U})$ for $\alpha \in \mathbf{R}$. For $\alpha \in [0, 1]$, this vector will terminate on the line segment between $U = (u_1, u_2)$ and $V = (v_1, v_2)$. For $\alpha > 1$, the vector will terminate above V and for $\alpha < 0$ it will terminate below V. An example of $\alpha = -1$ is shown in Figure 3.50. Suppose now that (x, y) is any point in $\mathcal{L}$. Then for some α,

$$(\mathbf{x}, \mathbf{y}) = \mathbf{U} + \alpha(\mathbf{V} - \mathbf{U}) = (1 - \alpha)\mathbf{U} + \alpha\mathbf{V}$$
$$= (1 - \alpha)(u_1, u_2) + \alpha(v_1, v_2)$$
$$= ((1 - \alpha)u_1 + \alpha v_1, (1 - \alpha)u_2 + \alpha v_2).$$

Thus,

$$x = (1 - \alpha)u_1 + \alpha v_1 \qquad \text{and} \qquad y = (1 - \alpha)u_2 + \alpha v_2$$

are parametric equations of the line $\mathcal{L}$. We may eliminate the parameter α to obtain a single constraining equation describing $\mathcal{L}$ as follows. From the first equation we have

$$x = u_1 + \alpha(v_1 - u_1)$$

from which

$$\alpha = \frac{x - u_1}{v_1 - u_1},$$

provided that $v_1 - u_1 \neq 0$. Substituting this in the second equation, we obtain

$$y - u_2 = \frac{v_2 - u_2}{v_1 - u_1}(x - u_1),$$

or

$$y = mx + b,$$

where

$$m = (v_2 - u_2)/(v_1 - u_1) \qquad \text{and} \qquad b = u_2 - u_1 m.$$

Question: We have assumed in our discussion of eliminating the parameter that $v_1 - u_1 \neq 0$. What can you say about the line $\mathcal{L}$ and its nonparametric equation if $v_1 - u_1 = 0$?

EXERCISES 3.6

1. Find equations for and graph the two lines normal to V that are a distance α from the origin.
   a. $V = (2, -3)$, $\alpha = 4$.   b. $V = (-1, -6)$, $\alpha = 2$.
   c. $V = (2, 4)$, $\alpha = 1$.   d. $V = (-3, 2)$, $\alpha = 5$.

2. Find an equation for and graph the line that passes through P and is normal to V. (Find the distance the line is from O.)
   a. $P = (1, 4)$; $V = [1, 1]$.   b. $P = (-1, 2)$; $V = [7, -3]$.
   c. $P = (-3, 7)$; $V = [-2, 1]$.   d. $P = (5, -1)$; $V = [-2, 5]$.

3. Find the equation of a line that is perpendicular to the given line and intersects it at P.
   a. $y = -\frac{1}{2}x + 4$; $P = (2, 3)$.   b. $y = 3x - 1$; $P = (1, 2)$.
   c. $3y + 4x = 2$; $P = (-1, 2)$.   d. $4x - 5y = 2$; $P = (-2, -2)$.

4. Define the slope of a free vector $[a, b]$ to be b/a, if $a \neq 0$. Show that two vectors with nonzero slope are perpendicular iff they have slopes that are negative reciprocals.

5. The slope of a line determined by the fixed vector (A, B) is equal to the slope of the free vector containing (A, B). Show that lines are perpendicular iff they have slopes that are negative reciprocals.

6. Let $A = (2, 4)$ and $B = (1, 2)$. Graph the representative of $B - A$ that has its tail at $(2, 4)$.

7. a. Let $A = (1, 4)$. Graph the position vectors tA, where $t = 1$, $t = 2$, $t = 3$, $t = 4$, $t = -1$, $t = -2$, $t = -3$, and $t = -4$.
   b. Draw a line through the heads of these vectors.

8. a. Graph the vectors $\mathbf{A} = (1, 2)$ and $\mathbf{B} = (4, 1)$.
    b. Graph $\mathbf{X} = \mathbf{B} - \mathbf{A}$.
    c. Graph $t\mathbf{X}$ and $t\mathbf{X} + \mathbf{A}$, where $t = -1$, $t = 0$, $t = 1$, $t = 2$, and $t = 3$.
    d. Graph $\mathcal{K} = \{t\mathbf{X} + \mathbf{A} : t \in \mathbf{R}\}$.

9. Graph $\mathcal{K} = \{t\mathbf{X} + \mathbf{A} : t \in \mathbf{R}\}$, where X and A are as given.
    a. $\mathbf{X} = (4, 1) - (1, -1);\ \mathbf{A} = (1, -1)$.
    b. $\mathbf{X} = (2, 1) - (-1, -3);\ \mathbf{A} = (3, 2)$.
    c. $\mathbf{X} = (7, 1);\ \mathbf{A} = (-1, -2)$.
    d. $\mathbf{X} = (-3, 5);\ \mathbf{A} = (2, -4)$.

10. a. Graph the fixed vector $((7, 1), (-3, 4))$ and the line $\mathcal{L}$ it determines.
    b. Find $\mathbf{X}$ and $\mathbf{A}$ so this line is given by $\mathcal{L} = \{t\mathbf{X} + \mathbf{A} : t \in \mathbf{R}\}$.
    c. If $\mathbf{Z} = (\mathbf{x}, \mathbf{y})$ represents an arbitrary element of $\mathcal{L}$, then determine x and y as functions of a parameter t.
    d. Eliminate the parameter t mentioned in Exercise 10c and give a single constraint for the coordinates x and y for a point on $\mathcal{L}$.

11. Find parametric and nonparametric equations for the line containing the two points given.
    a. $(1, 3), (7, 5)$.   b. $(-3, 1), (-2, 4)$.
    c. $(-1, -4), (6, -1)$.   d. $(2, -2), (3, -1)$.

3.7 SYSTEMS OF LINEAR EQUATIONS AND INTRODUCTION TO ELEMENTARY MATRIX ALGEBRA

We now consider a special case of a broad subject that has far-reaching applications in mathematics. Often in the study of physical phenomena, equations or inequalities arise that involve more than one unknown number. We now consider the situation in which two equations are given involving two unknown numbers. A solution to an equation that involves two unknowns can be viewed as a coordinate vector in $\mathbf{R}^2$. For example, the equation

$$2x + 3y = 0$$

has many coordinate vectors as solutions (that is, ordered pair solutions (x, y)). Some of these are $(0, 0)$, $(3, -2)$, $(6, -4)$. If the plane has been given a Euclidean coordinatization, this solution set can be viewed geometrically as a line in the plane.

In asking for solutions to a system of several equations, we are seeking coordinate vectors that simultaneously satisfy all of the equations in the system. For example, the set of solutions to the system

$$2x - y = 1$$
$$x + y = 5$$

may be described as

$$\{(x, y) : 2x - y = 1 \text{ and } x + y = 5\}$$
$$= \{(x, y) : 2x - y = 1\} \cap \{(x, y) : x + y = 5\} = \{(2, 3)\}.$$

A graphical interpretation is simply that the two lines described by $2x - y = 1$ and $x + y = 5$ intersect at the point $(2, 3)$. (See Figure 3.50a.)

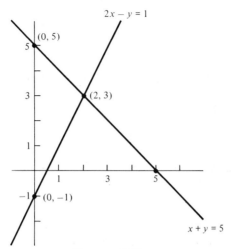

FIGURE 3.50a

The graphical interpretation of solutions for two linear equations in two unknowns suggests certain facts about such solutions. There will be none, exactly one, or infinitely many solutions, according as the corresponding lines are parallel and distinct, not parallel, and parallel and the same, respectively. If the lines both have slopes, then there is a unique solution to the system iff the slopes are not equal.

Example: Consider the system

$$a_1x + b_1y = c_1$$
$$a_2x + b_2y = c_2.$$

By putting these equations in the slope intercept form ($y = mx + b$), we can obtain the slopes of the lines (assuming they both have slopes). Thus the system is equivalent to

$$y = -\frac{a_1}{b_1}x + \frac{c_1}{b_1}$$

$$y = -\frac{a_2}{b_2}x + \frac{c_2}{b_2}.$$

The condition of nonequal slopes is that

$$-\frac{a_1}{b_1} \neq -\frac{a_2}{b_2}$$

or equivalently

$$a_1 b_2 - a_2 b_1 \neq 0,$$

a condition we will examine in some detail later.

Matrices

Before we proceed with a discussion of systems of two equations in two unknowns, we wish to introduce the notion of a matrix.

3.7-1   Definition: The symbol

$$\begin{bmatrix} \alpha & \beta \\ \gamma & \delta \end{bmatrix}$$

is called a two by two *matrix* (plural: matrices). The symbols

$$[\alpha \; \beta] \qquad \text{and} \qquad \begin{bmatrix} \alpha \\ \beta \end{bmatrix}$$

are one by two and two by one matrices respectively, which in addition can be interpreted as vectors in $\langle \mathbf{R}^2, \mathbf{R} \rangle$.

Remark: A real 2×2 (2 by 2) matrix may be defined as a function $F : \{1, 2\} \times \{1, 2\} \to R$, where we agree to the convention:

$$F((1, 1)) = a_{11}, \qquad F((1, 2)) = a_{12}, \qquad F((2, 1)) = a_{21}, \qquad F((2, 2)) = a_{22}.$$

The values of F are listed as

$$\begin{bmatrix} a_{11} & a_{12} \\ a_{21} & a_{22} \end{bmatrix}.$$

3.7-2   Definition: The *sum* of two real 2×2 matrices

$$A = \begin{bmatrix} a_{11} & a_{12} \\ a_{21} & a_{22} \end{bmatrix} \qquad \text{and} \qquad B = \begin{bmatrix} b_{11} & b_{12} \\ b_{21} & b_{22} \end{bmatrix}$$

is the 2×2 matrix

$$A + B = \begin{bmatrix} a_{11} + b_{11} & a_{12} + b_{12} \\ a_{21} + b_{21} & a_{22} + b_{22} \end{bmatrix}.$$

Example:

$$\begin{bmatrix} 5 & 0 \\ -1 & 7 \end{bmatrix} + \begin{bmatrix} 1 & 1 \\ -2 & 2 \end{bmatrix} = \begin{bmatrix} 6 & 1 \\ -3 & 9 \end{bmatrix}.$$

3.7-3   Theorem: The set $\mathfrak{M}$ of 2×2 matrices is a commutative group under addition.

Proof: One needs only to verify that the various group properties are exhibited by $\mathfrak{M}$. (You are asked to do so in the exercises.) Note that in most cases, this is a direct result of the fact that $\mathbf{R}$ is a commutative group under ordinary addition. You can readily verify that the matrix

$$\begin{bmatrix} 0 & 0 \\ 0 & 0 \end{bmatrix}$$

is the additive identity matrix, and that the additive inverse of the matrix

$$\begin{bmatrix} a_{11} & a_{12} \\ a_{21} & a_{22} \end{bmatrix} \text{ is } \begin{bmatrix} -a_{11} & -a_{12} \\ -a_{21} & -a_{22} \end{bmatrix}.$$

We feel that it is natural to insist that $A + A = 2A$. That is,

$$\begin{bmatrix} a_{11} & a_{12} \\ a_{21} & a_{22} \end{bmatrix} + \begin{bmatrix} a_{11} & a_{12} \\ a_{21} & a_{22} \end{bmatrix} = \begin{bmatrix} 2a_{11} & 2a_{12} \\ 2a_{21} & 2a_{22} \end{bmatrix} = 2 \begin{bmatrix} a_{11} & a_{12} \\ a_{21} & a_{22} \end{bmatrix}.$$

3.7-4   Definition:

$$\alpha \begin{bmatrix} a_{11} & a_{12} \\ a_{21} & a_{22} \end{bmatrix} = \begin{bmatrix} \alpha a_{11} & \alpha a_{12} \\ \alpha a_{21} & \alpha a_{22} \end{bmatrix}.$$

Example:

$$4 \begin{bmatrix} 0 & -1 \\ 2 & 3 \end{bmatrix} = \begin{bmatrix} 0 & -4 \\ 8 & 12 \end{bmatrix}.$$

$$-1 \begin{bmatrix} 0 & -1 \\ 2 & 3 \end{bmatrix} = \begin{bmatrix} 0 & 1 \\ -2 & -3 \end{bmatrix}.$$

Remark: We define *subtraction* of matrices by

$$A - B = A + (-1)B.$$

Example:

$$\begin{bmatrix} 1 & -2 \\ 7 & 4 \end{bmatrix} - \begin{bmatrix} 2 & 8 \\ -11 & 0 \end{bmatrix} = \begin{bmatrix} 1 & -2 \\ 7 & 4 \end{bmatrix} + \begin{bmatrix} -2 & -8 \\ 11 & 0 \end{bmatrix} = \begin{bmatrix} -1 & -10 \\ 18 & 4 \end{bmatrix}.$$

The definition of matrix multiplication is not so simple as that for addition.

3.7-5   Definition: The *product* of two real 2×2 matrices

$$A = \begin{bmatrix} a_{11} & a_{12} \\ a_{21} & a_{22} \end{bmatrix} \quad \text{and} \quad B = \begin{bmatrix} b_{11} & b_{12} \\ b_{21} & b_{22} \end{bmatrix}$$

is the 2×2 matrix

$$AB = \begin{bmatrix} a_{11}b_{11} + a_{12}b_{21} & a_{11}b_{12} + a_{12}b_{22} \\ a_{21}b_{11} + a_{22}b_{21} & a_{21}b_{12} + a_{22}b_{22} \end{bmatrix}.$$

Remark: This definition asserts that each element in AB is the result of taking the dot product of a *row vector* of A times a *column vector* of B. Thus, for example, if

$$AB = C = \begin{bmatrix} c_{11} & c_{12} \\ c_{21} & c_{22} \end{bmatrix},$$

we have

$$c_{11} = (a_{11}, a_{12}) \cdot (b_{11}, b_{21}) = (a_{11}, a_{12}) \cdot \begin{bmatrix} b_{11} \\ b_{21} \end{bmatrix} = a_{11}b_{11} + a_{12}b_{21},$$

where the dot product of coordinate vectors is patterned from the dot product of position vectors.

Example:

$$\begin{bmatrix} 2 & 1 \\ -1 & 5 \end{bmatrix}\begin{bmatrix} 1 & -1 \\ 3 & 4 \end{bmatrix} = \begin{bmatrix} 2+3 & -2+4 \\ -1+15 & 1+20 \end{bmatrix} = \begin{bmatrix} 5 & 2 \\ 14 & 21 \end{bmatrix}.$$

$$\begin{bmatrix} 1 & -1 \\ 3 & 4 \end{bmatrix}\begin{bmatrix} 2 & 1 \\ -1 & 5 \end{bmatrix} = \begin{bmatrix} 2+1 & 1-5 \\ 6-4 & 3+20 \end{bmatrix} = \begin{bmatrix} 3 & -4 \\ 2 & 23 \end{bmatrix}.$$

Note in this example, that $AB \neq BA$.

Example:

$$\begin{bmatrix} 1 & 0 \\ 0 & 1 \end{bmatrix}\begin{bmatrix} a_{11} & a_{12} \\ a_{21} & a_{22} \end{bmatrix} = \begin{bmatrix} a_{11} & a_{12} \\ a_{21} & a_{22} \end{bmatrix} = \begin{bmatrix} a_{11} & a_{12} \\ a_{21} & a_{22} \end{bmatrix}\begin{bmatrix} 1 & 0 \\ 0 & 1 \end{bmatrix}.$$

That is, $\begin{bmatrix} 1 & 0 \\ 0 & 1 \end{bmatrix}$ is a *multiplicative identity matrix* (usually denoted by I).

3.7-6   Theorem: Suppose A, B, and C are real 2×2 matrices, and α and β are real numbers. Then

  i. $A(BC) = (AB)C$ (so we may simply write ABC),
  ii. $\alpha(AB) = (\alpha A)B = A(\alpha B)$,
  iii. $A(B + C) = AB + AC$,
  iv. $(\alpha + \beta)A = \alpha A + \beta A$,
  v. $\alpha(A + B) = \alpha A + \alpha B$.

PROOF: The proof is left for the most part for the reader. We shall prove part iii as an example. Suppose

$$A = \begin{bmatrix} a_{11} & a_{12} \\ a_{21} & a_{22} \end{bmatrix}, \qquad B = \begin{bmatrix} b_{11} & b_{12} \\ b_{21} & b_{22} \end{bmatrix}, \qquad C = \begin{bmatrix} c_{11} & c_{12} \\ c_{21} & c_{22} \end{bmatrix}.$$

Now,

$A(B + C)$

$$= \begin{bmatrix} a_{11} & a_{12} \\ a_{21} & a_{22} \end{bmatrix}\begin{bmatrix} b_{11}+c_{11} & b_{12}+c_{12} \\ b_{21}+c_{21} & b_{22}+c_{22} \end{bmatrix}$$

$$= \begin{bmatrix} a_{11}(b_{11}+c_{11})+a_{12}(b_{21}+c_{21}) & a_{11}(b_{12}+c_{12})+a_{12}(b_{22}+c_{22}) \\ a_{21}(b_{11}+c_{11})+a_{22}(b_{21}+c_{21}) & a_{21}(b_{12}+c_{12})+a_{22}(b_{22}+c_{22}) \end{bmatrix}$$

$$= \begin{bmatrix} (a_{11}b_{11}+a_{12}b_{21})+(a_{11}c_{11}+a_{12}c_{21}) & (a_{11}b_{12}+a_{12}b_{22})+(a_{11}c_{12}+a_{12}c_{22}) \\ (a_{21}b_{11}+a_{22}b_{21})+(a_{21}c_{11}+a_{22}c_{21}) & (a_{21}b_{12}+a_{22}b_{22})+(a_{21}c_{12}+a_{22}c_{22}) \end{bmatrix}$$

$$= \begin{bmatrix} a_{11}b_{11}+a_{12}b_{21} & a_{11}b_{12}+a_{12}b_{22} \\ a_{21}b_{11}+a_{22}b_{21} & a_{21}b_{12}+a_{22}b_{22} \end{bmatrix} + \begin{bmatrix} a_{11}c_{11}+a_{12}c_{21} & a_{11}c_{12}+a_{12}c_{22} \\ a_{21}c_{11}+a_{22}c_{21} & a_{21}c_{12}+a_{22}c_{22} \end{bmatrix}$$

$$= \begin{bmatrix} a_{11} & a_{12} \\ a_{21} & a_{22} \end{bmatrix}\begin{bmatrix} b_{11} & b_{12} \\ b_{21} & b_{22} \end{bmatrix} + \begin{bmatrix} a_{11} & a_{12} \\ a_{21} & a_{22} \end{bmatrix}\begin{bmatrix} c_{11} & c_{12} \\ c_{21} & c_{22} \end{bmatrix}$$

$$= AB + AC.$$

Our definition for multiplication of matrices may be extended so that the product

$$\begin{bmatrix} a_1 & b_1 \\ a_2 & b_2 \end{bmatrix} \begin{bmatrix} x \\ y \end{bmatrix}$$

is also defined by making a comparison with

$$\begin{bmatrix} a_1 & b_1 \\ a_2 & b_2 \end{bmatrix} \begin{bmatrix} x & 0 \\ y & 0 \end{bmatrix}.$$

That is, we define

$$\begin{bmatrix} a_1 & b_1 \\ a_2 & b_2 \end{bmatrix} \begin{bmatrix} x \\ y \end{bmatrix} = \begin{bmatrix} a_1 x + b_1 y \\ a_2 x + b_2 y \end{bmatrix}.$$

Thus, using vectors and matrix multiplication, the system of equations

$$a_1 x + b_1 y = c_1$$
$$a_2 x + b_2 y = c_2$$

is equivalent to the *matrix equation*

$$\begin{bmatrix} a_1 & b_1 \\ a_2 & b_2 \end{bmatrix} \begin{bmatrix} x \\ y \end{bmatrix} = \begin{bmatrix} c_1 \\ c_2 \end{bmatrix}.$$

Matrix Equations and the Determinant

We shall now determine a necessary and sufficient condition on the matrix

$$\begin{bmatrix} a_1 & b_1 \\ a_2 & b_2 \end{bmatrix}$$

to determine whether the system above has a unique solution. We have seen graphically that this coincides precisely with the case that the lines $a_1 x + b_1 y = c_1$ and $a_2 x + b_2 y = c_2$ are not parallel.

Recall that if a and b are fixed, the family of lines obtained by varying the parameter c in an equation $ax + by = c$ is a family of parallel lines. The change of c has no effect on the slope (or the nonexistence of slope) of the lines. Thus, if we wish to determine a condition that will tell us when two equations

$$a_1 x + b_1 y = c_1$$
$$a_2 x + b_2 y = c_2$$

yield lines that are not parallel, we can ask the equivalent question: When will the two equations

$$a_1 x + b_1 y = 0$$
$$a_2 x + b_2 y = 0$$

determine lines that are not parallel?

Let us view the system in matrix form:

$$\begin{bmatrix} a_1 & b_1 \\ a_2 & b_2 \end{bmatrix} \begin{bmatrix} x \\ y \end{bmatrix} = \begin{bmatrix} 0 \\ 0 \end{bmatrix}.$$

Thus, we notice that the line

$$\{(x, y) : a_1x + b_1y = 0\}$$

is simply the collection of all vectors (x, y) perpendicular to the matrix row vector (a_1, b_1). (Explain, using the dot product!) Also, the line $a_2x + b_2y = 0$ is the collection of all vectors perpendicular to the matrix row vector (a_2, b_2). (See Figure 3.51.) Thus, the two lines in question will be nonparallel

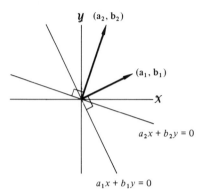

FIGURE 3.51

provided that the two matrix row vectors (a_1, b_1) and (a_2, b_2) are nonparallel. The vector $(b_2, -a_2)$ is perpendicular to (a_2, b_2) since

$$(b_2, -a_2) \cdot (a_2, b_2) = b_2a_2 - a_2b_2 = 0.$$

Hence, (a_1, b_1) is not parallel to (a_2, b_2) if and only if (a_1, b_1) is not perpendicular to $(b_2, -a_2)$. This is precisely the condition that $(a_1, b_1) \cdot (b_2, -a_2) \neq 0$. That is,

$$a_1b_2 - a_2b_1 \neq 0,$$

which is the condition mentioned earlier in connection with lines having nonequal slope. This is a very important condition and the number $a_1b_2 - a_2b_1$ is called the *determinant* of the matrix $\begin{bmatrix} a_1 & b_1 \\ a_2 & b_2 \end{bmatrix}$.

3.7-7 Definition: The *determinant* of a 2×2 matrix is defined and denoted as follows:

$$\det \begin{bmatrix} a_1 & b_1 \\ a_2 & b_2 \end{bmatrix} = \begin{vmatrix} a_1 & b_1 \\ a_2 & b_2 \end{vmatrix} = a_1b_2 - a_2b_1.$$

We have established the following very important theorem regarding systems of equations.

3.7-8 Theorem: Let A be a 2×2 matrix, and let X and C be 2×1 matrices. Then the matrix equation

$$AX = C$$

has exactly one solution X iff

$$|A| \neq 0.$$

1. Find $A + B$, AB, and $3A$ where

$$A = \begin{bmatrix} 1 & 3 \\ 2 & -2 \end{bmatrix} \quad \text{and} \quad B = \begin{bmatrix} 2 & -4 \\ 0 & 1 \end{bmatrix}.$$

2. Find $A + B$, AB, and BA, where

$$A = \begin{bmatrix} -1 & 1 \\ 2 & 3 \end{bmatrix} \quad \text{and} \quad B = \begin{bmatrix} 2 & -4 \\ 0 & -1 \end{bmatrix}.$$

3. Find $2A + 4B$, where

$$A = \begin{bmatrix} 1 & 2 \\ 3 & -1 \end{bmatrix} \quad \text{and} \quad B = \begin{bmatrix} -1 & -2 \\ 6 & 3 \end{bmatrix}.$$

4. Let $\mathfrak{M}$ denote the set of all real 2×2 matrices. Show that $\langle \mathfrak{M}, \mathbf{R} \rangle$ is a vector space where addition and scalar multiplication are as defined in this section.

5. Determine AB and BA. Also compute $|A|$, $|B|$, $|AB|$, and $|BA|$.

a. $A = \begin{bmatrix} 1 & 1 \\ -2 & 1 \end{bmatrix} \quad B = \begin{bmatrix} 2 & 0 \\ 1 & -2 \end{bmatrix}$

b. $A = \begin{bmatrix} 3 & 4 \\ -2 & 1 \end{bmatrix} \quad B = \begin{bmatrix} 1 & 7 \\ -2 & 4 \end{bmatrix}$

c. $A = \begin{bmatrix} 1 & 5 \\ 6 & 1 \end{bmatrix} \quad B = \begin{bmatrix} 2 & 2 \\ 2 & 2 \end{bmatrix}$

6. Write each system of equations as a matrix equation.
a. $2x + 4y = 2$ b. $-3x - 2y = 1$
$ 4x - 2y = 1.$ $ 4x + 5y = -2.$

7. Compute the determinant of each given matrix

$$\begin{bmatrix} a_1 & b_1 \\ a_2 & b_2 \end{bmatrix}$$

and graph the lines $a_1x + b_1y = 0$, and $a_2x + b_2y = 0$. Also graph each row vector of the matrix.

a. $\begin{bmatrix} 1 & 2 \\ 3 & -1 \end{bmatrix}$ b. $\begin{bmatrix} 2 & 2 \\ 0 & 1 \end{bmatrix}$

c. $\begin{bmatrix} 2 & 3 \\ 6 & 9 \end{bmatrix}$ d. $\begin{bmatrix} -1 & -2 \\ 3 & 1 \end{bmatrix}$

8. Write each pair of equations as a matrix equation and show that the equation has a unique solution.
a. $2x - 3y = 1$ b. $x - 2y = 0$
$ 3x + y = 4.$ $ 2x = 1.$

c. $-3x - 2y = 3$ d. $4x - 4y = 1$
    $-5x + y = 1.$ $-x - y = 3.$

9. For 2×2 matrices A and B, show that $|AB| = |A|\,|B|$.

3.8   MISCELLANEOUS GEOMETRIC TOPICS AND THEIR RELATIONSHIP TO VECTORS AND DETERMINANTS

In this section we shall make use of vector operations to solve certain area, distance, and projection problems.

Determinants and Area

We first consider an interesting geometric interpretation for a two by two matrix $\begin{bmatrix} a & b \\ x & y \end{bmatrix}$ with respect to its two row vectors (a, b) and (x, y).

Consider two vectors $\mathbf{A} = (x, y)$ and $\mathbf{B} = (a, b)$, which determine an angle θ (see Figure 3.52). We will show that the area of the parallelogram having

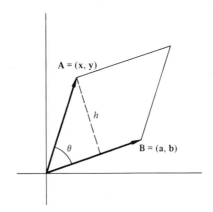

FIGURE 3.52

adjacent sides $\mathbf{A}$ and $\mathbf{B}$, as shown in Figure 3.52, has area given by $\left\| \begin{matrix} a & b \\ x & y \end{matrix} \right\|$ (absolute value of the determinant). First, notice that the area is given by $|\mathbf{B}|h = |\mathbf{B}|\,|\mathbf{A}| \sin \theta$. This can be expressed in terms of the dot product as follows.

$$|\mathbf{B}|\,|\mathbf{A}| \sin \theta = |\mathbf{B}|\,|\mathbf{A}| \sqrt{1 - \cos^2 \theta} = |\mathbf{B}|\,|\mathbf{A}| \sqrt{1 - \left(\frac{\mathbf{A} \cdot \mathbf{B}}{|\mathbf{A}|\,|\mathbf{B}|} \right)^2},$$

since $\mathbf{A} \cdot \mathbf{B} = |\mathbf{A}| \, |\mathbf{B}| \cos \theta$. We have then that the square of the area is given by

$$|\mathbf{A}|^2 |\mathbf{B}|^2 \left(1 - \frac{(\mathbf{A} \cdot \mathbf{B})^2}{|\mathbf{A}|^2 |\mathbf{B}|^2}\right)$$

$$= |\mathbf{A}|^2 |\mathbf{B}|^2 - (\mathbf{A} \cdot \mathbf{B})^2$$
$$= (x^2 + y^2)(a^2 + b^2) - (ax + by)^2$$
$$= x^2 a^2 + y^2 b^2 + x^2 b^2 + y^2 a^2 - (ax)^2 - 2axby - (by)^2$$
$$= (ay)^2 - 2aybx + (bx)^2 = (ay - bx)^2 = \begin{vmatrix} a & b \\ x & y \end{vmatrix}^2.$$

3.8-1   Theorem: If $\mathbf{A} = (x, y)$, $\mathbf{B} = (a, b)$ are two position vectors, then the area of the parallelogram having $\mathbf{A}$ and $\mathbf{B}$ as adjacent sides is given by

$$\sqrt{|\mathbf{A}|^2 |\mathbf{B}|^2 - (\mathbf{A} \cdot \mathbf{B})^2} = \left\| \begin{matrix} a & b \\ x & y \end{matrix} \right\|.$$

Remark: It is clear then, geometrically, that the determinant will be zero if and only if one row vector is a scalar multiple of the other (that is, if $\mathbf{A}$ and $\mathbf{B}$ lie on the same line).

Finding a Vector Perpendicular to a Given Vector

We wish now to anticipate an operation on three space vectors, to be considered later, of combining determinants and basis vectors into a procedure for obtaining vectors normal (perpendicular) to a given vector. Suppose $\mathbf{I} = (1, 0)$ and $\mathbf{J} = (0, 1)$ are the usual basis vectors for two-dimensional space. We wish to find a vector $\mathbf{U}$ normal to a given vector $\mathbf{V} = (a, b)$. That is, we are searching for a nonzero vector $\mathbf{U}$ satisfying $\mathbf{U} \cdot \mathbf{V} = 0$. Suppose we formally write

$$\begin{vmatrix} \mathbf{I} & \mathbf{J} \\ a & b \end{vmatrix}$$

to mean $b\mathbf{I} - a\mathbf{J}$. (This is consistent with our earlier definition of determinants of 2×2 matrices.) Note that

$$(b\mathbf{I} - a\mathbf{J}) \cdot (a\mathbf{I} + b\mathbf{J}) = ba - ab = 0.$$

Thus, the vector given by $\begin{vmatrix} \mathbf{I} & \mathbf{J} \\ a & b \end{vmatrix}$ is normal to $(a, b) = a\mathbf{I} + b\mathbf{J}$.

Remark: Recall that the "vector of coefficients" (a, b) for the line $ax + by = 0$ is normal to the line. This can be seen by noting that

$$\begin{vmatrix} \mathbf{I} & \mathbf{J} \\ a & b \end{vmatrix} = b\mathbf{I} - a\mathbf{J}$$

yields a point $(b, -a)$ on the line. One can view the line $ax + by = 0$ as the line generated by all position vectors $(\mathbf{x}, \mathbf{y})$ normal to $(\mathbf{a}, \mathbf{b})$. Thus, the line is given by

$$\{(x, y) : (\mathbf{x}, \mathbf{y}) \cdot (\mathbf{a}, \mathbf{b}) = 0\} = \{(x, y) : ax + by = 0\}\,.$$

Projection of a Vector on a Line

Suppose we wish to determine the free vector that results when a given free vector is "projected" to a given line. That is, suppose $\mathbf{V}$ is a free vector and $\mathcal{L}$ a line. If a line is drawn from the head of $\mathbf{V}$ (that is, some representation of $\mathbf{V}$), which is perpendicular to $\mathcal{L}$, then it intersects $\mathcal{L}$ at the point B (Figure 3.53). Similarly, we have a point A on $\mathcal{L}$ that is the "perpendicular projection"

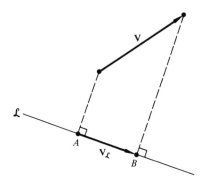

FIGURE 3.53

onto $\mathcal{L}$ of the tail. In this fashion we have identified a free vector $(\mathbf{A}, \mathbf{B})$, which we will call $\mathbf{V}_{\mathcal{L}}$. Notice, that any representation of $\mathbf{V}$ and any line parallel to $\mathcal{L}$ would yield the same free vector, although by a different representation. Thus, we may assume without loss of generality that $\mathcal{L}$ passes through the origin, and $\mathbf{V}$ has its tail at the origin. (See Figure 3.54.)

Suppose the line $\mathcal{L}$ is described by the equation $ax + by = 0$ (assuming that it passes through the origin). This line contains the points $(0, 0)$ and $(b, -a)$. It follows that the vector $[\mathbf{b}, -\mathbf{a}]$ is parallel to $\mathcal{L}$. By multiplying $[\mathbf{b}, -\mathbf{a}]$ by the appropriate scalar, we will obtain the desired projection $\mathbf{V}$. The length of $\mathbf{V}_{\mathcal{L}}$ is given by $|\mathbf{V}_{\mathcal{L}}| = |\mathbf{V}| \cos \theta$, where θ is the angle between $\mathbf{V}$ and $\mathbf{V}_{\mathcal{L}}$, as shown in Figure 3.54. But $|\mathbf{V}| \cos \theta$ reminds us of a dot product: indeed, $|\mathbf{V}| \cos \theta = \mathbf{T} \cdot \mathbf{V}$, where $\mathbf{T}$ is a unit vector along $\mathcal{L}$. The unit vector

$$\mathbf{T} = \frac{1}{\sqrt{b^2 + a^2}} [\mathbf{b}, -\mathbf{a}]$$

is parallel to the line $ax + by = c$, and the projection $\mathbf{V}_{\mathcal{L}}$ of a vector $\mathbf{V}$ on $\mathcal{L}$ has length

$$|\mathbf{V}_{\mathcal{L}}| = |\mathbf{T} \cdot \mathbf{V}|\,.$$

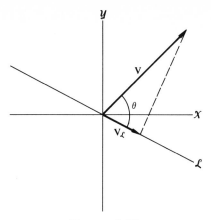

FIGURE 3.54

The projection $\mathbf{V}_{\mathcal{L}}$ is thus given by

$$\mathbf{V}_{\mathcal{L}} = (\mathbf{T} \cdot \mathbf{V})\mathbf{T}.$$

Note that this is simply the projection of $\mathbf{V}$ onto $\mathbf{X} = [\mathbf{b}, -\mathbf{a}]$, as discussed in Section 3.5.

Remark: It might appear at first that by taking a unit vector parallel to the line, different from

$$\mathbf{T} = \frac{1}{\sqrt{b^2 + a^2}}\,[\mathbf{b}, -\mathbf{a}],$$

one might obtain different vector projections. However, this is not the case. For example, an equivalent description of the line $ax + by = c$ is $-ax - by = -c$. Thus, following the procedure above, we obtain a unit vector parallel to the line $\mathcal{L}$ and given by

$$\frac{1}{\sqrt{b^2 + a^2}}\,[-\mathbf{b}, \mathbf{a}] = -\mathbf{T}.$$

But notice that

$$(\mathbf{T} \cdot \mathbf{V})\mathbf{T} = (-\mathbf{T} \cdot \mathbf{V})(-\mathbf{T}),$$

so that the vector projection remains the same regardless of the sense of the parallel unit vector $\mathbf{T}$.

Example: Suppose $\mathcal{L}$ is described by $4x + 3y = -1$ and $\mathbf{V} = [-1, 3]$. Now

$$\mathbf{T} = \frac{1}{\sqrt{9 + 16}}\,[\mathbf{3}, -\mathbf{4}] = \frac{1}{5}\,[\mathbf{3}, -\mathbf{4}],$$

thus

$$\mathbf{V}_{\mathfrak{L}} = (\mathbf{T} \cdot \mathbf{V})\mathbf{T} = \left(\left[\frac{3}{5}, \frac{-4}{5}\right] \cdot [-1, 3]\right)\left[\frac{3}{5}, \frac{-4}{5}\right] = -3\left[\frac{3}{5}, \frac{-4}{5}\right]$$

$$= \left[\frac{-9}{5}, \frac{12}{5}\right].$$

(See Figure 3.55.)

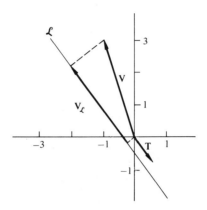

FIGURE 3.55

Example: The projection of $[-1, -1]$ on the line described by $y = 0$ (taking $\mathbf{T} = [1, 0]$) is

$$([1, 0] \cdot [-1, -1])[1, 0] = [-1, 0].$$

Notice that $[-1, 0]$ is simply the horizontal component of the vector $[-1, -1]$. We should expect the projection of $[-1, -1]$ on the vertical

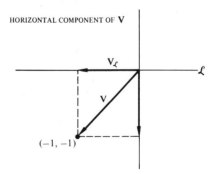

FIGURE 3.56

line $x = 0$ to result in the vertical component of $[-1, -1]$; namely $[0, -1]$. (Verify that this is the case.) (See Figure 3.56.)

Distance from a Point to a Line

A notion related to that of finding the projection of a vector on a line is the determination of the perpendicular distance from a point to a given line. In order to develop the formula for this distance, we shall project a vector having tail at some arbitrary point on the line and head at the point to a second line perpendicular to the given line. In order to find the distance d from the point P to the line $\mathcal{L}$, we find the length of the projection on the line normal to $\mathcal{L}$. (See Figure 3.57.)

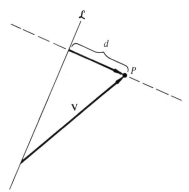

FIGURE 3.57

Suppose the line is described by the equation $ax + by = c$, and the point P has coordinate (p, q). Let (u, v) be any convenient point on $\mathcal{L}$; then the vector $\mathbf{V} = ((\mathbf{u}, \mathbf{v}), (\mathbf{p}, \mathbf{q})) = [\mathbf{p} - \mathbf{u}, \mathbf{q} - \mathbf{v}]$ has a representation with tail on $\mathcal{L}$ and head at P. The vector

$$\mathbf{T} = \frac{1}{\sqrt{a^2 + b^2}} [\mathbf{a}, \mathbf{b}]$$

is a unit vector normal to $\mathcal{L}$. It follows that the projection we seek is the vector

$$\mathbf{V_T} = (\mathbf{T} \cdot \mathbf{V})\mathbf{T},$$

so that the desired distance is given by

$$|\mathbf{V_T}| = |\mathbf{T} \cdot \mathbf{V}| \, |\mathbf{T}| = |\mathbf{T} \cdot \mathbf{V}| = \left| \frac{a(p - u) + b(q - v)}{\sqrt{a^2 + b^2}} \right|.$$

The important thing to remember here is not the explicit formula, but rather the technique used to develop the formula. In summary, the steps in finding the distance from a point to a line are as follows:

1. Find a unit vector $\mathbf{T}$, normal to the line.

2. Find a fixed vector **V** from some point in the line to the given point.

3. Find the length of the projection of **V** on **T**.

Example: The distance from $(5, -3)$ to the line $-2x + y = 18$ is determined as follows:

    a. a unit normal vector is $\mathbf{T} = (1/\sqrt{5})[-2, 1]$,

    b. a vector from a convenient point on the line (say $(0, 18)$) to the point $(5, -3)$ is $\mathbf{V} = ((0, 18), (5, -3)) = [5, -21]$,

    c. $d = |\mathbf{T} \cdot \mathbf{V}| = \left| \dfrac{1}{\sqrt{5}}(-10 - 21) \right| = \dfrac{31}{\sqrt{5}}$.

EXERCISES 3.8

1. Graph the pair of vectors given and draw the parallelogram they determine. Compute the area of the parallelogram.
    a. $(-2, -1)$, $(-2, 1)$.   b. $(2, 1)$, $(1, -3)$.
    c. $(6, 0)$, $(0, 4)$.   d. $(2, -1)$, $(-2, -4)$.

2. Show that Theorem 3.8-1 holds when column vectors of the determinant are used instead of row vectors.

3. For each matrix, graph the pair of row vectors, the pair of column vectors, and the parallelograms they determine. Find the areas of the parallelograms.

    a. $\begin{bmatrix} 1 & 2 \\ -2 & 4 \end{bmatrix}$.   b. $\begin{bmatrix} -2 & 3 \\ 1 & -1 \end{bmatrix}$.

    c. $\begin{bmatrix} 6 & 4 \\ 2 & -1 \end{bmatrix}$.   d. $\begin{bmatrix} -2 & -2 \\ -1 & 0 \end{bmatrix}$.

4. Determine the projection of the given vector on the given line. Graph the vectors and the line.
    a. $2x + 3y = 4$; $\mathbf{V} = [1, -2]$.   b. $-3x - 4y = 1$; $\mathbf{V} = [2, 1]$.
    c. $x - y = 2$; $\mathbf{V} = [-1, 6]$.   d. $4x + 7y = 0$; $\mathbf{V} = [-2, -3]$.

5. Find the distance from the given point to the given line.
    a. $(2, 3)$; $4x - 2y = 1$.   b. $(-1, 4)$; $6x + 3y = 2$.
    c. $(-2, -2)$; $x + 4y = -1$.   d. $(5, 4)$; $-2x + y = 2$.

6. How would you define the angle between a vector and a line?

7. Show that projecting a vector to a line perpendicular to it results in the zero vector.

8. For a given vector **W**, $\mathbf{W} \neq \mathbf{0}$, assume that $\mathbf{W} \cdot \mathbf{U} = \mathbf{W} \cdot \mathbf{V}$. Prove or disprove:
    a. $\mathbf{U} = \mathbf{V}$.   b. $\mathbf{U} \cdot \mathbf{V} \neq 0$.   c. **U** and **V** are parallel.

9. Suppose $\mathcal{L}$ is a line containing the points (a, b) and (c, d).
    a. Find a line normal to $\mathcal{L}$.
    b. Find the line normal to $\mathcal{L}$ containing the point (a, b).

3.9 BASIS VECTORS AND COORDINATE SYSTEMS

In this section we further develop the idea of expressing a vector as a linear combination of other vectors and relate this notion to coordinatizations.

It may be possible to express every vector in a vector space as a linear combination of several given *basis* vectors. Questions then arise concerning how many basis vectors are necessarily required for this, and how the basis vectors should be chosen.

We begin by recalling the notion of *linear independence* of vectors. The vectors $V_1, V_2, \ldots, V_n$ in a vector space are said to be *linearly independent* iff

$$a_1 V_1 + a_2 V_2 + \cdots + a_n V_n = 0 \Rightarrow a_1 = a_2 = \cdots = a_n = 0.$$

The vectors are called linearly dependent if they are not linearly independent.

Example: The coordinate vectors $(0, 1)$ and $(1, 1)$ in $\mathbf{R}^2$ are linearly independent, since

$$a(0, 1) + b(1, 1) = (0, 0)$$

implies that

$$(0, a) + (b, b) = (b, a + b) = (0, 0).$$

From this we have $b = 0$ and $a + b = 0$, which gives $a = b = 0$. Thus, the only way one can combine these two vectors to obtain the zero vector is to use zero scalars.

Example: $(0, 1)$ and $(0, -7)$ are not linearly independent since it is possible to choose numbers a and b not both zero such that

$$a(0, 1) + b(0, -7) = (0, 0).$$

What is a possible choice for a and b in this example? Are a and b unique?

Remark: If one of the vectors in a set is the zero vector, then the vectors are linearly dependent, since for any vectors $V_1, V_2, \ldots, V_{n-1}, \mathbf{0}$, we have

$$0V_1 + 0V_2 + \cdots + 0V_{n-1} + 1\mathbf{0} = \mathbf{0}.$$

It may be possible that a collection of linearly dependent vectors has a linearly independent subcollection. For example,

$$(0, 1), (1, 1), (1, 0)$$

are linearly dependent, but any pair of these vectors is linearly independent (see Exercise 5).

A graphical interpretation of linear independence and dependence of two vectors in $\mathbf{R}^2$ may be obtained by observing corresponding position vectors when a coordinatization of the plane has been specified. It is easily seen that collinear position vectors are linearly dependent, and that dependent vectors are collinear.

Basis Vectors and Dimension

We have noted that the coordinate vectors $(1, 0)$ and $(0, 1)$ are linearly independent and that any vector in $\mathbf{R}^2$ can be written as a linear combination of these vectors. For, suppose that (x, y) is a vector in $\mathbf{R}^2$. Then $x \in \mathbf{R}$ and $y \in \mathbf{R}$ are scalars, and $(x, y) = x(1, 0) + y(0, 1)$.

3.9-1   **Definition:** A collection of vectors $V_1, V_2, \ldots, V_n$ in a vector space is said to *span* the space if any vector in the space may be expressed as a linear combination of $V_1, V_2, \ldots, V_n$.

Example: $(0, 1)$, $(1, 1)$, and $(1, 0)$ span $\langle \mathbf{R}^2, \mathbf{R} \rangle$, as do $(0, 1)$ and $(1, 0)$. Thus, it is possible to span $\mathbf{R}^2$ with various collections of vectors. However, it turns out that any collection spanning $\langle \mathbf{R}^2, \mathbf{R} \rangle$ must have at least two linearly independent vectors. For this reason we call $\langle \mathbf{R}^2, \mathbf{R} \rangle$ "two-dimensional."

3.9-2   **Definition:** The dimension of a (finite dimensional) vector space is the minimal number of linearly independent vectors that can be used to span the space.

Example: Any subspace $\mathcal{S}$ of $\mathbf{R}^2$ where $\mathcal{S} = \{\alpha V : \alpha \in \mathbf{R}\}$, $(V \neq O)$, has dimension 1, since V spans $\mathcal{S}$.

Remark: By convention, the vector space $\langle \{(0, 0)\}, \mathbf{R} \rangle$ (also a subspace of $\langle \mathbf{R}^2, \mathbf{R} \rangle$) is usually assigned dimension zero.

We call a collection of vectors spanning a space a *basis* of the vector space if they are linearly independent.

3.9-3   **Definition:** A *basis* for a vector space $\langle \mathcal{V}, F \rangle$ is a set of linearly independent vectors spanning the space.

We shall now investigate the relationships between the vectors forming a basis for a space and the dimension of the space. First let us prove a fact we illustrated geometrically in the previous section.

3.9-4   **Lemma:** If (x_1, y_1) and (x_2, y_2) are linearly independent, then $x_1y_2 - x_2y_1 = 0$. That is,

$$\begin{vmatrix} x_1 & y_1 \\ x_2 & y_2 \end{vmatrix} = 0.$$

PROOF: Consider the contrapositive. Suppose $x_1y_2 = x_2y_1$. Then we can show that (x_1, y_1) and (x_2, y_2) are linearly dependent. We consider two cases.

CASE 1. $x_1 = 0$. Then $x_2 = 0$ or $y_1 = 0$. If $y_1 = 0$, the dependence follows since one of the vectors is the zero vector. If $y_1 \neq 0$, then $x_2 = 0$. But the vectors $(0, y_1)$ and $(0, y_2)$ are dependent (see Exercise 7).

CASE 2. $x_1 \neq 0$. We know that for some scalar α, $x_2 = \alpha x_1$. But $x_1y_2 = x_2y_1$ implies that

$$y_2 = \frac{x_2y_1}{x_1} = \frac{\alpha x_1 y_1}{x_1} = \alpha y_1.$$

Thus, $(x_2, y_2) = \alpha(x_1, y_1)$, and the dependence follows.

3.9-5   **Theorem:** Any two linearly independent vectors in $\mathbf{R}^2$ span the space and thus are a basis for the space.

PROOF: Suppose that the given vectors are denoted by $V_1 = (x_1, y_1)$, $V_2 = (x_2, y_2)$, and suppose $U = (u, v)$ is any vector in the space. We wish to show that for some scalars α and β,

$$\alpha V_1 + \beta V_2 = U \, (\alpha(x_1, y_1) + \beta(x_2, y_2) = (u, v)).$$

That is, the system

$$\alpha x_1 + \beta x_2 = u$$
$$\alpha y_1 + \beta y_2 = v$$

has a solution. (In matrix form this is the equation

$$\begin{bmatrix} x_1 & x_2 \\ y_1 & y_2 \end{bmatrix} \begin{bmatrix} \alpha \\ \beta \end{bmatrix} = \begin{bmatrix} u \\ v \end{bmatrix}.)$$

For a solution, we need only take

$$\alpha = \frac{u y_2 - x_2 v}{x_1 y_2 - x_2 y_1} \quad \text{and} \quad \beta = \frac{x_1 v - y_1 u}{x_1 y_2 - x_2 y_1}.$$

That is,

$$\alpha = \frac{\begin{vmatrix} u & x_2 \\ v & y_2 \end{vmatrix}}{\begin{vmatrix} x_1 & x_2 \\ y_1 & y_2 \end{vmatrix}} \quad \text{and} \quad \beta = \frac{\begin{vmatrix} x_1 & u \\ y_1 & v \end{vmatrix}}{\begin{vmatrix} x_1 & x_2 \\ y_1 & y_2 \end{vmatrix}}.$$

(You should verify that these values satisfy the equation.)

3.9-6 Theorem: Any basis for the space $\mathbf{R}^2$ contains exactly two vectors.

PROOF: Left as an exercise.

In summary, even though a basis for the two-dimensional space $\langle \mathbf{R}^2, \mathbf{R} \rangle$ is not unique, it is the case that any basis consists of precisely two linearly independent vectors. It is common to take a special basis pair for $\langle \mathbf{R}^2, \mathbf{R} \rangle$, which is suggested by our coordinatization of the plane: namely, the pair $(1, 0) = I$ and $(0, 1) = J$. Our discussion regarding basis vectors and dimension of $\mathbf{R}^2$ can easily be applied to the space of position vectors. The distinction between these two-dimensional spaces is important as we see in the following discussion on coordinates.

Change of Coordinates

The notion of basis vectors is very closely related to coordinatization of the plane. The plane having been coordinatized in a particular fashion, it is natural to think of each position vector as a linear combination of the vectors $\mathbf{I}$ and $\mathbf{J}$. Thus, each position vector $\mathbf{V} = a\mathbf{I} + b\mathbf{J}$ is associated with a coordinate vector (a, b). It is useful to associate position vectors with coordinate vectors in other ways as well.

3.9-7 Definition: Let **A** and **B** be two linearly independent position vectors. Then the pair (**A**, **B**) is called an *ordered basis*. If **V** = *a***A** + *b***B**, then (*a*, *b*) is called the *coordinate* of **V** with respect to the ordered basis (**A**, **B**).

Question: For a given ordered basis (**A**, **B**), how do we know that a vector **V** has exactly one coordinate (*a*, *b*)?

Geometrically, a basis for the set of position vectors consists of two nonzero vectors not lying on the same line through the origin. Any position vector **V** is some linear combination of two such vectors. If **A** and **B** form

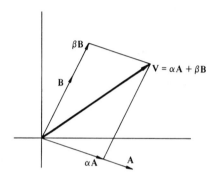

FIGURE 3.58

a basis, as shown in Figure 3.58, and **V** is an arbitrary vector, then by the proper selection of α and β, we have

$$\mathbf{V} = \alpha\mathbf{A} + \beta\mathbf{B}.$$

Thus, the coordinate for the vector **V** with respect to the ordered basis (**A**, **B**) is (α, β). With respect to a different ordered basis, **V** would have a different coordinate.

Example: Let **A** = (1, 1), **B** = (−1, 2), **C** = (1, 2), and **D** = (2, −1). If **V** = (3, 4), then **V** = $\frac{10}{3}$**A** + $\frac{1}{3}$**B**, and hence the coordinate for **V** with respect to the basis (**A**, **B**) is ($\frac{10}{3}$, $\frac{1}{3}$). Also **V** = $\frac{11}{5}$**C** + $\frac{2}{5}$**D**, and hence the coordinate for **V** with respect to the basis (**C**, **D**) is ($\frac{11}{5}$, $\frac{2}{5}$). What is the coordinate of **V** with respect to the *standard basis* (**I**, **J**)?

Notice that finding the coordinate (*x*, *y*) for a given vector **V** = (c_1, c_2) with respect to a basis **A** = (a_1, a_2), **B** = (b_1, b_2) (actually the ordered basis (**A**, **B**)) is exactly the problem of solving the system of linear equations

$$a_1 x + b_1 y = c_1,$$
$$a_2 x + b_2 y = c_2,$$

written in matrix form as

$$\begin{bmatrix} a_1 & b_1 \\ a_2 & b_2 \end{bmatrix} \begin{bmatrix} x \\ y \end{bmatrix} = \begin{bmatrix} c_1 \\ c_2 \end{bmatrix}.$$

Let us interpret this information from a slightly different point of view. We have a vector **V** in mind, and it has coordinate (x, y) with respect to the basis (A, B) and it has coordinate (c_1, c_2) with respect to the standard basis (I, J). We have then that the coordinate for **V** in one system can be obtained from its coordinate in another system by multiplication of a particular matrix. That is, in the example above,

$$\begin{bmatrix} a_1 & b_1 \\ a_2 & b_2 \end{bmatrix} \begin{bmatrix} x \\ y \end{bmatrix} = \begin{bmatrix} c_1 \\ c_2 \end{bmatrix}$$

indicates that multiplication of $\begin{pmatrix} x \\ y \end{pmatrix}$, the coordinate with respect to the basis (A, B), by the matrix

$$\begin{bmatrix} a_1 & b_1 \\ a_2 & b_2 \end{bmatrix} = M$$

yields the coordinate

$$\begin{bmatrix} c_1 \\ c_2 \end{bmatrix},$$

which is the coordinate of the same vector **V** with respect to the standard basis (I, J). It seems reasonable that there might be some matrix K that would reverse this process. That is, we might expect to find a 2×2 matrix K such that

$$K \begin{pmatrix} c_1 \\ c_2 \end{pmatrix} = \begin{pmatrix} x \\ y \end{pmatrix},$$

thus K sends the standard coordinate of **V** to its coordinate with respect to (A, B). If K is some matrix such that

$$KM = \begin{pmatrix} 1 & 0 \\ 0 & 1 \end{pmatrix} = I \qquad \text{(the identity matrix)},$$

then we have found the matrix we desire since

$$M \begin{pmatrix} x \\ y \end{pmatrix} = \begin{pmatrix} c_1 \\ c_2 \end{pmatrix}$$

from which

$$KM \begin{pmatrix} x \\ y \end{pmatrix} = K \begin{pmatrix} c_1 \\ c_2 \end{pmatrix}$$

and then

$$I \begin{pmatrix} x \\ y \end{pmatrix} = K \begin{pmatrix} c_1 \\ c_2 \end{pmatrix},$$

thus giving

$$\begin{pmatrix} x \\ y \end{pmatrix} = K \begin{pmatrix} c_1 \\ c_2 \end{pmatrix}.$$

The problem of changing coordinates and the existence of the multiplicative identity matrix I suggests the question of whether there are multiplicative inverse matrices. We consider this question in more detail later. It turns out that not all matrices have multiplicative inverses. However, such an inverse, when it exists, is useful in solving systems of linear equations. We will also see that matrix multiplication may be viewed as a transformation on $\langle R^2, R \rangle$. For the present, we shall concentrate on the problem of coordinate changes and existence of inverses.

Let us proceed with an example. Consider the basis (A, B) where $A = (1, 1)$ and $B = (1, 3)$. The vector $V = (4, 5)$ has standard coordinate $(4, 5)$ and in order to find the coordinate of V with respect to the basis (A, B), we must find x and y such that

$$x(1, 1) + y(1, 3) = (4, 5).$$

That is, we must solve the system of equations

$$1x + 1y = 4,$$
$$1x + 3y = 5,$$

written matrix form

$$\begin{bmatrix} 1 & 1 \\ 1 & 3 \end{bmatrix} \begin{bmatrix} x \\ y \end{bmatrix} = \begin{bmatrix} 4 \\ 5 \end{bmatrix}.$$

Using elementary methods, one can easily determine that $(x, y) = (\frac{7}{2}, \frac{1}{2})$ is a solution to the system. Notice that

$$\begin{bmatrix} \frac{3}{2} & -\frac{1}{2} \\ -\frac{1}{2} & \frac{1}{2} \end{bmatrix} \begin{bmatrix} 1 & 1 \\ 1 & 3 \end{bmatrix} = \begin{bmatrix} 1 & 0 \\ 0 & 1 \end{bmatrix}.$$

That is, we have found (without telling you how) a multiplicative inverse for the matrix

$$\begin{bmatrix} 1 & 1 \\ 1 & 3 \end{bmatrix}.$$

If we multiply both sides of our matrix equation by this inverse, we have

$$\begin{bmatrix} \frac{3}{2} & -\frac{1}{2} \\ -\frac{1}{2} & \frac{1}{2} \end{bmatrix} \begin{bmatrix} 1 & 1 \\ 1 & 3 \end{bmatrix} \begin{bmatrix} x \\ y \end{bmatrix} = \begin{bmatrix} \frac{3}{2} & -\frac{1}{2} \\ -\frac{1}{2} & \frac{1}{2} \end{bmatrix} \begin{bmatrix} 4 \\ 5 \end{bmatrix}.$$

After completing the multiplication, we have

$$\begin{bmatrix} 1 & 0 \\ 0 & 1 \end{bmatrix} \begin{bmatrix} x \\ y \end{bmatrix} = \begin{bmatrix} 6 & -\frac{5}{2} \\ -2 & +\frac{5}{2} \end{bmatrix}$$

or equivalently

$$\begin{bmatrix} x \\ y \end{bmatrix} = \begin{matrix} \frac{7}{2} \\ \frac{1}{2} \end{matrix},$$

which we have already seen to be the correct solution.

This method can be used to solve the more general system

$$1x + 1y = \alpha$$
$$1x + 3y = \beta$$

or, in matrix form, the equation

$$\begin{bmatrix} 1 & 1 \\ 1 & 3 \end{bmatrix} \begin{bmatrix} x \\ y \end{bmatrix} = \begin{bmatrix} \alpha \\ \beta \end{bmatrix}.$$

That is, the matrix

$$\begin{bmatrix} 1 & 1 \\ 1 & 3 \end{bmatrix}$$

transforms the coordinate (x, y) in the $(\mathbf{A}, \mathbf{B})$ basis to the standard basis coordinate (α, β), and the multiplicative inverse

$$\begin{bmatrix} \frac{3}{2} & -\frac{1}{2} \\ -\frac{1}{2} & \frac{1}{2} \end{bmatrix}$$

transforms the standard coordinate (α, β) to the $(\mathbf{A}, \mathbf{B})$ coordinate (x, y).

Thus, we have seen that by matrix multiplication, we can solve systems of equations that in turn are related to changing coordinates. We shall pursue these topics in more detail in the next section.

EXERCISES 3.9

1. Show that the three vectors given are linearly dependent. Graph the vectors.
   a. $(1, 2), (2, 3), (-1, -1)$. b. $(1, 0), (-2, -1), (2, 1)$.
   c. $(2, 1), (-1, 3), (-4, 2)$.

2. Show that the two vectors given are linearly independent. Graph the vectors.
   a. $(1, 1), (-1, 2)$. b. $(-2, -4), (3, 1)$.
   c. $(2, 1), (3, 4)$. d. $(-2, 5), (1, -3)$.

3. Let $A = (1, 2)$, $B = (-1, 1)$. Find the coordinate of the vector $\mathbf{V}$ with respect to the basis $(\mathbf{A}, \mathbf{B})$.
   a. $\mathbf{V} = (-1, -3)$. b. $\mathbf{V} = (1, 1)$.
   c. $\mathbf{V} = (2, 1)$. d. $\mathbf{V} = (2, -1)$.

4. Find a matrix that will transform the coordinate (x, y) of a vector $\mathbf{V} = (\alpha, \beta)$ with respect to the basis $(\mathbf{A}, \mathbf{B})$ to its standard coordinate (α, β).
   a. $A = (2, 1)$, $B = (1, 3)$. b. $A = (1, 2)$, $B = (-3, 1)$.
   c. $A = (-1, -1)$, $B = (5, 2)$. d. $A = (2, 3)$, $B = (4, -2)$.

5. a. Show that the vectors $(0, 1), (1, 1), (1, 0)$ are linearly dependent.
   b. Show that any two of the vectors above are linearly independent.

6. How many one-dimensional subspaces of the two-dimensional vector space $\langle \mathbf{R}^2, \mathbf{R} \rangle$ are there? Describe some.

7. Show that any two vectors $(0, a)$ and $(0, b)$ are linearly dependent.

8. Show that V_1 and V_2 are linearly independent iff

$$\alpha_1 V_1 + \alpha_2 V_2 = 0 \Rightarrow \alpha_1{}^2 + \alpha_2{}^2 = 0.$$

9. Prove Theorem 3.9-6.

10. Suppose $\mathbf{V}$ is a fixed-position vector. Define

$$\mathbb{S} = \{\mathbf{U} : \mathbf{U} \cdot \mathbf{V} = 0\}.$$

   a. Show that $\langle \mathbb{S}, \mathbf{R} \rangle$ is a vector space.
   b. Under what conditions is $\langle \mathbb{S}, \mathbf{R} \rangle$ a proper subspace (i) of dimension 1? (ii) of dimension 0?

11. Find $A = (a, b)$ and
$B = a(2, 5)$

such that

$$A \cdot B = 0, \qquad |A| = |B| = 1, \qquad \text{and} \qquad a > 0.$$

3.10 INVERSES OF NONSINGULAR MATRICES AND TRANSPOSE OF A MATRIX

Inverse of a Matrix

In the preceding section, we saw that some matrices have multiplicative inverses and that it might be useful to be able to determine these inverses.

Example: Let

$$\begin{bmatrix} 1 & 1 \\ 0 & 1 \end{bmatrix} = A \qquad \text{and} \qquad \begin{bmatrix} 1 & -1 \\ 0 & 1 \end{bmatrix} = B.$$

Then

$$AB = I = \begin{bmatrix} 1 & 0 \\ 0 & 1 \end{bmatrix},$$

so

$$B = A^{-1}.$$

Note also that $BA = I$, so

$$B^{-1} = (A^{-1})^{-1} = A.$$

It is also clear that not all matrices have inverses.

Example: $\begin{bmatrix} 1 & 1 \\ 0 & 0 \end{bmatrix}$ has no inverse, since for any 2×2 matrix $\begin{bmatrix} a & b \\ c & d \end{bmatrix}$,

$$\begin{bmatrix} 1 & 1 \\ 0 & 0 \end{bmatrix}\begin{bmatrix} a & b \\ c & d \end{bmatrix} = \begin{bmatrix} a+c & b+d \\ 0 & 0 \end{bmatrix},$$

and for no values of a, b, c, d can this product matrix be I.

3.10-1 Definition: If a matrix has an inverse, it is said to be *nonsingular;* otherwise it is called *singular.*

Example:

$$\begin{bmatrix} 1 & 1 \\ 0 & 0 \end{bmatrix} \qquad \text{and} \qquad \begin{bmatrix} 0 & 0 \\ 0 & 1 \end{bmatrix}$$

are singular, whereas

$$\begin{bmatrix} 1 & 1 \\ 0 & 1 \end{bmatrix} \qquad \text{and} \qquad \begin{bmatrix} 2 & 4 \\ -1 & 3 \end{bmatrix}$$

are nonsingular.

Before developing methods for determining whether a 2×2 matrix is singular, and if not, calculating the inverse, let us recall how knowledge of the inverse can be useful in solving systems of linear equations. We have discussed how a system of linear equations can be written as $AX = C$, where

$$A = \begin{bmatrix} a_{11} & a_{12} \\ a_{21} & a_{22} \end{bmatrix} \quad \text{(the } coefficient\ matrix\text{)},$$

$$X = \begin{bmatrix} x \\ y \end{bmatrix} \quad \text{(the vector of } unknowns\text{)},$$

$$C = \begin{bmatrix} c_1 \\ c_2 \end{bmatrix} \quad \text{(the vector of } constants\text{)}.$$

Thus, the matrix equation $AX = C$ represents the system of equations written in the traditional form as

$$a_{11}x + a_{12}y = c_1,$$
$$a_{21}x + a_{22}y = c_2.$$

It seems natural to wonder whether this matrix equation can be solved by first finding a matrix B such that $BA = I$, and then multiplying both sides of the equation on the left by B. That is, $B(AX) = BC$. Since multiplication of matrices is associative, we have $(BA)X = BC$, and thus $IX = BC$, from which we can immediately determine the solution by looking at BC.

Example: Suppose that we are asked to solve the system

$$2x + 3y = 2,$$
$$x + 2y = 1.$$

This can be written in matrix form as

$$\begin{bmatrix} 2 & 3 \\ 1 & 2 \end{bmatrix} \begin{bmatrix} x \\ y \end{bmatrix} = \begin{bmatrix} 2 \\ 1 \end{bmatrix},$$

or $AX = C$, where

$$A = \begin{bmatrix} 2 & 3 \\ 1 & 2 \end{bmatrix}, \quad X = \begin{bmatrix} x \\ y \end{bmatrix}, \quad \text{and} \quad C = \begin{bmatrix} 2 \\ 1 \end{bmatrix}.$$

Note that $A^{-1} = \begin{bmatrix} 2 & -3 \\ -1 & 2 \end{bmatrix}$, since

$$\begin{bmatrix} 2 & 3 \\ 1 & 2 \end{bmatrix} \begin{bmatrix} 2 & -3 \\ -1 & 2 \end{bmatrix} = \begin{bmatrix} 1 & 0 \\ 0 & 1 \end{bmatrix} = I,$$

although the method used to "find" A^{-1} remains rather mysterious at this point. The solution to the system is thus given by

$$A^{-1}AX = \begin{bmatrix} 2 & -3 \\ -1 & 2 \end{bmatrix} \begin{bmatrix} 2 & 3 \\ 1 & 2 \end{bmatrix} \begin{bmatrix} x \\ y \end{bmatrix} = A^{-1}C = \begin{bmatrix} 2 & -3 \\ -1 & 2 \end{bmatrix} \begin{bmatrix} 2 \\ 1 \end{bmatrix} = \begin{bmatrix} 1 \\ 0 \end{bmatrix}.$$

That is, the unique solution of the system is $x = 1$ and $y = 0$. Of course, the solution can also be found by elementary methods.

Properties of the Inverse

The problem of determining whether a given square matrix has an inverse is easily solved using the determinant function introduced earlier. Knowing that A^{-1} exists, and actually finding A^{-1} are two very different problems. We will discuss methods of constructing A^{-1} when it exists. In general, finding A^{-1} is not easy when the dimension of A is large. We will limit our consideration in this text to 2×2 and 3×3 matrices, since the computational difficulty becomes significant for larger matrices.

We can say a great deal about multiplicative inverses of matrices, even though we as yet have given no systematic procedure for finding them. Some properties of inverses are given in the following theorem. We state and prove the theorem for real 2×2 matrices, although the result is not limited to this case.

3.10-2   Theorem: Suppose A and B are 2×2 nonsingular matrices, and k is a nonzero real number. Then,
   a. The product AB has an inverse, and moreover

$$(AB)^{-1} = B^{-1}A^{-1}.$$

   b. $(kA)^{-1} = \dfrac{1}{k} A^{-1}.$

PROOF: Part (a). In this part we need to show that

$$(AB)(B^{-1}A^{-1}) = I.$$

This will automatically imply that AB has an inverse. By the associative property of matrix multiplication, the matrix on the left-hand side of the equation can be written

$$A(BB^{-1})A^{-1} = AIA^{-1} = AA^{-1} = I.$$

Part (b) we leave as an exercise for the student.

The determinant function will enable us to determine when a matrix has an inverse and to provide a method of computing the inverse if it exists. Keep in mind that one of the advantages in being able to compute A^{-1}, given the matrix A, is that it leads to the solution of the system of linear equations written in matrix form $AX = C$.

We define the determinant function for larger matrices in a later chapter; however, the simple case of a 2×2 matrix provides much insight into the more general situation.

Let us investigate some real 2×2 matrices and try to determine conditions under which a matrix will be nonsingular. Consider the matrix

$$A = \begin{bmatrix} a & b \\ c & d \end{bmatrix}.$$

We wish to find a matrix

$$B = \begin{bmatrix} x & y \\ z & w \end{bmatrix}$$

such that

$$\begin{bmatrix} x & y \\ z & w \end{bmatrix}\begin{bmatrix} a & b \\ c & d \end{bmatrix} = \begin{bmatrix} 1 & 0 \\ 0 & 1 \end{bmatrix}.$$

That is,

$$\begin{bmatrix} xa + yc & xb + yd \\ za + wc & zb + wd \end{bmatrix} = \begin{bmatrix} 1 & 0 \\ 0 & 1 \end{bmatrix} = I.$$

Equivalently, we wish to find solutions for the following two systems of equations.

$$\begin{array}{ll} ax + cy = 1 & az + cw = 0 \\ bx + dy = 0 & bz + dw = 1 \end{array}$$

(or written in matrix form,

$$\begin{bmatrix} a & c \\ b & d \end{bmatrix}\begin{bmatrix} x \\ y \end{bmatrix} = \begin{bmatrix} 1 \\ 0 \end{bmatrix} \quad \begin{bmatrix} a & c \\ b & d \end{bmatrix}\begin{bmatrix} z \\ w \end{bmatrix} = \begin{bmatrix} 0 \\ 1 \end{bmatrix}).$$

From these, using elementary methods, we can deduce that the only possible solutions are given by

$$x = \frac{d}{ad - bc}, \qquad y = \frac{-b}{ad - bc},$$

$$z = \frac{-c}{ad - bc}, \qquad w = \frac{a}{ad - bc}.$$

Notice it must be assumed that $\begin{vmatrix} a & b \\ c & d \end{vmatrix} = ad - bc \neq 0$. If $ad - bc = 0$, then there is no solution, and hence no inverse for the matrix.

The foregoing discussion has achieved a dual purpose. We have shown that

1. $\begin{bmatrix} a & b \\ c & d \end{bmatrix}^{-1}$ exists iff $\begin{vmatrix} a & b \\ c & d \end{vmatrix} \neq 0$.

2. If $|A| \neq 0$, then A^{-1} is given by

$$A^{-1} = \begin{bmatrix} a & b \\ c & d \end{bmatrix}^{-1} = \frac{1}{|A|}\begin{bmatrix} d & -b \\ -c & a \end{bmatrix}.$$

We have thus established a way to solve a system of two linear equations in two unknowns. Later we shall extend this process to three equations in three unknowns. At present, using the information we have so far developed, let us solve some systems.

Example: Solve the system of equations

$$\begin{array}{l} 2x - 2y = 1 \\ -1x + 2y = 3. \end{array}$$

This system can be written in matrix form $AX = C$, as follows:

$$\begin{bmatrix} 2 & -2 \\ -1 & 2 \end{bmatrix} \begin{bmatrix} x \\ y \end{bmatrix} = \begin{bmatrix} 1 \\ 3 \end{bmatrix}.$$

We compute $|A| = 4 - 2 = 2 \neq 0$, so A^{-1} exists. From above, we have

$$A^{-1} = \frac{1}{2} \begin{bmatrix} 2 & 2 \\ 1 & 2 \end{bmatrix} = \begin{bmatrix} 1 & 1 \\ \frac{1}{2} & 1 \end{bmatrix}.$$

Thus,

$$\begin{bmatrix} 1 & 1 \\ \frac{1}{2} & 1 \end{bmatrix} \begin{bmatrix} 2 & -2 \\ -1 & 2 \end{bmatrix} \begin{bmatrix} x \\ y \end{bmatrix} = \begin{bmatrix} 1 & 1 \\ \frac{1}{2} & 1 \end{bmatrix} \begin{bmatrix} 1 \\ 3 \end{bmatrix},$$

from which

$$\begin{bmatrix} 1 & 0 \\ 0 & 1 \end{bmatrix} \begin{bmatrix} x \\ y \end{bmatrix} = \begin{bmatrix} 4 \\ \frac{7}{2} \end{bmatrix}.$$

Thus, the solution to the system is $x = 4$ and $y = \frac{7}{2}$.

Example: Solve the system

$$\begin{bmatrix} 2 & 2 \\ 3 & -1 \end{bmatrix} \begin{bmatrix} x \\ y \end{bmatrix} = \begin{bmatrix} 2 \\ 4 \end{bmatrix}.$$

We compute

$$\begin{bmatrix} 2 & 2 \\ 3 & -1 \end{bmatrix}^{-1} = \frac{1}{-8} \begin{bmatrix} -1 & -2 \\ -3 & 2 \end{bmatrix} = \begin{bmatrix} \frac{1}{8} & \frac{1}{4} \\ \frac{3}{8} & -\frac{1}{4} \end{bmatrix}.$$

The solution is thus given by

$$\begin{bmatrix} x \\ y \end{bmatrix} = \begin{bmatrix} \frac{1}{8} & \frac{1}{4} \\ \frac{3}{8} & -\frac{1}{4} \end{bmatrix} \begin{bmatrix} 2 \\ 4 \end{bmatrix} = \begin{bmatrix} \frac{2}{8} + \frac{4}{4} \\ \frac{6}{8} - \frac{4}{4} \end{bmatrix} = \begin{bmatrix} \frac{5}{4} \\ -\frac{2}{4} \end{bmatrix} = \begin{bmatrix} \frac{5}{4} \\ -\frac{1}{2} \end{bmatrix}.$$

Changing Coordinates

In the previous section, we saw that we could use matrix multiplication to change coordinates. We considered only the case in which a matrix M was used to map the coordinate $\begin{bmatrix} x \\ y \end{bmatrix}$ of a vector $\mathbf{V} = (\alpha, \beta)$ with respect to some basis $(\mathbf{A}, \mathbf{B})$ to its standard coordinate (α, β). That is, if

$$\mathbf{V} = x\mathbf{A} + y\mathbf{B} = \alpha\mathbf{I} + \beta\mathbf{J},$$

then we found a matrix M such that

$$M \begin{bmatrix} x \\ y \end{bmatrix} = \begin{bmatrix} \alpha \\ \beta \end{bmatrix}.$$

We now consider the more general case, in which two arbitrary ordered bases are considered. Assume that a vector $\mathbf{V} = (\alpha, \beta)$ has coordinate (x, y) with respect to $(\mathbf{A}, \mathbf{B})$ and has coordinate (u, v) with respect to $(\mathbf{C}, \mathbf{D})$. That is,

$$\mathbf{V} = x\mathbf{A} + y\mathbf{B} = u\mathbf{C} + v\mathbf{D}.$$

If

$$M \begin{bmatrix} x \\ y \end{bmatrix} = \begin{bmatrix} \alpha \\ \beta \end{bmatrix} \quad \text{and} \quad K \begin{bmatrix} u \\ v \end{bmatrix} = \begin{bmatrix} \alpha \\ \beta \end{bmatrix},$$

Then

$$K^{-1}K \begin{bmatrix} u \\ v \end{bmatrix} = \begin{bmatrix} u \\ v \end{bmatrix} = K^{-1} \begin{bmatrix} \alpha \\ \beta \end{bmatrix}.$$

It follows that

$$K^{-1}M \begin{bmatrix} x \\ y \end{bmatrix} = K^{-1} \begin{bmatrix} \alpha \\ \beta \end{bmatrix} = \begin{bmatrix} u \\ v \end{bmatrix}.$$

Thus, the matrix $K^{-1}M$ transforms the coordinate (x, y) of **V** with respect to the basis $(\mathbf{A}, \mathbf{B})$ to its coordinate (u, v) with respect to the basis $(\mathbf{C}, \mathbf{D})$.

Example: Let $\mathbf{A} = (2, 1)$, $\mathbf{B} = (-1, 1)$, $\mathbf{C} = (3, 2)$, and $\mathbf{D} = (1, -1)$. Find a matrix that transforms the $(\mathbf{A}, \mathbf{B})$ coordinate of a point (position vector) to its $(\mathbf{C}, \mathbf{D})$ coordinate.

Solution: We have for an arbitrary vector, **V**, with $(\mathbf{A}, \mathbf{B})$ coordinate (x, y) and $(\mathbf{C}, \mathbf{D})$ coordinate (u, v),

$$x(2, 1) + y(-1, 1) = u(3, 2) + v(1, -1).$$

From this we have

$$2x - 1y = 3u + 1v,$$
$$1x + 1y = 2u - 1v,$$

or in matrix form,

$$\begin{bmatrix} 2 & -1 \\ 1 & 1 \end{bmatrix} \begin{bmatrix} x \\ y \end{bmatrix} = \begin{bmatrix} 3 & 1 \\ 2 & -1 \end{bmatrix} \begin{bmatrix} u \\ v \end{bmatrix}.$$

Let us multiply both sides of the equation by

$$\begin{bmatrix} 3 & 1 \\ 2 & -1 \end{bmatrix}^{-1} = \frac{1}{-5} \begin{bmatrix} -1 & -1 \\ -2 & 3 \end{bmatrix} = \begin{bmatrix} \frac{1}{5} & \frac{1}{5} \\ \frac{2}{5} & -\frac{3}{5} \end{bmatrix}$$

to obtain

$$\begin{bmatrix} \frac{1}{5} & \frac{1}{5} \\ \frac{2}{5} & -\frac{3}{5} \end{bmatrix} \begin{bmatrix} 2 & -1 \\ 1 & 1 \end{bmatrix} \begin{bmatrix} x \\ y \end{bmatrix} = \begin{bmatrix} \frac{3}{5} & 0 \\ \frac{1}{5} & -1 \end{bmatrix} \begin{bmatrix} x \\ y \end{bmatrix} = \begin{bmatrix} u \\ v \end{bmatrix}.$$

Now, if we wish to express, for example, the vector

$$5(2, 1) + 3(-1, 1)$$

as a linear combination of $(3, 2)$ and $(1, -1)$, we merely compute

$$\begin{bmatrix} \frac{3}{5} & 0 \\ \frac{1}{5} & -1 \end{bmatrix} \begin{bmatrix} 5 \\ 3 \end{bmatrix} = \begin{bmatrix} 3 \\ -2 \end{bmatrix}.$$

We can check this as follows:

$$5(2, 1) + 3(-1, 1) = (10, 5) + (-3, 3) = (7, 8);$$

also

$$3(3, 2) - 2(1, -1) = (9, 6) + (-2, 2) = (7, 8).$$

Transpose of a Matrix

We now introduce a particularly simple but useful notion regarding matrices: the construction of a matrix by interchanging rows and columns in a given matrix.

3.10-3   Definition: The *transpose* of a 2 × 2 matrix

$$\begin{bmatrix} a & b \\ c & d \end{bmatrix}$$

is the 2 × 2 matrix

$$\begin{bmatrix} a & c \\ b & d \end{bmatrix}$$

(The transpose of a matrix A is denoted by A^t.) This notion extends to matrices of all dimensions; for example,

$$\begin{bmatrix} a \\ b \end{bmatrix}^t = (a, b).$$

Example:

$$\begin{bmatrix} 1 & 0 \\ 5 & -7 \end{bmatrix}^t = \begin{bmatrix} 1 & 5 \\ 0 & -7 \end{bmatrix}.$$

Example:

$$\begin{bmatrix} \cos \theta & \sin \theta \\ -\sin \theta & \cos \theta \end{bmatrix}^t = \begin{bmatrix} \cos \theta & -\sin \theta \\ \sin \theta & \cos \theta \end{bmatrix}.$$

Perhaps the most obvious fact about the transpose of a matrix is that $(A^t)^t = A$. The following theorem lists other interesting properties of the transpose.

3.10-4   Theorem: For 2 × 2 matrices A and B

  i. $(A + B)^t = A^t + B^t$.
  ii. $(AB)^t = B^t A^t$.
  iii. $(A^{-1})^t = (A^t)^{-1}$ (assuming the matrix A is nonsingular).
  iv. $|A| = |A^t|$.

The proof is left as an exercise.

3.10-5   Definition: A matrix A such that $A = A^t$ is said to be *symmetric*.
   We shall have occasion later to see how certain symmetric matrices arise in analytic geometry.

3.10-6   Definition: An *orthogonal* matrix is a nonsingular matrix A such that $A^{-1} = A^t$.

3.10-7   Theorem: An orthogonal matrix has a determinant of either 1 or -1.

PROOF: Let A be an orthogonal matrix. Then

$$1 = |I| = |AA^t| = |A|\,|A^t| = |A|\,|A| = |A|^2.$$

Thus, $|A| = \pm 1$.

Example: The matrix

$$\begin{bmatrix} \cos\theta & \sin\theta \\ -\sin\theta & \cos\theta \end{bmatrix}$$

is an orthogonal matrix. This matrix will occur later in connection with rotation of coordinates.

Example: The matrix

$$\begin{bmatrix} 1 & 0 \\ 0 & -1 \end{bmatrix}$$

is orthogonal and has determinant -1.

EXERCISES 3.10

1. Compute $|A|$ and use the method developed in this section to find A^{-1}. Test your result.

a. $A = \begin{bmatrix} 1 & 2 \\ 4 & 1 \end{bmatrix}.$
        b. $A = \begin{bmatrix} -1 & -3 \\ 2 & 0 \end{bmatrix}.$

c. $A = \begin{bmatrix} 1 & 2 \\ 1 & -2 \end{bmatrix}.$
        d. $A = \begin{bmatrix} -1 & 6 \\ 2 & -3 \end{bmatrix}.$

e. $A = \begin{bmatrix} 2 & 1 \\ 1 & -1 \end{bmatrix}.$
        f. $A = \begin{bmatrix} 4 & 6 \\ 3 & -2 \end{bmatrix}.$

2. Use the method of this section to solve the following systems of equations.

a. $2x + 3y = 4$
   $-x + y = 1.$
        b. $5x + 2y = 2$
   $2x - y = 3.$

c. $2x + y = 7$
   $x - y = 2.$
        d. $6x + 2y = 0$
   $3x + 7y = -1.$

e. $-x - 3y = 2$
   $4x + 2y = 3.$
        f. $3x - 2y = 1$
   $4x + 2y = 0.$

3. a. Write a system of equations that cannot be solved using these methods.
   b. Graph the lines determined by the equations in the system.

4. Find a matrix that will transform the coordinate of a vector with respect to the basis (A, B) to its coordinate with respect to (C, D), where
   a. $A = (1, 2)$, $B = (-3, 1)$, $C = (-1, -1)$, $D = (2, 1)$.
   b. $A = (5, 7)$, $B = (-1, -2)$, $C = (-3, -3)$, $D = (1, 2)$.
   c. $A = (-2, 1)$, $B = (3, 4)$, $C = (1, 7)$, $D = (-2, -7)$.
   d. $A = (2, 3)$, $B = (6, 4)$, $C = (3, -2)$, $D = (5, -1)$.

5. Write each of the following as a linear combination of $(2, -1)$ and $(1, 3)$, where $A = (1, 1)$ and $B = (-2, 3)$.
   a. $5A + 4B.$
        b. $6A - 3B.$
   c. $-2A + 4B.$
        d. $A - 7B.$

6. Show for a 2×2 nonsingular matrix A and a nonzero real number k that $(kA)^{-1} = (1/k)A^{-1}$.

7. Compute $|A|$ and $|A^t|$.

  a. $A = \begin{bmatrix} 2 & 5 \\ 7 & 1 \end{bmatrix}$.

  b. $A = \begin{bmatrix} -1 & 3 \\ -2 & 7 \end{bmatrix}$.

  c. $A = \begin{bmatrix} 1 & 3 \\ -2 & 4 \end{bmatrix}$.

  d. $A = \begin{bmatrix} 3 & 4 \\ 4 & -1 \end{bmatrix}$.

8. Compute $(AB)^t$ and $A^t B^t$.

  a. $A = \begin{bmatrix} 2 & 1 \\ 3 & -1 \end{bmatrix}$. $B = \begin{bmatrix} 4 & -1 \\ 7 & 1 \end{bmatrix}$.

  b. $A = \begin{bmatrix} 5 & 3 \\ 2 & -3 \end{bmatrix}$. $B = \begin{bmatrix} 1 & 4 \\ 3 & -1 \end{bmatrix}$.

9. Prove Theorem 3.10-4.

10. Show that a product of orthogonal matrices is orthogonal.

11. Prove or disprove the converse of Theorem 3.10-7.

IV

TRANSLATIONS AND ROTATIONS AND INTRODUCTION TO THREE-DIMENSIONAL SPACE

4.1 TRANSLATION OF COORDINATES

We have previously discussed general notions of coordinatizations: the process of matching points in the plane with ordered pairs of real numbers. We have also pointed out the distinction between a point and its coordinate ordered pair, although we often used the same notation for both when this apparently led to no confusion. In the first part of this chapter, we shall concentrate on the distinction between points and coordinates and examine the relationships between coordinates of a given point and certain different coordinatizations.

Suppose the plane has been coordinatized with x-axis $\mathcal{X}$ and y-axis $\mathcal{Y}$. Assume that a different coordinatization has also been given with x'-axis $\mathcal{X}'$ and y'-axis $\mathcal{Y}'$ such that $\mathcal{X}'$ is parallel to $\mathcal{X}$ and $\mathcal{Y}'$ is parallel to $\mathcal{Y}$. Assume that $\mathcal{X}'$ and $\mathcal{Y}'$ intersect in a point O', which has coordinate (h, k) in the $\mathcal{X}-\mathcal{Y}$ system, as shown in Figure 4.1.

We wish now to determine general formulas that relate the $\mathcal{X}-\mathcal{Y}$ coordinate of a point to the $\mathcal{X}'-\mathcal{Y}'$ coordinate. Consider an arbitrary point P having $\mathcal{X}-\mathcal{Y}$ coordinate (x, y) and $\mathcal{X}'-\mathcal{Y}'$ coordinate (x', y'). It is easily seen that

$$[\mathbf{x}, \mathbf{y}] = [\mathbf{h}, \mathbf{k}] + [\mathbf{x}', \mathbf{y}'],$$

as shown in Figure 4.2. From this equation, we have

$$x = h + x' \quad \text{and} \quad y = k + y'$$

or equivalently

$$x' = x - h \quad \text{and} \quad y' = y - k.$$

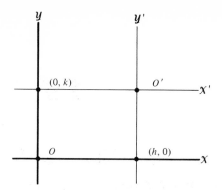

FIGURE 4.1

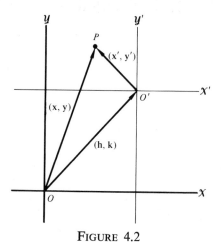

FIGURE 4.2

Let us view this as establishing a function T that maps coordinate *2-tuples* (ordered pairs) by the formula

$$T\begin{bmatrix} x \\ y \end{bmatrix} = \begin{bmatrix} x - h \\ y - k \end{bmatrix} = \begin{bmatrix} x' \\ y' \end{bmatrix}.$$

That is, T is a function that assigns the x–y coordinate of any point P to its corresponding x'–y' coordinate. The map T^{-1}, given by

$$T^{-1}\begin{bmatrix} x' \\ y' \end{bmatrix} = \begin{bmatrix} x' + h \\ y' + k \end{bmatrix} = \begin{bmatrix} x \\ y \end{bmatrix},$$

assigns the x'–y' coordinate of any point to its x–y coordinate. The maps T and T^{-1} are called *transformation-of-coordinates maps*. In this particular case they belong to the subclass of transformations called *translations*.

Translation of Coordinate Systems Applied to Graphing

Let us now use the idea of translation to simplify the analytic description of certain sets of points. Here, we need to keep in mind the distinction between a point and its coordinate under a given coordinatization. For example, consider the set

$$S = \{(x, y) : x^2 - 4x + y^2 - 2y + 4 = 0\}.$$

In order to graph S, we must determine the points in the plane that correspond to the ordered pairs in S under a particular coordinatization.

In general, it is very difficult to find by trial and error, for example, many members of the set S of coordinates (x, y) satisfying the constraint

$$x^2 - 4x + y^2 - 2y + 4 = 0.$$

However, if we are sufficiently clever, we notice that this equation is equivalent to

$$(x - 2)^2 + (y - 1)^2 = 1.$$

(In a moment we will discuss how one might go about being so clever.) Since we know immediately how to graph the set of points whose coordinates (x', y') are subject to the constraint

$$x'^2 + y'^2 = 1,$$

we can first graph the set

$$S' = \{(x', y') : x'^2 + y'^2 = 1\}$$

in a Cartesian coordinate system with axes x' and y', and later relate this to the original system. (See Figure 4.3.)

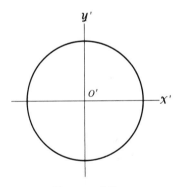

FIGURE 4.3

Let us now change coordinates by the equations

$$x = x' + 2 \quad \text{and} \quad y = y' + 1$$

(that is, if a point P has coordinate (x', y') in the $\mathfrak{X}'$–$\mathcal{Y}'$ system, then it has coordinate $(x, y) = (x' + 2, y' + 1)$ in a system with axes $\mathfrak{X}$ and $\mathcal{Y}$.) The two systems are shown in Figure 4.4. Since $x' = x - 2$ and $y' = y - 1$, we see that the graph of

$$\mathcal{S} = \{(x, y) : (x - 2)^2 + (y - 1)^2 = 1\}$$

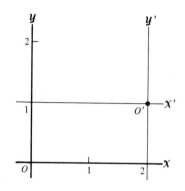

FIGURE 4.4

in the $\mathfrak{X}$–$\mathcal{Y}$ coordinate system is exactly the same set of points as the graph of the set

$$\mathcal{S}' = \{(x', y') : x'^2 + y'^2 = 1\}$$

in the $\mathfrak{X}'$–$\mathcal{Y}'$ system. Hence, to graph the set $\mathcal{S}$, we draw the axes for both coordinate systems in proper relation to each other, and simply graph $\mathcal{S}'$ in the $\mathfrak{X}'$–$\mathcal{Y}'$ system. (See Figure 4.5.)

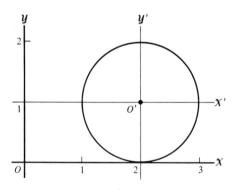

FIGURE 4.5

Later we shall make a great deal of use of this idea. We will find that a figure with a very difficult description in one coordinate system may have a simple description in another. In such a case, it may be possible to simplify the constraint by relating the two coordinatizations (perhaps with a system of equations), and thus do the graphing easily with the second set of coordinates.

With regard to translations, if the constraining equation for the coordinates of a set of points in a coordinatization with axes $\mathcal{X}$ and $\mathcal{Y}$ is given by $f(x, y) = 0$, then the equation $f(x' + h, y' + k) = 0$ is the constraining equation for the coordinates of the *same* set of points in a system coordinatized with parallel axes $\mathcal{X}'$ and $\mathcal{Y}'$, where the origin O' is at the point with $\mathcal{X}$–$\mathcal{Y}$ coordinate (h, k). The objective in making such a substitution is to produce a simpler and perhaps more familiar equation that can be more easily graphed. For this reason, the application of this procedure is usually approached in a somewhat reverse fashion. Typically, one is given an equation $f(x, y) = 0$, which by algebraic manipulation is put into a form $g(x - h, y - k) = 0$. From this, it can easily be seen that the substitution $x' = x - h$ and $y' = y - k$ will lead to the equation $g(x', y') = 0$. In many cases, the new equation will be familiar and readily graphed.

Example: Graph the set of points whose $\mathcal{X}$–$\mathcal{Y}$ coordinates satisfy the equation

$$9x^2 - 36x + 4y^2 + 24y + 36 = 0.$$

As may be readily verified, we can write this equation in the equivalent form

$$9(x - 2)^2 + 4(y + 3)^2 = 36.$$

This suggests that we translate coordinates by the equations

$$x' = x - 2 \quad \text{and} \quad y' = y + 3,$$

and hence obtain the equation

$$9x'^2 + 4y'^2 = 36.$$

This can of course, be put into the familiar equation for an ellipse:

$$\frac{x'^2}{4} + \frac{y'^2}{9} = 1.$$

We then graph this equation using axes $\mathcal{X}'$ and $\mathcal{Y}'$, whose origin O' is the point with $\mathcal{X}$–$\mathcal{Y}$ coordinate $(2, -3)$. (See Figure 4.6.)

Completing the Square

We now discuss an algebraic method that may be useful in putting equations in a form desirable for determining a convenient translation of coordinates. Consider an expression of the form $x^2 + bx + c$. We wish to write this equivalently in the form $(x - p)^2 + q$. By expanding this expression and equating it to the former, we have

$$x^2 - 2px + p^2 + q = x^2 + bx + c.$$

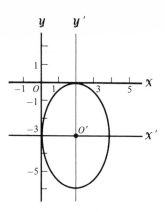

FIGURE 4.6

From this, we see that by taking $-2p = b$, and $p^2 + q = c$, we will have the desired form. That is, if we take $p = -(b/2)$ and $q = c - (b^2/4)$, then $x^2 + bx + c$ and $(x - p)^2 + q$ will be equal for any substituted value of x. In actually applying this process, one can either compute p and q and then *substitute* their values in the desired form, or perhaps more desirably, view the process as the reverse of expanding the binomial $(x - p)^2$. For obvious reasons, this process is called "completing the square."

Example: Write $x^2 - 4x + 2$ in the form $(x - p)^2 + q$. One recognizes easily that on expanding $(x - 2)^2$ he will obtain the desired $x^2 - 4x$. However, in order to obtain a condition of equality with $x^2 - 4x + 2$ we need to add or subtract the proper number. Thus, since $(x - 2)^2 = x^2 - 4x + 4$, we see that $(x - 2)^2 - 2 = x^2 - 4x + 2$.

In the event that we wish to work with the expression $ax^2 + bx + c$, we simply factor out a to obtain $a\left(x^2 + \dfrac{b}{a}x + \dfrac{c}{a}\right)$ and then apply the above procedure to

$$x^2 + \frac{b}{a}x + \frac{c}{a}.$$

Summary

By applying the completion of the square techniques developed in this section and using the previous information regarding translations and conic sections with centers at the origin, one can easily graph any relation given by an equation of the form

$$Ax^2 + By^2 + Dx + Ey + F = 0 \qquad \text{(where } A \neq 0 \text{ or } B \neq 0\text{)}.$$

By appropriately completing squares in each variable and making the corresponding translation, we give the equation the form

$$ax'^2 + by'^2 + f = 0$$

or one of the forms

$$ax'^2 + ey' = 0 \quad \text{or} \quad by'^2 + dx' = 0.$$

We recognize these as being the familiar equations for conic sections with center at the x'-y' origin.

Example: Graph the equation $2x^2 + 12x - 4y + 10 = 0$. By completing the square on x, we have

$$2(x + 3)^2 - 18 - 4y + 10 = 0,$$

which can be written as

$$2(x + 3)^2 - 4(y + 2) = 0 \quad \text{or} \quad (x + 3)^2 = 2(y + 2).$$

If we now change coordinates by the translation

$$x' = x + 3 \quad \text{and} \quad y' = y + 2,$$

we obtain the equation

$$x'^2 = 2y',$$

which is the parabola shown in Figure 4.7. When we superimpose this coordinatization on the original x-y system, we place O' at the point with x-y coordinate $(-3, -2)$, obtaining the graph as shown in Figure 4.8.

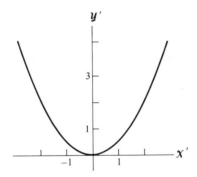

FIGURE 4.7

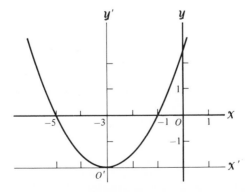

FIGURE 4.8

1. Draw coordinate axes $\mathfrak{X}$, $\mathfrak{Y}$ and $\mathfrak{X}'$, $\mathfrak{Y}'$ as they are related by the transformation of coordinates map T, where

  a. $T\begin{bmatrix} x \\ y \end{bmatrix} = \begin{bmatrix} x - 4 \\ y - 3 \end{bmatrix} = \begin{bmatrix} x' \\ y' \end{bmatrix}.$

  b. $T\begin{bmatrix} x \\ y \end{bmatrix} = \begin{bmatrix} x + 2 \\ y - 5 \end{bmatrix} = \begin{bmatrix} x' \\ y' \end{bmatrix}.$

  c. $T^{-1}\begin{bmatrix} x' \\ y' \end{bmatrix} = \begin{bmatrix} x' - 4 \\ y' + 6 \end{bmatrix} = \begin{bmatrix} x \\ y \end{bmatrix}.$

2. Write each of the following expressions in the form $a(x - p)^2 + q$.
   a. $x^2 + 6x - 7$.
   b. $x^2 - 14x - 2$.
   c. $3x^2 - 6x + 1$.
   d. $5x^2 + 30x + 4$.

3. Write each of the following equations in the form

$$(x - h)^2 + (y - k)^2 = r^2.$$

   a. $x^2 + 10x + y^2 - 6y - 2 = 0$.
   b. $x^2 + y^2 - 16x + 2y - 35 = 0$.
   c. $x^2 - 8y + 6x + y^2 - 15 = 0$.

4. For each Equation in Exercise 3, determine a translation of coordinates that will reduce the equation to the form $x'^2 + y'^2 = r^2$, and graph the corresponding set of points, showing both coordinate systems.

5. Use techniques developed in this section and your knowledge of ellipses to graph the relations described by the following equations.
   a. $3x^2 + 18x + 4y^2 - 8y - 50 = 0$.
   b. $6x^2 + 4y^2 - 12x + 4y - 1 = 0$.
   c. $2x^2 + 3y^2 - 8x + 6y - 5 = 0$.

6. Graph each of the following hyperbolas.
   a. $2x^2 - 2y^2 - 4x - 8y = 8$.
   b. $x^2 - y^2 - 4x + 6y = 30$.
   c. $3y^2 - 2x^2 + 2x + 3y = 6$.

7. Graph each of the following parabolas.
   a. $x^2 - 4x - 11y = 7$.
   b. $4y^2 - 4y + 6x + 3 = 0$.
   c. $5x^2 - 3x + 2y = 4$.

4.2 CONIC SECTIONS IN POLAR COORDINATES

A Unifying Definition

Recall that we defined a parabola to be a set of points each of which has the same distance from a certain point (its focus) as from a given line (its directrix). We will now show that ellipses and hyperbolas can be defined in a similar fashion, providing yet another unifying feature of the conic sections. As we shall see, methods using polar coordinates lend themselves very well to the study of conic sections.

4.2-1 Definition: A *conic section* $\mathcal{S}$ is a set of points having the property that for any point X in $\mathcal{S}$, the ratio of the distance between X and a fixed point F (called the *focus*) to the distance between X and a fixed line (called the *directrix*) is some fixed positive number e (called the *eccentricity* of the conic section).

Derivation of Standard Equations

At present we shall consider only the special case in which the focus is the origin (pole in polar coordinates) and the directrix is parallel to one of the axes. Later we shall relax these assumptions.

Let the directrix $\mathfrak{D}$ be the line perpendicular to the polar axis, which is a positive distance p to the right of the pole. That is, in Cartesian coordinates, $\mathfrak{D} = \{(x, y) : x = p\}$ and in polar coordinates $\mathfrak{D} = \{(r, \theta) : r \cos \theta = p\}$.

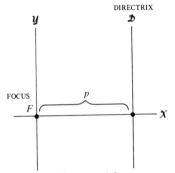

FIGURE 4.9

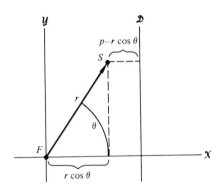

FIGURE 4.10

(See Figure 4.9.) A point S will be in the conic section provided that the ratio of its distance from F to its distance from $\mathfrak{D}$ is the fixed number e. (See Figure 4.10.)

Thus, we have the ratio

$$\frac{r}{p - r \cos \theta} = e,$$

giving us a constraint on the polar coordinates of any point in the conic section being described. This equation can be put in the form

$$r = \frac{ep}{1 + e \cos \theta},$$

which is the *standard form* for a conic section (in polar coordinates) as described, with *directrix vertical* and to the *right of the pole*.

By using similar arguments, one can derive other standard forms:

$$r = \frac{ep}{1 - e \cos \theta} \qquad \text{(directrix *vertical* and to the *left* of the pole),}$$

$$r = \frac{ep}{1 - e \sin \theta} \qquad \text{(directrix *horizontal* and *below* the pole),}$$

$$r = \frac{ep}{1 + e \sin \theta} \qquad \text{(directrix *horizontal* and *above* the pole).}$$

Comparison with Cartesian Forms

We shall now show that equations of the form $r = ep/(1 + e \cos \theta)$ actually describe curves of the type we earlier called conic sections. We show that an ellipse is determined in the case $e < 1$, a parabola if $e = 1$, and a hyperbola if $e > 1$. We do this by changing from a polar constraint to one on the Cartesian coordinates. That is, we substitute for r and θ according to the formulas

$$x = r \cos \theta \qquad \text{and} \qquad y = r \sin \theta.$$

On multiplying both sides of the equation $r = ep/(1 + e \cos \theta)$ by $1 + e \cos \theta$, we have

$$r + er \cos \theta = ep.$$

Since $x = r \cos \theta$, and $r = \pm\sqrt{x^2 + y^2}$, when we change to Cartesian coordinates, we have

$$\pm\sqrt{x^2 + y^2} + ex = ep.$$

This equation takes the familiar form

$$\pm\sqrt{x^2 + y^2} = e(p - x), \tag{1}$$

or

$$x^2 + y^2 = e^2(p - x)^2. \tag{2}$$

Remark: Only the plus sign is needed in Equation (1) if $e \leqslant 1$ (why?). In this case, $x < p$, and all points of the conic lie to the left of the directrix. In case $e > 1$, we need to allow r to be less than 0, in which case we also get points that are to the right of the directrix.

Since Equation (2) is an equation of the second degree with no xy term, it describes a curve of the type previously discussed. However, we can also write this equation in the form

$$(1 - e^2)x^2 + 2pe^2x + y^2 = e^2p^2. \tag{3}$$

If $e = 1$, we then have the equation

$$y^2 = -2p\left(x - \frac{p}{2}\right),$$

which is a parabola extending to the left with vertex at the point $(p/2, 0)$ and with axis $\mathfrak{X}$. (See Figure 4.11.)

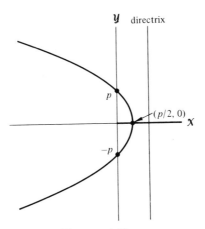

FIGURE 4.11

If $e \neq 1$, then Equation (3) can be written in the form

$$(1 - e^2)\left(x + \frac{pe^2}{1 - e^2}\right)^2 + y^2 = \frac{e^2 p^2}{1 - e^2},$$

or equivalently

$$\frac{\left(x + \dfrac{pe^2}{1 - e^2}\right)^2}{\left(\dfrac{ep}{1 - e^2}\right)^2} + \frac{y^2}{\dfrac{(ep)^2}{1 - e^2}} = 1.$$

If $0 < e < 1$, then $1 - e^2 > 0$, and we have an ellipse with major axis $\mathfrak{X}$, center at $\left(-\dfrac{pe^2}{1 - e^2}, 0\right)$, and vertex at $\left(\dfrac{ep}{1 + e}, 0\right)$ (explain). (See Figure 4.12.)

If $e > 1$, then $1 - e^2 < 0$, thus [noting that $e^2 - 1 = -(1 - e^2)$] we may write our equation in the form

$$\frac{\left(x - \dfrac{pe^2}{e^2 - 1}\right)^2}{[ep/(1 - e^2)]^2} - \frac{y^2}{(ep)^2/(e^2 - 1)} = 1.$$

Thus, we have the equation of a hyperbola with major axis $\mathfrak{X}$, center at $\left(\dfrac{pe^2}{e^2 - 1}, 0\right)$ and asymptotes with slope $\pm\sqrt{e^2 - 1}$. (See Figure 4.13.)

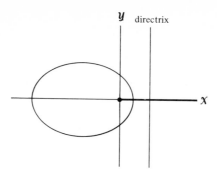

FIGURE 4.12

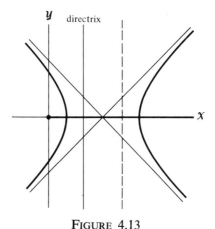

FIGURE 4.13

Remark: If we had allowed only $r > 0$, we would obtain only the left half of this hyperbola.

Remark: The slope of the asymptotes can also be obtained by solving the equation for $\cos \theta$, and observing the result as $r \to \infty$. That is,

$$\lim_{r \to \infty} \cos \theta = \lim_{r \to \infty} \left(\frac{p}{r} - \frac{1}{e} \right) = -\frac{1}{e}.$$

Thus, one asymptote is tilted at an angle θ where $\cos \theta = -(1/e)$, from which $\tan \theta = -\sqrt{e^2 - 1}$. Thus, the asymptotes have slope $\pm \sqrt{e^2 - 1}$.

Similar remarks and graphs can be deduced concerning the other three standard forms.

Example: Graph the curve whose polar coordinates satisfy the equation

$$r = \frac{6}{1 + 2 \sin \theta} = \frac{2 \cdot 3}{1 + 2 \sin \theta}.$$

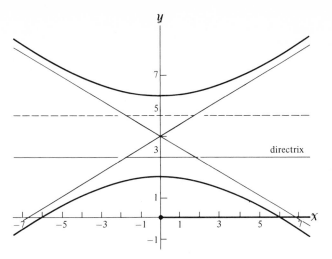

FIGURE 4.14

This is in the form for a conic section with eccentricity two (hyperbola) and directrix three units above and parallel to the x-axis. When $\theta = \pi/2$, we have $r = 2$. In this case the asymptotes have slope

$$\pm\sqrt{e^2 - 1} = \pm\sqrt{4 - 1} = \pm\sqrt{3}.$$

(See Figure 4.14.)

EXERCISES 4.2

1. Graph each curve in polar coordinates.

a. $r = \dfrac{6}{1 - \cos\theta}.$

b. $r = \dfrac{8}{2 + \cos\theta}.$

c. $r = \dfrac{18}{4 - 5\cos\theta}.$

d. $r = \dfrac{6}{1 + 2\sin\theta}.$

e. $r = \dfrac{12}{3 + 2\sin\theta}.$

f. $r = \dfrac{3}{2 + 2\sin\theta}.$

g. $r = \dfrac{15}{3 + 2\sin\theta}.$

h. $r = \dfrac{9}{1 - 2\cos\theta}.$

i. $r = \dfrac{3}{1 - 3\sin\theta}.$

j. $r = \dfrac{6}{1 - 2\sin\theta}.$

2. Change the equation

$$r = \frac{ep}{1 - e\sin\theta}$$

to Cartesian coordinates and put it into standard form for the equations of conic sections in the three cases $e = 1$, $e < 1$, $e > 1$.

3. Explain how the polar equation for a hyperbola gives both branches of the hyperbola.

4. Let $\mathcal{H}$ be an arbitrary chord of a conic section that intersects the conic section at points A and B and passes through a focal point F. Show that the sum $(1/a) + (1/b)$ is the same for all such chords where $a = d(A, F)$ and $b = d(B, F)$.

5. a. Graph $y = 2/(1 - 2 \cos x)$ in Cartesian coordinates.

  b. Explain how this graph is related to the hyperbolic polar curve $r = 2/(1 - 2 \cos \theta)$.

4.3 ROTATION OF COORDINATES

Rotation Formulas

We now consider a special class of coordinate transformations called *rotations*. Suppose two Cartesian coordinate systems with axes $\mathcal{X}$, $\mathcal{Y}$ and $\mathcal{X}'$, $\mathcal{Y}'$ are given. Assume they have the same unit length, and a common origin, but with the $\mathcal{X}'$–$\mathcal{Y}'$ system rotated counterclockwise from the $\mathcal{X}$–$\mathcal{Y}$ system by an angle of measure θ. (See Figure 4.15.) We should like to derive some equations

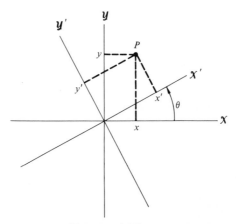

FIGURE 4.15

that relate the coordinates of the two systems. If the point P is considered as a position vector with respect to the common origin of the two systems, then we have

$$\mathbf{P} = x\mathbf{I} + y\mathbf{J} = x'\mathbf{I}' + y'\mathbf{J}',$$

where $\mathbf{I}$, $\mathbf{J}$, and $\mathbf{I}'$, $\mathbf{J}'$ are mutually perpendicular pairs of unit vectors, as shown in Figure 4.16. Since $\mathbf{I}'$ and $\mathbf{J}'$ are unit vectors, then by the definition of sine and cosine, we have

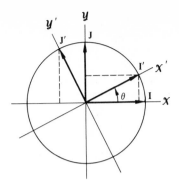

FIGURE 4.16

$$I' = \cos \theta \, I + \sin \theta \, J,$$

and

$$J' = -\sin \theta \, I + \cos \theta \, J.$$

Let us now substitute these values in the equation

$$xI + yJ = x'I' + y'J'$$

to obtain

$$xI + yJ = x'(\cos \theta \, I + \sin \theta \, J) + y'(-\sin \theta \, I + \cos \theta \, J).$$

If we express this equation in the form

$$\alpha I + \beta J = 0,$$

we have

$$(x' \cos \theta - y' \sin \theta - x)I + (x' \sin \theta + y' \cos \theta - y)J = 0.$$

Since I and J are linearly independent, and can thus be combined to equal 0 only if both scalars α and β are 0, we have

$$x' \cos \theta - y' \sin \theta - x = 0$$

and

$$x' \sin \theta + y' \cos \theta - y = 0.$$

We thus have the rotation-of-coordinates transformation equations.

4.3-1 Theorem: If (x', y') is the x'–y' coordinate of a point whose x–y coordinate is (x, y), where the x'–y' axes are rotated from the x–y axes by an angle of measure θ, then

$$x' \cos \theta - y' \sin \theta = x$$

and

$$x' \sin \theta + y' \cos \theta = y.$$

Let us write this in matrix and vector form as

$$\begin{bmatrix} \cos \theta & -\sin \theta \\ \sin \theta & \cos \theta \end{bmatrix} \begin{bmatrix} x' \\ y' \end{bmatrix} = \begin{bmatrix} x \\ y \end{bmatrix};$$

thus, multiplication by the matrix

$$T = \begin{bmatrix} \cos \theta & -\sin \theta \\ \sin \theta & \cos \theta \end{bmatrix}$$

can be viewed as a transformation that maps the x'–y' coordinate of a point P to its x–y coordinate. Note that the inverse of this matrix is its transpose:

$$T^{-1} = \begin{bmatrix} \cos \theta & \sin \theta \\ -\sin \theta & \cos \theta \end{bmatrix}.$$

Multiplication of this matrix transforms the x–y coordinate of a point to its x'–y' coordinate, thus

$$T^{-1} \begin{bmatrix} x \\ y \end{bmatrix} = \begin{bmatrix} \cos \theta & \sin \theta \\ -\sin \theta & \cos \theta \end{bmatrix} \begin{bmatrix} x \\ y \end{bmatrix} = \begin{bmatrix} x' \\ y' \end{bmatrix}.$$

In particular, we have then the equations

$$x \cos \theta + y \sin \theta = x',$$
$$-x \sin \theta + y \cos \theta = y',$$

which can be used to compute x' and y', if x, y, and θ are given. These equations can also be gotten simply either by solving the previous system for x' and y', or by a process similar to our derivation of Theorem 4.3-1. We summarize this as follows.

4.3-2   Theorem: If (x, y) is the x–y coordinate of a point whose x'–y' coordinate is (x', y'), where the x'–y' axes are rotated from the x–y axes by an angle θ, then

$$x \cos \theta + y \sin \theta = x',$$

and

$$-x \sin \theta + y \cos \theta = y'.$$

Some Trigonometric Formulas

Let us now use vector methods to derive some well-known trigonometric formulas. Let **A** be the unit vector

$$\mathbf{A} = \cos \alpha \, \mathbf{I} + \sin \alpha \, \mathbf{J},$$

and let **B** be the unit vector

$$\mathbf{B} = \cos \beta \, \mathbf{I} + \sin \beta \, \mathbf{J}.$$

(See Figure 4.17.)
Since

$$\mathbf{A} \cdot \mathbf{B} = |\mathbf{A}| \, |\mathbf{B}| \cos \theta,$$

where θ is the angle between **A** and **B**, and since $|\mathbf{A}| = |\mathbf{B}| = 1$, and $\theta = \beta - \alpha$, we have

$$\mathbf{A} \cdot \mathbf{B} = \cos \theta = \cos (\beta - \alpha) = \cos (\alpha - \beta) = \cos \alpha \cos \beta + \sin \alpha \sin \beta.$$

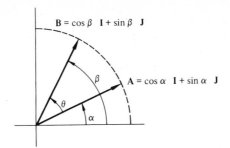

FIGURE 4.17

Using additional information about sine and cosine shifts by $\pi/2$, we have

$$\sin(\alpha - \beta) = \cos\left(\alpha - \beta - \frac{\pi}{2}\right) = \cos\left(\alpha - \left(\beta + \frac{\pi}{2}\right)\right)$$

$$= \cos\left(\beta + \frac{\pi}{2}\right)\cos\alpha + \sin\left(\beta + \frac{\pi}{2}\right)\sin\alpha$$

$$= -\sin\beta\cos\alpha + \cos\beta\sin\alpha,$$

from which

$$\sin(\alpha - \beta) = \sin\alpha\cos\beta - \cos\alpha\sin\beta.$$

Thus, we have

4.3-3   Theorem: If α and β are real numbers, then

$$\cos(\alpha - \beta) = \cos\alpha\cos\beta + \sin\alpha\sin\beta,$$

and

$$\sin(\alpha - \beta) = \sin\alpha\cos\beta - \cos\alpha\sin\beta.$$

EXERCISES 4.3

1. Find the x'–y' coordinate of the point whose x–y coordinate is given, where the x'–y' axes are rotated from x–y by an angle whose radian measure is $\pi/3$. Graph the axes and the point.
   a. (2, 5).   b. (3, −1).   c. (−2, −3).

2. Find the x'–y' coordinate of the point whose x–y coordinate is given, where the x'–y' axes are rotated from x–y by an angle of measure $2\pi/3$. Graph the axes and the point.
   a. (4, −1).   b. (−2, −3).   c. (−7, 3).

3. Find the x–y coordinate of the point whose x'–y' coordinate is given, where the x'–y' axes are rotated from x–y by an angle of $-(\pi/6)$. Graph the axes and the point.
   a. (−1, −3).   b. (4, 6).   c. (1, 7).

4. Find the x–y coordinate of the point whose x'–y' coordinate is given, where the axes are rotated by $\pi/4$. Graph.
   a. (3, 3).   b. (2, −4).   c. (7, 6).

5. Solve, by substitution, the equations in Theorem 4.3-1 for x' and y' to obtain the equations in Theorem 4.3-2.

6. Derive the equations in Theorem 4.3-2 by writing **I** and **J** as a linear combination of **I'** and **J'**, and then using a method analogous to the derivation of Theorem 4.3-1.

7. Show that

$$\cos(\alpha + \beta) = \cos \alpha \cos \beta - \sin \alpha \sin \beta,$$

and

$$\sin(\alpha + \beta) = \sin \alpha \cos \beta + \cos \alpha \sin \beta.$$

8. Show that $\sin 2\theta = 2 \sin \theta \cos \theta$, and $\cos 2\theta = \cos^2 \theta - \sin^2 \theta$.

4.4 GRAPHING CONICS USING ROTATION OF AXES

We are now prepared to determine the graph for any equation of the form

$$Ax^2 + By^2 + Cxy + Dx + Ey + F = 0$$

(called the *general equation of the second degree*). We have studied the special case in which $C = 0$. We will now show that if $C \neq 0$, then by a rotation of axes change of coordinates, we may obtain a transformed equation in which $C' = 0$. We may then simply proceed as before.

4.4-1 Theorem: If

$$Ax^2 + By^2 + Cxy + Dx + Ey + F = 0,$$

where $C \neq 0$ is the constraining equation for a set, then by any rotation of axes

$$x = x' \cos \theta - y' \sin \theta,$$
$$y = x' \sin \theta + y' \cos \theta,$$

where

$$\cot 2\theta = \frac{A - B}{C},$$

a new constraining equation will result, which is of the form

$$A'x'^2 + B'y'^2 + D'x' + E'y' + F' = 0.$$

PROOF. Substituting for x and y using the transformation equations gives

$$A(x' \cos \theta - y' \sin \theta)^2 + B(x' \sin \theta + y' \cos \theta)^2$$
$$+ C(x' \cos \theta - y' \sin \theta)(x' \sin \theta + y' \cos \theta)$$
$$+ D(x' \cos \theta - y' \sin \theta) + E(x' \sin \theta + y' \cos \theta) + F = 0.$$

By expanding and regrouping, we obtain an equation

$$A'x'^2 + B'y'^2 + C'x'y' + D'x' + E'y' + F' = 0,$$

where

$$C' = -2A \sin \theta \cos \theta + C(\cos^2 \theta - \sin^2 \theta) + 2B \sin \theta \cos \theta.$$

Using the identities $2 \sin \theta \cos \theta = \sin 2\theta$ and $\cos^2 \theta - \sin^2 \theta = \cos 2\theta$, we have

$$C' = C(\cos^2 \theta - \sin^2 \theta) + 2(B - A) \sin \theta \cos \theta$$
$$= C \cos 2\theta + (B - A) \sin 2\theta,$$

which is equal to zero provided that $C \cos 2\theta = (A - B) \sin 2\theta$, or equivalently

$$\cot 2\theta = \frac{A - B}{C}.$$

Example: Graph the equation

$$4x^2 + 11y^2 - 24xy + 72x - 116y + 204 = 0.$$

Using the result of the theorem, we know the xy term is eliminated by any rotation of axes by θ where

$$\cot 2\theta = \frac{4 - 11}{-24} = \frac{7}{24} = \frac{1}{\tan 2\theta}.$$

We may find such a θ as follows. Using the identity

$$\tan^2 \alpha + 1 = \sec^2 \alpha = \frac{1}{\cos^2 \alpha},$$

and solving for $\cos^2 \alpha$,

$$\cos^2 \alpha = \frac{1}{\tan^2 \alpha + 1},$$

we decide to select θ such that

$$\cos 2\theta = \frac{1}{\sqrt{(\frac{24}{7})^2 + 1}} = \frac{7}{25}.$$

Using the identities

$$\cos^2 \theta = \frac{1 + \cos 2\theta}{2} \quad \text{and} \quad \sin^2 \theta = \frac{1 - \cos 2\theta}{2},$$

we take

$$\cos \theta = \sqrt{\frac{1 + \frac{7}{25}}{2}} = \frac{4}{5} \quad \text{and} \quad \sin \theta = \sqrt{\frac{1 - \frac{7}{25}}{2}} = \frac{3}{5}.$$

(Is this the only selection of θ that will eliminate the xy term?) Let us now substitute for x and y according to the equations

$$x = \tfrac{4}{5}x' - \tfrac{3}{5}y' \quad \text{and} \quad y = \tfrac{3}{5}x' + \tfrac{4}{5}y',$$

thus getting

$$-5x'^2 + 20y'^2 - 12x' - 136y' + 204 = 0.$$

By completing squares and simplifying, we obtain

$$\frac{(y' - \frac{17}{5})^2}{1} - \frac{(x' + \frac{6}{5})^2}{4} = 1.$$

The translation $x'' = x' + \frac{6}{5}$, $y'' = y' - \frac{17}{5}$ will simplify this equation to

$$\frac{y''^2}{1} - \frac{x''^2}{4} = 1,$$

which is the hyperbola shown in Figure 4.18. Let us now graph this in the $\mathfrak{X}$–$\mathfrak{Y}$ system in view of the two transformations (a rotation and a translation) we used. (See Figure 4.19.)

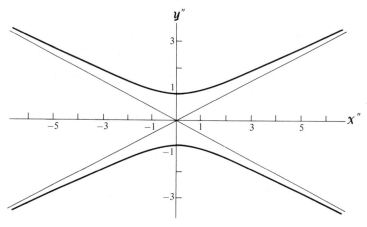

FIGURE 4.18

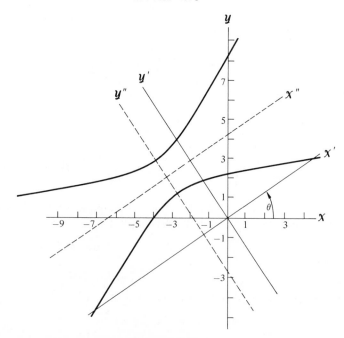

FIGURE 4.19

Example: Graph the equation $x^2 - 6xy + 9y^2 - 20\sqrt{10}x - 20 = 0$. We can eliminate the xy term by rotating axes by an angle θ, where

$$\cot 2\theta = \frac{1 - 9}{-6} = \frac{4}{3}.$$

To accomplish this, we need to know $\cos\theta$ and $\sin\theta$ so we can make the substitutions $x = x'\cos\theta - y'\sin\theta$ and $y = x'\sin\theta + y'\cos\theta$. It is also useful to know $\tan\theta$ for the purpose of drawing the graph. Consider a right triangle whose sides are in proper ratio so that $\cot 2\theta = \frac{4}{3}$, as shown in Figure 4.20. It is often desirable to use a right triangle with sides of

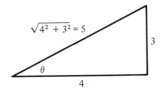

$$\sqrt{4^2 + 3^2} = 5$$

FIGURE 4.20

appropriate dimensions to compute relationships between trigonometric functions, rather than formally apply identities. From the figure, we see that $\cos 2\theta = \frac{4}{5}$, hence we take

$$\cos\theta = \sqrt{\frac{1 + \frac{4}{5}}{2}} = \frac{3}{\sqrt{10}} \quad \text{and} \quad \sin\theta = \sqrt{\frac{1 - \frac{4}{5}}{2}} = \frac{1}{\sqrt{10}}.$$

We also note that $\tan\theta = \frac{1}{3}$. We now substitute the values

$$x = x'\frac{3}{\sqrt{10}} - y'\frac{1}{\sqrt{10}} \quad \text{and} \quad y = x'\frac{1}{\sqrt{10}} + y'\frac{3}{\sqrt{10}}$$

throughout the equation for the curve. After appropriate computation and regrouping, we have

$$y' + 2y' - 6x' - 2 = 0.$$

Upon completing squares and so forth, we obtain

$$(y' + 1)^2 = 6(x' + \tfrac{1}{2}),$$

which can be translated to an equation of the form

$$y''^2 = 6x''.$$

We thus have the parabola shown in Figure 4.21.

A Characterizing Matrix

It is interesting to notice a particular invariant property, under translation and rotation of coordinates, of the second-degree expression used to deter-

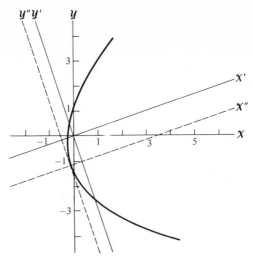

FIGURE 4.21

mine a conic section. If we write the three second-degree terms of the general quadratic equation in the form $Ax^2 + \frac{C}{2}xy + \frac{C}{2}xy + By^2$, or perhaps

$$Ax^2 + \frac{C}{2}xy$$

$$+\frac{C}{2}xy + By^2,$$

then we are reminded of the two by two matrix

$$\begin{bmatrix} A & C/2 \\ C/2 & B \end{bmatrix}.$$

This matrix turns out to be of considerable importance with regard to translation and rotation of axes. For example, if $C = 0$, the matrix is called a *diagonal matrix*, in which case no rotation is required to change the equation to standard form. For the present, let us concentrate on the determinant of this matrix. If one changes coordinates, either by a rotation or translation, this determinant,

$$\begin{vmatrix} A & C/2 \\ C/2 & B \end{vmatrix} = AB - \frac{C^2}{4},$$

remains unchanged. More precisely, we have the following theorem.

4.4-2   Theorem: If x and y are replaced in the expression

$$Ax^2 + By^2 + Cxy + Dx + Ey + F,$$

according to the translation-of-coordinates formulas, $x = x' + a$ and $y = y' + b$, or the rotation-of-coordinates formulas $x = x' \cos \theta -$

$y' \sin \theta$ and $y = x' \sin \theta + y' \cos \theta$, and there results the expression

$$A'x'^2 + B'y'^2 + C'x'y' + D'x' + E'y' + F',$$

then

$$\begin{vmatrix} A & C/2 \\ C/2 & B \end{vmatrix} = \begin{vmatrix} A' & C'/2 \\ C'/2 & B' \end{vmatrix}.$$

PROOF: (Translation) Left for the reader. (Rotation) Substitute the rotation formulas in the first expression to obtain

$$A(x' \cos \theta - y' \sin \theta)^2 + B(x' \sin \theta + y' \cos \theta)^2$$
$$+ C(x' \cos \theta - y' \sin \theta)(x' \sin \theta + y' \cos \theta)$$
$$+ D(x' \cos \theta - y' \sin \theta) + E(x' \sin \theta + y' \cos \theta) + F.$$

First, notice that the values of A', B', and C' are unaffected by D, E, and F. We have then

$$A' = A \cos^2 \theta + B \sin^2 \theta + C \cos \theta \sin \theta,$$
$$B' = A \sin^2 \theta + B \cos^2 \theta - C \sin \theta \cos \theta,$$

and

$$C' = 2(B - A) \cos \theta \sin \theta + C(\cos^2 \theta - \sin^2 \theta).$$

After considerable computation, we have

$$A'B' - \frac{C'^2}{4} = \left(AB - \frac{C^2}{4} \right)(\cos^2 \theta + \sin^2 \theta)^2 = AB - \frac{C^2}{4},$$

thus establishing the desired result.

It is now easy to use this result to predict in advance whether an equation will determine an ellipse, a parabola, or a hyperbola.

4.4-3 Theorem: The equation

$$Ax^2 + By^2 + Cxy + Dx + Ey + F = 0$$

will determine an ellipse, a parabola, or a hyperbola, according to whether

$$\begin{vmatrix} A & C/2 \\ C/2 & B \end{vmatrix}$$

is positive, zero, or negative, respectively.

PROOF: Since this determinant is unchanged by translations and rotations, we can restrict our attention to equations in the standard form with center at O and with axis $\mathfrak{X}$ or $\mathfrak{Y}$. We have the following possible forms (taking $a > 0$ and $b > 0$):

1. $ax^2 + by^2 = 1$ (ellipses and circles)

$$\begin{vmatrix} a & 0 \\ 0 & b \end{vmatrix} = ab > 0.$$

2. $ax^2 + py = 0$, or $by^2 + px = 0$ (parabolas)

$$\begin{vmatrix} a & 0 \\ 0 & 0 \end{vmatrix} = \begin{vmatrix} 0 & 0 \\ 0 & b \end{vmatrix} = 0.$$

3. $ax^2 - by^2 = 1$, or $-ax^2 + by^2 = 1$ (hyperbolas)

$$\begin{vmatrix} a & 0 \\ 0 & -b \end{vmatrix} = \begin{vmatrix} -a & 0 \\ 0 & b \end{vmatrix} = -ab < 0.$$

We close this section with the following remark.

Remark: Using matrix multiplication, any equation

$$Ax^2 + Cxy + By^2 + Dx + Ey = -F$$

can be written

$$[x \ \ y]\begin{bmatrix} A & C/2 \\ C/2 & B \end{bmatrix}\begin{bmatrix} x \\ y \end{bmatrix} + [D \ \ E]\begin{bmatrix} x \\ y \end{bmatrix} = -F.$$

EXERCISES 4.4

1. Graph:
   a. $31x^2 + 21y^2 + 10\sqrt{3}xy - 144 = 0$.
   b. $23x^2 - 3y^2 + 26\sqrt{3}xy - 144 = 0$.
   c. $x^2 + 3y^2 - 2\sqrt{3}xy - 4 = 0$.
   d. $x^2 + y^2 - 2xy - 4\sqrt{2} = 0$.
   e. $41x^2 + 24xy + 34y^2 + 25x + 50y - 25 = 0$.
   f. $-4x^2 + 6xy + 4y^2 - 8\sqrt{10}x + 6\sqrt{10}y - 45 = 0$.
   g. $3x^2 - 8xy - 3y^2 - 2\sqrt{5} - 4\sqrt{5}y = 0$.
   h. $4x^2 + 4xy + y^2 + 4\sqrt{5}x + 2\sqrt{5}y + 5 = 0$.
   i. $9x^2 - 24xy + 16y^2 - 3x + 4y - 6 = 0$.
   j. $x^2 + 24xy - 6y^2 + 4x + 48y + 35 = 0$.
   k. $73x^2 + 72xy + 52y^2 - 218x - 176y + 97 = 0$.
   l. $6x^2 + 13xy + 6y^2 - 7x - 8y + 2 = 0$.
   m. $2x^2 + 4xy + 4y^2 + 2x + 3 = 0$.

2. Show that $x^2 + y^2 = r^2$ is unaltered by rotation.

3. a. Show that the lines $x + y = 3$ and $x - y = 1$ are perpendicular.
   b. What translation of axes will translate the origin to the intersection of these two lines?
   c. Find an angle through which the axes in Exercise 3b may be rotated to make them coincide with the given lines.

4. Show that $A + B$ is invariant under translations and rotations in the expression $Ax^2 + By^2 + Cxy + Dx + Dy + F$.

5. Complete the details of the proof of Theorem 4.4-2.

6. Without graphing, decide whether the equation determines an ellipse, a parabola, or a hyperbola. Write the equation in matrix notation according to the remark at the close of this section.
   a. $2x^2 + 4xy + 5y^2 - 2x - 5y - 19 = 0$.

b. $x^2 + 4xy + 3y^2 - 2x - 3y - 21 = 0$.
c. $4x^2 + 4xy + y^2 + 8x - 6y = 1$.
d. $144x^2 - 120xy + 25y^2 - 29x - 27 = 1$.
e. $2x^2 - xy = 6x + 2y - y^2 - 7$.
f. $2xy = 3y^2 - 5x^2 - 9x + 7y$.

7. For what values of B does the equation

$$12x^2 + 36xy + By^2 + 6x + 6y + 3 = 0$$

represent an ellipse?

4.5 CARTESIAN COORDINATES AND THREE SPACE

The physical space in which we live is perceived by us to have three dimensions, which we commonly denote by names such as length, width, and height. It is useful to establish correspondences between sets of ordered triples of real numbers and points in this three-dimensional space. We shall now discuss the most common of three common methods of establishing such a correspondence.

Cartesian Coordinates

A Cartesian coordinatization of three-dimensional space is established as follows. First select a plane in the space and assume that a Cartesian coordinatization has been given for this plane (called the *x–y plane*). There exists a unique line Z in space perpendicular to this plane that passes through the origin of the selected plane coordinate system (see Figure 4.22).

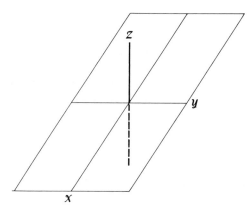

FIGURE 4.22

On this third axis (the line Z, called the *z*-axis), select a coordinatization with the same unit length as that used on the other axes, and with 0 at the point of intersection with the *x-y* plane. We have, then, three mutually perpendicular lines $\mathfrak{X}$, $\mathcal{Y}$, and $\mathcal{Z}$, called respectively the *x*-axis, the *y*-axis, and the *z*-axis. Each axis has a rigid coordinatization and they meet at a common point O called the *origin*. The zero on each line is at this origin, and all three lines have the same unit length. A variety of types of systems can occur, depending on the relative directions chosen to be the positive and negative directions on the axes. If the positive *x*-axis is rotated through an angle of $\pi/2$ into the positive *y*-axis, then we have a *right-handed* system if the positive *z*-axis is in the direction of the right thumb when one rotates his palm from the *x*-axis to the *y*-axis. Otherwise we have a *left-handed* system. Figure 4.23 shows a right-handed system, the type we shall use.

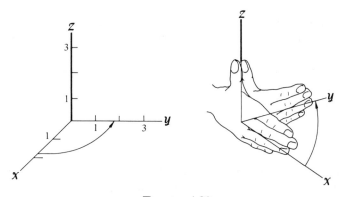

FIGURE 4.23

Remark: In discussing three space, we must assume certain knowledge about planes and lines in *space* analogous to the knowledge one has about lines in the Euclidean plane from the study of Euclidean geometry.

Each point P in space is associated with an ordered triple of real numbers (x, y, z) as follows. For a point P, there exists a unique line through P that is perpendicular to the selected *x–y* plane. This line pierces the plane at a point with planar coordinate (x, y). There exists a unique plane containing P that is parallel to the *x–y* plane (that is, that does not intersect the *x–y* plane). This plane intersects the *z*-axis at the number z. We then designate the coordinate of P to be the ordered triple (x, y, z). (See Figure 4.24.)

Coordinate Planes and Octants

With this coordinate system it is possible to consider graphs (sets of points) associated with sets of ordered triples. Let us consider a few very simple sets of ordered triples. Consider the set $\mathcal{P}$ of triples described by

$$\mathcal{P} = \{(x, y, z) : z = c\} \subset \mathbf{R} \times \mathbf{R} \times \mathbf{R}.$$

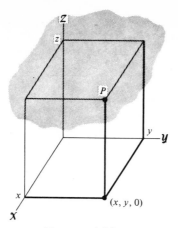

FIGURE 4.24

The graph of this set is the plane parallel to the x–y plane at height c above the x–y plane. Note in particular that

$$\{(x, y, z) : z = 0\}$$

describes the x–y *plane*. Similarly,

$$\{(x, y, z) : y = c\}$$

describes a plane that contains the axes $\mathfrak{X}$ and Z if $c = 0$, and otherwise does not intersect them. We call the set

$$\{(x, y, z) : y = 0\}$$

the x–z *plane*, and the set

$$\{(x, y, z) : x = 0\}$$

the y–z *plane*. The three planes, the x–y plane, the y–z plane, and the x–z plane are called *coordinate planes*.

In a way analogous to the assignment of quadrants in the plane, we assign octants to space.

4.5-1   **Definition:** A point in space with coordinate (x, y, z) is said to be in *octant*

I if $x > 0, y > 0, z > 0$;
II if $x < 0, y > 0, z > 0$;
III if $x < 0, y < 0, z > 0$;
IV if $x > 0, y < 0, z > 0$;
V if $x > 0, y > 0, z < 0$;
VI if $x < 0, y > 0, z < 0$;
VII if $x < 0, y < 0, z < 0$;
VIII if $x > 0, y < 0, z < 0$.

These octants are separated by the three coordinate planes $x = 0$, $y = 0$, and $z = 0$. (See Figure 4.25.)

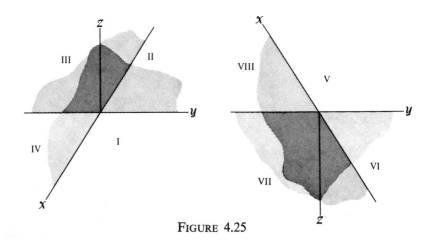

FIGURE 4.25

Remark: A point P with coordinate (a, b, c) can be viewed as the intersection of the three planes $x = a$, $y = b$, and $z = c$. (See Figure 4.26.)

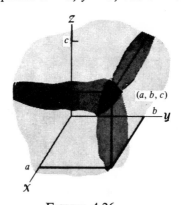

FIGURE 4.26

Distances

We can use a Cartesian coordinatization to assign distances in space in a manner analogous to the way we did for the plane. Consider two points P and Q in space, with coordinates (a, b, c) and (x, y, z). The square of the distance between these points can be derived using the Pythagorean theorem, and the rectangular box shown in Figure 4.27. The distance from P to Q is given

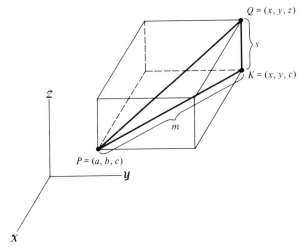

FIGURE 4.27

by $m^2 + s^2$, where m is the distance from P to K, and s is the distance from K to Q. However,

$$m^2 = (x - a)^2 + (y - b)^2 \qquad \text{and} \qquad s^2 = (z - c)^2.$$

(Explain!) Hence,

$$m^2 + s^2 = (x - z)^2 + (y - b)^2 + (z - c)^2.$$

4.5-2   **Definition:** If P and Q are points in space with Cartesian coordinates (a, b, c) and (x, y, z), then the distance from P to Q, $d(P, Q)$, is given by

$$d(P, Q) = \sqrt{(x - a)^2 + (y - b)^2 + (z - c)^2}.$$

Example:

$$d((1, 3, 4), (-2, 7, 1)) = \sqrt{(-3)^2 + 4^2 + (-3)^2}$$
$$= \sqrt{9 + 16 + 9} = \sqrt{34}.$$

Example: Since a sphere is defined as a set of points in space all of which are the same distance from some center point, it follows that

$$\{(x, y, z) : (x - a)^2 + (y - b)^2 + (z - c)^2 = r^2\}$$

graphs as a sphere of radius r with center at the point with coordinate (a, b, c).

Example: The graph of the set $\mathcal{K} = \{(x, y, z) : x^2 + y^2 = 1\}$ is the circular cylinder with $\mathbb{Z}$ as the axis of symmetry (see Figure 4.27(b)).

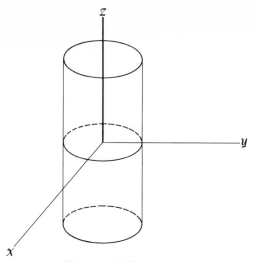

FIGURE 4.27b

Graphing Techniques

One graphing technique for graphing sets of ordered triples in Cartesian coordinates is to *cut* the figure with some planes parallel to one or more of the three coordinate planes. For example, let us graph the set

$$\mathcal{E} = \{(x, y, z) : 4x^2 + 9y^2 + z^2 = 36\} \, .$$

If we set $z = 0$ in the equation $4x^2 + 9y^2 + z^2 = 36$, we obtain

$$4x^2 + 9y^2 = 36 \, ,$$

or equivalently

$$\frac{x^2}{9} + \frac{y^2}{4} = 1 \, ,$$

which is an equation for an ellipse with vertices at $(\pm 3, 0)$ and $(0, \pm 2)$. When we set $z = 0$ in the equation, we add the constraint $z = 0$; that is, we are asking what kind of a plane figure will be traced out in the plane $z = 0$ by the given spacial figure. We see in this case that we have an ellipse. Further, let us cut the figure $4x^2 + 9y^2 + z^2 = 36$ by a plane parallel to the $z = 0$ plane but slightly above. Let us set $z = 3$. Hence, we obtain the equation

$$4x^2 + 9y^2 = 27 \, ,$$

which also describes an ellipse, but one of smaller dimensions. Let us also cut the figure by the plane $z = 5$. This gives an equation of an ellipse,

$$4x^2 + 9y^2 = 11 \, .$$

Let us graph these three figures, indicating the planes in which they appear (see Figure 4.28). We see, then, that by cutting the figure with increasingly

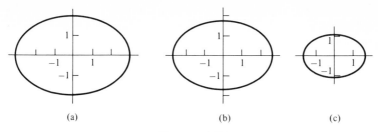

(a)   (b)   (c)

FIGURE 4.28

higher planes (above the x–y plane), we obtain ellipses that are smaller. If $z = 6$, we have only the point $(0, 0)$. If $z > 6$, we do not cut the figure at all. (See Figure 4.29.) We complete our knowledge of this figure (called an

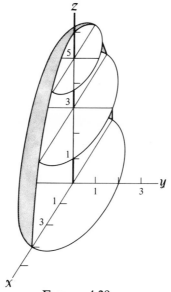

FIGURE 4.29

ellipsoid) by noting that (x, y, z) satisfies the equation iff $(x, y, -z)$ does. That is, we have symmetry through the x–y plane.

Example: Graph the equation $x^2 + z^2 = y$ in Cartesian coordinates.
Solution: Let us first cut this figure with various planes $y = c$. Clearly, if if $y < 0$, no point (x, y, z) satisfies the equation. Thus, no plane $y = c$, where $c < 0$, intersects the figure. If we set $y = 9$ (cut the figure with the plane $y = 9$), we have

$$x^2 + z^2 = 9.$$

Thus, in this case, we have a circle of radius 3. In fact, if we cut the figure with planes $x = c$ as c grows larger, we simply obtain larger and larger circles. (See Figure 4.30.)

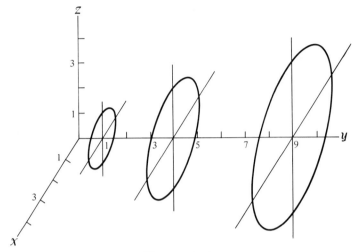

FIGURE 4.30

We gain more information by cutting the figure with some planes parallel to the x–y plane. For example, let us cut by the planes $z = 0$, $z = 1$, and $z = 2$. We obtain respectively the three equations

$$y = x^2, \qquad y - 1 = x^2, \qquad \text{and} \qquad y - 4 = x^2,$$

which are equations of parabolas. (See Figure 4.31.)

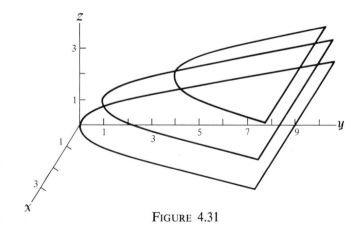

FIGURE 4.31

Thus, the graph of $x^2 + z^2 = y$ is the *circular paraboloid* shown in Figure 4.32.

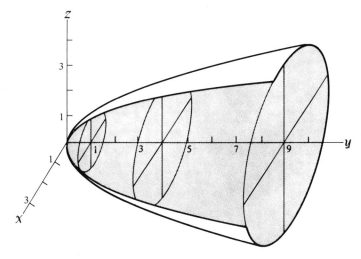

FIGURE 4.32

Example: The graph of the set $\mathcal{B} = \{(x, y, z) : x = y = z\}$ is a line through $(0, 0, 0)$, as shown in Figure 4.33. Notice that $\mathcal{B}$ is the set of all scalar multiples of the coordinate vector $(1, 1, 1)$ ($\mathcal{B} = \alpha(1, 1, 1) : \alpha \in \mathbf{R}\}$). Note that $\mathcal{B} \in \mathcal{V}$, where

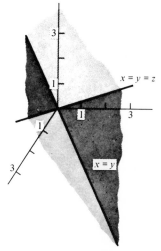

FIGURE 4.33

$$\mathcal{V} = \{(x, y, z) : x = y\},$$

which is a vertical plane. Any plane parallel to the x–y plane cuts $\mathcal{V}$, leaving the line $x = y$ in that plane.

Graphing Functions

It is common to consider the graphs of functions and relations from $\mathbf{R} \times \mathbf{R}$ to $\mathbf{R}$ or from $\mathbf{R}$ to $\mathbf{R} \times \mathbf{R}$ as subsets of three-dimensional space. For example, if $f : \mathbf{R} \to \mathbf{R} \times \mathbf{R}$, we call f a *vector-valued* function. This function associates with each domain value $x \in \mathbf{R}$, a vector value $f(x) = (y, z)$ in $\mathbf{R} \times \mathbf{R}$. By identifying each ordered pair $(x, (y, z))$ in f with an ordered triple (x, y, z) in $\mathbf{R}^3$, we may form a graph of f.

Example: The parametric equations of the unit circle in the plane

$$x = \cos t, \qquad y = \sin t$$

may be viewed as defining a function $f : \mathbf{R} \to \mathbf{R} \times \mathbf{R}$, where for each preimage $t \in \mathbf{R}$, the value image $f(t)$ is the coordinate vector $(x, y) = (\cos t, \sin t)$. The set of ordered triples

$$f = \{(t, x, y) : x = \cos t, y = \sin t\} = \{(t, \cos t, \sin t) : t \in \mathbf{R}\}$$

is a spiral in three-dimensional space as shown in Figure 4.34. (We have made some convenient axis changes to correspond with the usual unit circle in the x–y plane.)

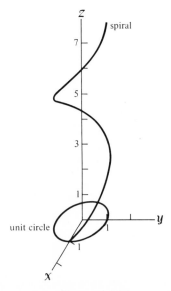

FIGURE 4.34

Remark: Notice how the elimination of the parameter t may be viewed as a projection of this spiral in space to a circle in the x–y plane.

On the other hand, if f is a function from $\mathbf{R} \times \mathbf{R}$ to $\mathbf{R}$, we call f a function of two variables. With each domain vector (x, y) is associated a value $z = f((x, y))$, usually denoted simply by $f(x, y)$. Again, the pairs $((x, y), f(x, y))$ may be viewed as triples (x, y, z) and graphed in three-dimensional space.

Example: Suppose $f : \mathbf{R} \times \mathbf{R} \to \mathbf{R}$ is described by $f(x, y) = x^2 + y^2$. Then the graph of f is the set of points associated with

$$\{(x, y, z) : z = x^2 + y^2\},$$

which is the paraboloid shown in Figure 4.35.

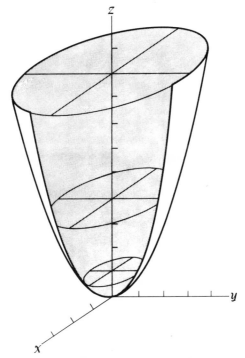

FIGURE 4.35

We shall not consider graphs of functions and relations in $\mathbf{R}^3$ at greater length here, but shall consider these matters in more detail in the next chapter.

EXERCISES 4.5

1. Draw a left-handed Cartesian coordinate system for space.

2. Decide which octant or which coordinate plane each point lies in.

a. $(1, 2, -7)$.   b. $(-1, -2, 4)$.
c. $(0, 1, 3)$.   d. $(2, -1, -6)$.
e. $(-1, -4, -7)$.   f. $(2, 4, 1)$.
g. $(-4, 2, 3)$.   h. $(3, -4, 5)$.

3. Compute the distance between the given pairs of points.
   a. $(2, 1, -4)$, $(-6, -4, 3)$.   b. $(1, 5, 7)$, $(0, 4, 2)$.
   c. $(0, 0, 0)$, $(-3, 4, 1)$.   d. $(-1, 0, 2)$, $(3, 1, 0)$.

4. Show that distances in space satisfy the following conditions: (a) $d(A, B) \geqslant 0$; (b) $d(A, B) = d(B, A)$; (c) $d(A, B) + d(B, C) \geqslant d(A, C)$.

5. Graph or describe the graph of the following sets of Cartesian coordinates.
   a. $\{(x, y, z) : y = 0\}$.   b. $\{(x, y, z) : z = y\}$.
   c. $\{(x, y, z) : x \leqslant 2\}$.   d. $\{(x, y, z) : x^2 + y^2 = 4\}$.
   e. $\{(x, y, z) : z = 2x - 3y - 5\}$.   f. $\{(x, y, z) : x^2 + y^2 + z^2 = 9\}$.

6. By making some well-selected planar cuts, graph the following sets of Cartesian coordinates.
   a. $y = 4x^2 + 9z^2$ (elliptic paraboloid).
   b. $9x^2 + 16y^2 + 25z^2 = 1$ (ellipsoid).

   c. $\dfrac{x^2}{16} + \dfrac{y^2}{9} - \dfrac{z^2}{4} = 1$ (hyperboloid of one sheet).

   d. $\dfrac{x^2}{16} - \dfrac{y^2}{9} - \dfrac{z^2}{4} = 1$ (hyperboloid of two sheets).

   e. $x^2 - 2y^2 = 3z$ (hyperbolic paraboloid).

7. Graph the following functions of two variables.
   a. $f(x, y) = x^2 + y$.   b. $f((x, y) = x^2 - y^2$.
   c. $f(x, y) = 2x^2 + 1$.

8. Graph in the first octant. (HINT: Make cuts with the three coordinate planes.)
   a. $4x^2 + 4y^2 + 16z^2 = 16$.   b. $4x^2 - 4y^2 + z^2 = 4$.
   ^{t} c. $-x^2 - y^2 + 4z^2 = 4$.   d. $9x^2 - 4y^2 - 36z^2 = 36$.

9. Graph the following vector-valued functions.
   a. $f(t) = (4 \cos t, 4 \sin t)$.   b. $f(t) = (0, t^2)$.
   c. $f(t) = (t^2, t^2)$.   d. $f(t) = (2t, 3t)$.

10. The *projection* of a set $S \subset \mathbf{R} \times \mathbf{R} \times \mathbf{R}$ onto the x–y plane is the set $\{(x, y, 0) : (x, y, z) \in S\}$. Graph each of the following sets and its projection onto the x–y plane.
    a. $\{(x, y, z) : x^2 + y^2 + z^2 = 1\}$.   b. $\{(x, y, z) : x = y^2 + z^2\}$.
    c. $\{(x, y, z) : x - y = z^2\}$.

4.6 SPHERICAL AND CYLINDRICAL COORDINATES

We devote the present section to a discussion of two other coordinatizations of three-dimensional space that have proved useful in applying mathematics to scientific fields.

Spherical Coordinates

Each point in three-dimensional space can be located by a method similar to that used in astronomy. We can give the angular bearings to the point measured from certain reference lines, together with the distance to the point.

Suppose a Cartesian coordinate system has been established, and consider a point P with Cartesian coordinate (x, y, z). Let ρ be the length of the line segment $\mathcal{S}$ connecting the origin O and the point P ($\rho = \sqrt{x^2 + y^2 + z^2}$). (See Figure 4.36.)

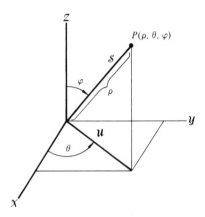

FIGURE 4.36

Let θ be the measure of the angle from the x-axis to the projection $\mathcal{U}$ of $\mathcal{S}$ onto the x–y plane ($\mathcal{U} = \{(x, y, 0) : (x, y, z) \in \mathcal{S}\}$), and let φ measure the angle from the z-axis to $\mathcal{S}$. The ordered triple (ρ, θ, φ) is called a *spherical coordinate* of P. Notice that the segment $\mathcal{U}$ has length $\rho \sin \varphi$ and so the spherical coordinates of a point P are related to the Cartesian coordinates by the equations

$$z = \rho \cos \varphi;$$
$$x = (\rho \sin \varphi) \cos \theta;$$
$$y = (\rho \sin \varphi) \sin \theta.$$

(Do you agree?)

4.6-1 Definition: If a point P in space has Cartesian coordinate (x, y, z), then any triple (ρ, θ, φ) such that

$$x = \rho \sin \varphi \cos \theta$$
$$y = \rho \sin \varphi \sin \theta,$$

and

$$z = \rho \cos \varphi$$

is called a *spherical coordinate* of P. The point with coordinate (0, 0, 0) is called the *pole*.

Remark: As in the case for polar coordinates in the plane, the spherical coordinatization described above does not establish a 1–1 correspondence between points in three-dimensional space and the ordered triples in $\mathbf{R}^3$. Thus, for example, the point with coordinate $(4, \pi/3, \pi/6)$ also has coordinates $(4, \pi/3 + \pi, -\pi/6)$ and $(-4, \pi/3, -\pi + \pi/6)$ among others.

We can describe sets of points in space by constraining equations in terms of the spherical coordinates of the points.

Example: The graph of the relation described in terms of spherical coordinates by $\{(\rho, \theta, \varphi) : \rho = 4\}$ is simply a sphere with center at the pole and radius 4. (See Figure 4.37.)

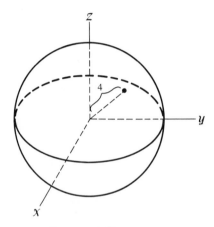

FIGURE 4.37

Example: The set of points described by the spherical constraint $\varphi = \pi/4$, $\rho \geqslant 0$, is the conical surface shown in Figure 4.38.

Cylindrical Coordinates

A cylindrical coordinate system is closely associated with a polar coordinatization of the x–y plane. We establish a reference Cartesian coordinatization of space and a polar coordinatization of the x–y plane. A point P is then located by a triple (r, θ, z), where z is the third component of the Cartesian coordinate (x, y, z), and (r, θ) is a polar coordinate of the projection of P on the x–y plane. (See Figure 4.39.)

4.6-2 Definition: If a point P has Cartesian coordinate (x, y, z), then any triple (r, θ, z) such that

$$x = r \cos \theta,$$
$$y = r \sin \theta,$$

and

$$z = z$$

is called a *cylindrical coordinate* of *P*.

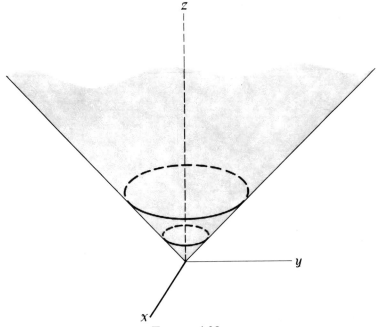

FIGURE 4.38

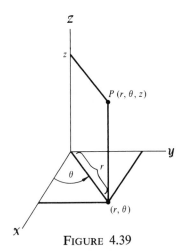

FIGURE 4.39

Note that a point having coordinate (r, θ, z) also has coordinates $(r, \theta + 2\pi, z)$ and $(-r, \theta + \pi, z)$, among others.

As in the cases of Cartesian coordinates and spherical coordinates, we may be interested in graphing various sets of ordered triples of real numbers in terms of cylindrical coordinates.

Example: The set $\{(r, \theta, z) : r = 2\}$ is a cylinder, as shown in Figure 4.40.

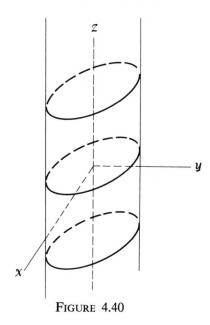

FIGURE 4.40

Example: The set $\{(r, \theta, z) : z = r^2,\ 0 < \theta < \pi/2\}$ has as its graph in cylindrical coordinates the surface shown in Figure 4.41.

EXERCISES 4.6

1. Locate in space and determine the Cartesian coordinate of the point with a spherical coordinate as given.

   a. $\left(3, \dfrac{\pi}{6}, \dfrac{\pi}{3}\right)$.   b. $\left(-4, \dfrac{\pi}{4}, 0\right)$.

   c. $\left(2, \dfrac{-\pi}{3}, \dfrac{-\pi}{2}\right)$.   d. $\left(-2, \dfrac{\pi}{3}, \dfrac{-\pi}{4}\right)$.

2. Locate in space and determine the Cartesian coordinate of the point with a cyclindrical coordinate as given.

   a. $\left(3, \dfrac{\pi}{6}, 2\right)$.   b. $\left(4, \dfrac{\pi}{2}, 1\right)$.

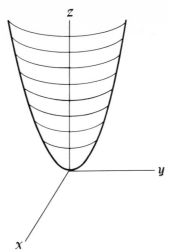

FIGURE 4.41

c. $\left(-4, \dfrac{\pi}{4}, -1\right)$.   d. $\left(2, \dfrac{-\pi}{3}, 3\right)$.

3. Graph the following in spherical coordinates.
   a. $\{(\rho, \theta, \varphi) : \theta = \pi/2\}$.   b. $\{(\rho, \theta, \varphi) : \varphi = \pi/4\}$.
   c. $\{(\rho, \theta, \varphi) : \theta = \varphi = \rho\}$.   d. $\{(\rho, \theta, \varphi) : \rho = -2\}$.
   e. $\{(\rho, \theta, \varphi) : \rho = \theta\}$.

4. Graph the following in cylindrical coordinates.
   a. $\{(r, \theta, z) : z = 2\}$.   b. $\{(r, \theta, z) : r = \theta\}$.
   c. $\{(r, \theta, z) : r = -z\}$.   d. $\{(r, \theta, z) : \theta = \pi/4\}$.
   e. $\{(r, \theta, z) : z = \theta, r = 1\}$.

5. Find a cylindrical coordinate of each of the following points given in Cartesian coordinates. (Use the Tan^{-1} function).
   a. $(3, 4, 5)$.   b. $(-3, 4, -1)$.
   c. $(12, 5, -6)$.   d. $(-5, -12, -3)$.

6. Find a spherical coordinate of each of the following points given in Cartesian coordinates.
   a. $(\sqrt{3}/2, 3/2, 1)$.   b. $(2, 2, 3)$.
   c. $(2\sqrt{3}, 2, 4)$.   d. $(3, \sqrt{3}, 6)$.

7. Write an equation in spherical coordinates for each of the following surfaces given in Cartesian coordinates.
   a. $x^2 + y^2 + z^2 = 9$.   b. $x^2 + y^2 = 1$.
   c. $x^2 + y^2 - z^2 = 4$.

8. Each of the following equations represents a surface given in cylindrical coordinates. Find the equation of that surface in Cartesian coordinates and sketch the surface.

   a. $r^2 = 1$.   b. $r^2 + z^2 = 4$.
   c. $r^2 = 4z$.   d. $r^2 - z^2 = 9$.

9. Find an equation in cylindrical coordinates of the surface generated by revolving the parabola $y^2 = 9z$ about the z-axis.

10. The equation of a surface in cylindrical coordinates is $r = 4 \sin \theta$. Find an equation of this surface in spherical coordinates.

4.7 SOLVING THREE EQUATIONS IN THREE UNKNOWNS BY ELIMINATION USING AN AUGMENTED MATRIX

Solutions of an Equation as Points in Space

We wish now to consider equations that have as solutions points in the vector space $\mathbf{R}^3$. For example, consider the equation

$$2x + 3y + z = 0.$$

A solution would consist of three components. That is, we need three numbers a, b, c (ordered properly) so that

$$2a + 3b + c = 0.$$

The best way to indicate this fact is to consider the three-tuple (vector in $\mathbf{R} \times \mathbf{R} \times \mathbf{R} = \mathbf{R}^3$)

$$\begin{bmatrix} a \\ b \\ c \end{bmatrix}$$

to be a solution. The solution set for the equation $2x + 3y + z = 0$ then is the set

$$\left\{ \begin{bmatrix} x \\ y \\ z \end{bmatrix} : 2x + 3y + z = 0 \right\}.$$

Some of many elements of this set are

$$\begin{bmatrix} 0 \\ 0 \\ 0 \end{bmatrix}, \begin{bmatrix} 1 \\ 0 \\ -2 \end{bmatrix}, \begin{bmatrix} 1 \\ 1 \\ -5 \end{bmatrix}.$$

In general, an equation

$$\alpha x + \beta y + \gamma z = 0$$

(called a *linear equation in three variables*) has many solutions that can be viewed as points in the vector space $\langle \mathbf{R}^3, \mathbf{R} \rangle$. Let us prove the following interesting theorem about solutions of such an equation.

4.7-1 Theorem: If

$$\begin{bmatrix} a \\ b \\ c \end{bmatrix} \quad \text{and} \quad \begin{bmatrix} a' \\ b' \\ c' \end{bmatrix}$$

are solutions for the linear equation

$$\alpha x + \beta y + \gamma z = 0,$$

then for any scalars (real numbers) p, and q,

$$p \begin{bmatrix} a \\ b \\ c \end{bmatrix} + q \begin{bmatrix} a' \\ b' \\ c' \end{bmatrix}$$

is also a solution.

PROOF:

$$p \begin{bmatrix} a \\ b \\ c \end{bmatrix} + q \begin{bmatrix} a' \\ b' \\ c' \end{bmatrix} = \begin{bmatrix} pa \\ pb \\ pc \end{bmatrix} + \begin{bmatrix} qa' \\ qb' \\ qc' \end{bmatrix} = \begin{bmatrix} pa + qa' \\ pb + qb' \\ pc + qc' \end{bmatrix}.$$

Now,

$$\alpha(pa + qa') + \beta(pb + qb') + \gamma(pc + qc')$$
$$= \alpha pa + \alpha qa' + \beta pb + \beta qb' + \gamma pc + \gamma qc'$$
$$= \alpha pa + \beta pb + \gamma pc + \alpha qa' + \beta qb' + \gamma qc'$$
$$= p(\alpha a + \beta b + \gamma c) + q(\alpha a' + \beta b' + \gamma c')$$
$$= p(0) + q(0) = 0$$

since

$$\begin{bmatrix} a \\ b \\ c \end{bmatrix} \quad \text{and} \quad \begin{bmatrix} a' \\ b' \\ c' \end{bmatrix}$$

are solutions to the equation

$$\alpha x + \beta y + \gamma z = 0.$$

Example: Consider the equation $x + 2y + 2z = 0$. The point (vector in $\mathbf{R}^3$)

$$\begin{bmatrix} 2 \\ 1 \\ -2 \end{bmatrix}$$

is a solution and hence

$$3 \begin{bmatrix} 2 \\ 1 \\ -2 \end{bmatrix} = \begin{bmatrix} 6 \\ 3 \\ -6 \end{bmatrix}$$

is also a solution. Further,

$$\begin{bmatrix} 2 \\ 1 \\ -2 \end{bmatrix} + \begin{bmatrix} 6 \\ 3 \\ -6 \end{bmatrix} = \begin{bmatrix} 8 \\ 4 \\ -8 \end{bmatrix}$$

is a solution.

Notice that if the vector A is a solution, then any scalar times A is a solution. The vector sum of two solutions is in turn a solution.

Question: Are there any solutions for $x + 2y + 2z = 0$ that cannot be obtained from

$$\begin{bmatrix} 2 \\ 1 \\ -2 \end{bmatrix}$$

by scalar multiplication?

The popular "elimination by addition and subtraction" method used to solve a system of equations is based on successive applications of the following two theorems.

4.7-2 Theorem: If any one of the equations in a system of linear equations is multiplied by a nonzero scalar, then the resulting system has exactly the same solution set.

PROOF: Without loss of generality, let us consider multiplication of the second equation. (We consider only the restricted case of three equations in three variables. The theorem was stated more generally, and is true in general, but we are interested here only in this special case.) Let $\begin{bmatrix} a \\ b \\ c \end{bmatrix}$ be a solution for the system of equations

$$\alpha_1 x + \beta_1 y + \gamma_1 z = \delta_1,$$
$$\alpha_2 x + \beta_2 y + \gamma_2 z = \delta_2,$$
$$\alpha_3 x + \beta_3 y + \gamma_3 z = \delta_3.$$

If s is a scalar, then

$$(s\alpha_2)a + (s\beta_2)b + (s\gamma_2)c = s\delta_2$$

and hence $\begin{bmatrix} a \\ b \\ c \end{bmatrix}$ is also a solution for the system

$$\alpha_1 x + \beta_1 y + \gamma_1 z = \delta_1,$$
$$(s\alpha_2)x + (s\beta_2)y + (s\gamma_2)z = s\delta_2,$$
$$\alpha_3 x + \beta_3 y + \gamma_3 z = \delta_3.$$

The fact that any solution for the latter system is also a solution for the former can be established by using the fact we have just shown and by multiplying the second equation by $1/s$.

Question: Where would the result fail if we did not insist that s be a nonzero scalar?

4.7-3 Theorem: If any one of the equations in a system of linear equations is replaced by an equation constructed by adding to the given equation another equation of the system, then the new system has the same solution set as the former.

Proof: Without loss of generality, let us consider adding the second equation of the system to the first. Since $\begin{bmatrix} a \\ b \\ c \end{bmatrix}$ is a solution, we must have

$$\alpha_1 a + \beta_1 b + \gamma_1 c = \delta_1,$$

and

$$\alpha_2 a + \beta_2 b + \gamma_2 c = \delta_2,$$

so that

$$(\alpha_1 a + \beta_1 b + \gamma_1 c) + (\alpha_2 a + \beta_2 b + \gamma_2 c) = \delta_1 + \delta_2,$$

or equivalently

$$(\alpha_1 + \alpha_2)a + (\beta_1 + \beta_2)b + (\gamma_1 + \gamma_2)c = \delta_1 + \delta_2.$$

Hence, the vector $\begin{bmatrix} a \\ b \\ c \end{bmatrix}$ is also a solution for the system

$$(\alpha_1 + \alpha_2)x + (\beta_1 + \beta_2)y + (\gamma_1 + \gamma_2)z = \delta_1 + \delta_2,$$
$$\alpha_2 x + \beta_2 y + \gamma_2 z = \delta_2,$$
$$\alpha_3 x + \beta_3 y + \gamma_3 z = \delta_3.$$

Again we apply this result "in reverse" to establish the fact that the two systems have exactly the same solutions.

By successively applying these two theorems, we can reduce the problem to a simpler one whose solutions we can determine by inspection. Sometimes we discover that the system is *inconsistent* (has no solution) and other times we find that the system is *dependent* (has many solutions). In Chapter V we investigate properties of the system that determine existence and uniqueness of solutions. For the present we shall practice solving some simple systems.

Example: Solve the following system of equations.

$$6x - 4y - 7z = 17$$
$$9x - 7y - 16z = 29$$
$$10x - 5y - 3z = 23.$$

We replace this system with

$$18x - 12y - 21z = 51 \qquad \text{(multiply by 3 from above)}$$
$$18x - 14y - 32z = 58 \qquad \text{(multiply by 2 from above)}$$
$$10x - 5y - 3z = 23,$$

and then by the system

$$18x - 12y - 21z = 51$$
$$2y + 11z = -7 \qquad \text{(replace the above by subtracting the second from the first)}$$
$$10x - 5y - 3z = 23,$$

then by

$$180x - 120y - 210z = 510 \quad \text{(multiply by 10)}$$
$$2y + 11z = -7$$
$$180x - 90y - 54z = 414, \quad \text{(multiply by 18)}$$

then

$$180x - 120y - 210z = 510$$
$$2y + 11z = -7$$
$$-30y - 156z = 96, \quad \text{(subtract third from first)}$$

then

$$18x - 12y - 21z = 51 \quad \text{(divide by 10)}$$
$$2y + 11z = -7$$
$$5y + 26z = -16, \quad \text{(divide by } -6)$$

then

$$18x - 12y - 21z = 51$$
$$12y + 66x = -42 \quad \text{(multiply by 6)}$$
$$5y + 26z = -16,$$

then

$$18x + 45z = 9 \quad \text{(add first and second)}$$
$$2y + 11z = -7 \quad \text{(divide by 6)}$$
$$5y + 26z = -16,$$

then

$$18x + 45z = 9$$
$$10y + 55z = -35 \quad \text{(multiply by 5)}$$
$$10y + 52z = -32, \quad \text{(multiply by 2)}$$

then

$$2x + 5z = 1 \quad \text{(divide by 9)}$$
$$2y + 11z = -7 \quad \text{(divide by 5)}$$
$$3z = -3, \quad \text{(subtract third from second)}$$

then

$$2x + 5z = 1$$
$$2y + 11z = -7$$
$$5z = -5, \quad \text{(multiply by } \tfrac{5}{3})$$

then

$$2x = 6 \quad \text{(subtract third from first)}$$
$$2y + 11z = -7$$
$$11z = -11, \quad \text{(multiply by } \tfrac{11}{5})$$

then

$$x = 3 \quad \text{(divide by 2)}$$
$$2y + 11z = -7$$
$$11z = -11,$$

then

$$x = 3$$
$$2y = 4 \quad \text{(subtract third from second)}$$
$$z = -1, \quad \text{(divide by 11)}$$

then

$$x \qquad\quad = 3$$
$$y \qquad = 2 \qquad \text{(divide by 2)}$$
$$z = -1.$$

Hence, by inspection, we see that the system has only the solution

$$\begin{bmatrix} 3 \\ 2 \\ -1 \end{bmatrix}.$$

It should be noted that in our transition from one system to another we often use two or more applications of the theorems. The rapidity of finding solutions by this method will vary considerably among students, depending on computational ability. It takes a great deal of experimentation and practice to know which step to take next in using this process. Perhaps the following explanation will be of some value.

In applying the reduction method shown above, one may follow these main steps:

1. Eliminate x from the second and third equations.
2. Eliminate y from the first and third equations.
3. Eliminate z from the first and second equations.

You should now look back over the previous example and see these main steps develop.

The Augmented Matrix

After solving several systems by the above method, one notices an interesting and important fact related to the process of finding solutions to a system of linear equations. In the process of applying the theorems for obtaining equivalent systems, one need not write the entire equation at each step with unknowns x, y, and z. Since we can always write the equation with the unknowns x, y, and z in a given order, it is sufficient merely to keep track of the coefficients at each stage.

Example: Let us solve the following system by applying the theorems, but keeping track of only the coefficients, using what is called the *augmented matrix* for the system.

$$x + 2y - z = 6$$
$$2x - y + 3z = -13$$
$$3x - 2y + 3z = -16$$

We write the system without the unknowns x, y, and z, and without plus signs in an *augmented matrix*.

$$\left[\begin{array}{ccc|c} 1 & 2 & -1 & 6 \\ 2 & -1 & 3 & -13 \\ 3 & -2 & 3 & -16 \end{array}\right]$$

We now apply Theorems 4.7-2 and 4.7-3, keeping the new system in matrix form.

$$\begin{bmatrix} 2 & 4 & -2 & | & 12 \\ 2 & -1 & 3 & | & -13 \\ 3 & -2 & 3 & | & -16 \end{bmatrix} \qquad \text{(multiply by 2)}$$

$$\begin{bmatrix} 2 & 4 & -2 & | & 12 \\ 0 & -5 & 5 & | & -25 \\ 3 & -2 & 3 & | & -16 \end{bmatrix} \qquad \text{(subtract first from second)}$$

$$\begin{bmatrix} 3 & 6 & -3 & | & 18 \\ 0 & 1 & -1 & | & 5 \\ 3 & -2 & 3 & | & -16 \end{bmatrix} \qquad \begin{aligned} &\text{(multiply by } \tfrac{3}{2}\text{)} \\ &\text{(divide by } -5\text{)} \end{aligned}$$

$$\begin{bmatrix} 3 & 6 & -3 & | & 18 \\ 0 & 1 & -1 & | & 5 \\ 0 & 8 & -6 & | & 34 \end{bmatrix} \qquad \text{(subtract third from first)}$$

$$\begin{bmatrix} 1 & 2 & -1 & | & 6 \\ 0 & 2 & -2 & | & 10 \\ 0 & 4 & -3 & | & 17 \end{bmatrix} \qquad \begin{aligned} &\text{(divide by 3)} \\ &\text{(multiply by 2)} \\ &\text{(divide by 2)} \end{aligned}$$

$$\begin{bmatrix} 1 & 0 & 1 & | & -4 \\ 0 & 4 & -4 & | & 20 \\ 0 & 4 & -3 & | & 17 \end{bmatrix} \qquad \begin{aligned} &\text{(subtract second from first)} \\ &\text{(multiply by 2)} \end{aligned}$$

$$\begin{bmatrix} 1 & 0 & 1 & | & -4 \\ 0 & 4 & -4 & | & 20 \\ 0 & 0 & 1 & | & -3 \end{bmatrix} \qquad \text{(subtract second from third)}$$

$$\begin{bmatrix} 1 & 0 & 1 & | & -4 \\ 0 & 1 & -1 & | & 5 \\ 0 & 0 & 1 & | & -3 \end{bmatrix} \qquad \text{(divide by 4)}$$

$$\begin{bmatrix} 1 & 0 & 0 & | & -1 \\ 0 & 1 & 0 & | & 2 \\ 0 & 0 & 1 & | & -3 \end{bmatrix} \qquad \begin{aligned} &\text{(subtract third from first)} \\ &\text{(add second and third)} \end{aligned}$$

Hence, the only solution is the vector $\begin{bmatrix} -1 \\ 2 \\ -3 \end{bmatrix}$.

Example: Solve the following system of equations.

$$\begin{aligned} x + 3y - 4z &= -13 \\ 2x - y + 2z &= 4 \\ 4x - 6y + z &= -1 \end{aligned}$$

The augmented matrix is

$$\begin{bmatrix} 1 & 3 & -4 & | & -13 \\ 2 & -1 & 2 & | & 4 \\ 4 & -6 & 1 & | & -1 \end{bmatrix}$$

and by the following steps applying the theorems we arrive at a solution.

$$\begin{bmatrix} 2 & 6 & -8 & -26 \\ -2 & 1 & -2 & -4 \\ 4 & -6 & 1 & -1 \end{bmatrix}$$ (multiply by 2)
(multiply by −1)

$$\begin{bmatrix} 2 & 6 & -8 & -26 \\ 0 & 7 & -10 & -30 \\ 4 & -6 & 1 & -1 \end{bmatrix}$$ (add first and second)

$$\begin{bmatrix} 4 & 12 & -16 & -52 \\ 0 & 7 & -10 & -30 \\ -4 & 6 & -1 & 1 \end{bmatrix}$$ (multiply by 2)

(multiply by −1)

$$\begin{bmatrix} 4 & 12 & -16 & -52 \\ 0 & 7 & -10 & -30 \\ 0 & 18 & -17 & -51 \end{bmatrix}$$ (add first and third)

$$\begin{bmatrix} 1 & 3 & -4 & -13 \\ 0 & 7 & -10 & -30 \\ 0 & 18 & -17 & -51 \end{bmatrix}$$ (divide by 4)

$$\begin{bmatrix} 7 & 21 & -28 & -91 \\ 0 & -21 & 30 & 90 \\ 0 & 18 & -17 & -51 \end{bmatrix}$$ (multiply by 7)
(multiply by −3)

$$\begin{bmatrix} 7 & 0 & 2 & -1 \\ 0 & -7 & 10 & 30 \\ 0 & 18 & -17 & -51 \end{bmatrix}$$ (add first and second)
(divide by 3)

$$\begin{bmatrix} 7 & 0 & 2 & -1 \\ 0 & -7 \cdot 18 & 180 & 540 \\ 0 & 18 \cdot 7 & -119 & -357 \end{bmatrix}$$ (multiply by 18)
(multiply by 7)

$$\begin{bmatrix} 7 & 0 & 2 & -1 \\ 0 & -7 & 10 & 30 \\ 0 & 0 & 61 & 183 \end{bmatrix}$$ (divide by 18)
(add second and third)

$$\begin{bmatrix} 7 & 0 & 2 & -1 \\ 0 & 7 & -10 & -30 \\ 0 & 0 & 1 & 3 \end{bmatrix}$$ (multiply by −1)
(divide by 61)

(multiply third by 2 and subtract from
first)

$$\begin{bmatrix} 7 & 0 & 0 & -7 \\ 0 & 7 & 0 & 0 \\ 0 & 0 & 1 & 3 \end{bmatrix}$$ (multiply third by 10 and add to second)

$$\begin{bmatrix} 1 & 0 & 0 & -1 \\ 0 & 1 & 0 & 0 \\ 0 & 0 & 1 & 3 \end{bmatrix}$$ (divide by 7)
(divide by 7)

It is obvious that $\begin{bmatrix} -1 \\ 0 \\ 3 \end{bmatrix}$ is the only vector such that

$$1x + 0y + 0z = -1$$
$$0x + 1y + 0z = 0$$
$$0x + 0y + 1z = 3.$$

Since at each step in arriving at this equation we wrote the augmented matrix for a system that has exactly the same solution set as the previous matrix, it follows that $\begin{bmatrix} -1 \\ 0 \\ 3 \end{bmatrix}$ is the only vector $\begin{bmatrix} x \\ y \\ z \end{bmatrix}$ such that

$$x + 3y - 4z = -13$$
$$2x - y + 2z = 4$$
$$4x - 6y + z = -1.$$

The three principal steps in this process are:

1. Arrive at zeros in all except the *first row* of *column one*.

2. Arrive at zeros in all except the *second row* of *column two*.

3. Arrive at zeros in all except the *third row* of *column three*.

In Chapter V we will establish some formal results that one can use to determine whether a system has a unique solution.

EXERCISES 4.7

1. Show that the position of any two equations in a system can be interchanged by applying Theorems 4.7-2 and 4.7-3.

2. Find vector solutions for the following systems of equations.

a. $3x + 2y \quad\quad = 13$
$\quad\quad 3y - 2z = 8$
$\quad 2x \quad\quad - 3z = 9.$

b. $3x + 4y + 5z = -21$
$\quad x + y - z = -11$
$\quad\quad y - 8z = -20.$

c. $12x - 4y + z = 3$
$\quad x - y - 2z = -1$
$\quad 5x - 2y \quad\quad = 0$

d. $2x - y + z = -9$
$\quad x - 2y + z = 0$
$\quad x - y + 2z = -11.$

e. $x - y + z = 9$
$\quad x - 2y + 3z = 32$
$\quad x - 4y + 5z = 62.$

f. $2x - 3y - 4z = -10$
$\quad 3x - 4y + 2z = -5$
$\quad 4x + 2y + 3z = -21.$

g. $9x + 4y = 10z + 11$
$\quad 12y - 5z = 6x - 9$
$\quad 15z + 3x = -8y - 16.$

h. $2x - y + z = 1$
$\quad x - y - z = 2$
$\quad 3x - 2y - z = -1.$

i. $x - 2y + z = 4$
$\quad 2x - 3y + z = 1$
$\quad 3x - 2y - z = 2.$

j. $3x - 2y \quad\quad = 1$
$\quad x - y - z = 4$
$\quad 3x + y \quad\quad = -4.$

k. $3x - 6y + 5z = 9$
$\quad 2x - y + z = -1$
$\quad x - 2y + 4z = 3.$

l. $x + y + z = 3$
$\quad x - y \quad\quad = 4$
$\quad 3x + y \quad\quad = 6.$

4.8 SOME SPECIAL TOPICS

The General Equation of the Second Degree

The equation

$$Ax^2 + By^2 + Cxy + Dx + Ey + F = 0$$

is called *the general equation of the second degree*. We have seen that by translation and rotation of coordinates, we can obtain an equation of the form

$$A'x^2 + B'y^2 + F = 0.$$

This equation can then (usually) be graphed as one of the special curves we called conic sections with center at the origin.

The question should have arisen by now as to the reason we call such curves *conic sections*. In the next chapter, when three-dimensional vector methods are available, we will show that all equations of the form

$$Ax^2 + By^2 + Cxy + Dx + Ey + F = 0$$

can be obtained by some planar cut of some right circular cone. A right circular cone is a three-dimensional figure of the type shown in Figure 4.42. A right circular cone has an axis and vertex as shown. Any plane perpendicular to the axis intersects the surface of the cone in a circle. Any plane containing the axis intersects the cone in two *edge* lines intersecting at the vertex. If a plane perpendicular to the axis is tilted slightly, then the cut is elliptical. If the intersecting plane is parallel to an edge but does not contain the vertex, then the cut is parabolic. A hyperbolic cut is obtained if the plane is steeper than the edges and does not contain the vertex. (See Figure 4.43.)

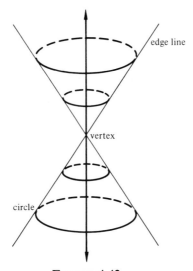

FIGURE 4.42

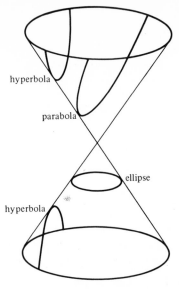

FIGURE 4.43

Degenerate Conics

When the plane used to cut the cone mentioned above passes through the vertex, circles and ellipses become points, parabolas become lines and hyperbolas become two intersecting lines. These curves are called *degenerate conics*, and it is easy to see how such curves can be obtained from the general equation of the second degree. For example, by appropriate choices of coefficients in the equation

$$Ax^2 + By^2 + Cxy + Dx + Ey + F = 0$$

we have the equation

$$x^2 = 0,$$

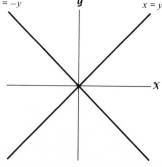

FIGURE 4.44

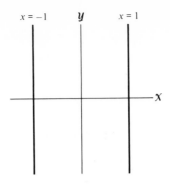

FIGURE 4.45

which is satisfied only by points on the line $x = 0$. If $A = 1$, $B = -1$, and $C = D = E = F = 0$, then we have the equation

$$x^2 - y^2 = 0,$$

which describes the two lines $x = y$ and $x = -y$. (See Figure 4.44.)

Some equations that can be gotten from the general second-degree equation do not seem to describe point sets that can be gotten from a planar cut of a cone. For example, consider the equation

$$x^2 = 1,$$

which describes the two parallel lines $x = 1$ and $x = -1$. (See Figure 4.45.) However, this can be viewed as a member of the family of parabolas

$$y + \alpha = \alpha x^2$$

as we take the limit as $\alpha \to \infty$. (See Figure 4.46.)

Circles through Three Points

Let us make an observation regarding circles and how they are related to the general quadratic equation

$$Ax^2 + By^2 + Cxy + Dx + Ey + F = 0.$$

Any circle can be described by such an equation where $C = 0$, since circles are invariant under rotation. If neither A nor $B = 0$, then by completing squares and changing coordinates, we obtain the equation in the form

$$Ax'^2 + By'^2 = F',$$

which is the equation of hyperbola or an ellipse (or circle). We obtain a circle only if $A = B$, in which case, the equation can be given in the form

$$x'^2 + y'^2 = r^2.$$

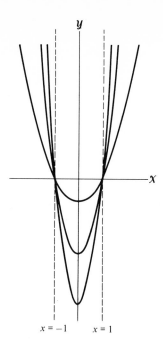

FIGURE 4.46

In general, then, any circle in the plane can be represented by an equation of the form

$$x^2 + y^2 + Dx + Ey + F = 0.$$

Let us use this fact to determine an equation of the circle that passes through three given noncollinear points, by finding the proper values of D, E, and F.

Example: Find an equation of the circle that passes through the three points $(1, 1)$, $(2, 3)$, $(-1, 1)$. We assume an equation of the above-mentioned form, and substitute the values of x and y for each of the given points.

$$1^2 + 1^2 + D(1) + E(1) + F = 0$$
$$2^2 + 3^2 + D(2) + E(3) + F = 0$$
$$(-1)^2 + 1^2 + D(-1) + E(1) + F = 0.$$

We thus have three linear equations in the three unknowns D, E, and F.

$$D + E + F = -2$$
$$2D + 3E + F = -13$$
$$-D + E + F = -2.$$

This system can be solved by the method of the previous section to yield the solution

$$D = 0, \qquad E = -\tfrac{11}{2}, \qquad \text{and} \qquad F = \tfrac{7}{2}.$$

V

VECTORS IN
THREE-DIMENSIONAL SPACE

In this chapter we shall extend most of the vector concepts discussed previously to the case of three-dimensional space. As we shall see, this extension is quite easily accomplished, and the results established for vectors in the plane have simple analogues in space. However, the three-dimensional case allows us to consider another interesting operation on vectors, the *cross product*, which has no nontrivial analogue in the two-dimensional spaces considered so far. We shall also be concerned with graphing concepts in three-dimensional spaces, and in solving systems of three equations in three unknowns.

5.1 POSITION VECTORS IN SPACE

We shall now extend to three-dimensional Euclidean space (hereafter called *space*) the geometric notions of vectors discussed earlier for two-dimensional space (the plane). This extension is quite natural, and it should be apparent that these notions could be extended to even higher-dimensional spaces without difficulty. For this reason, we shall not be so detailed in our remarks concerning vectors and space as we were for vectors in the plane. It is suggested that the student keep the two-dimensional case in mind as we proceed, and that he frequently compare these spaces.

Suppose we have made a Cartesian coordinatization of three-dimensional space, so that each point in space is associated with a unique ordered triple

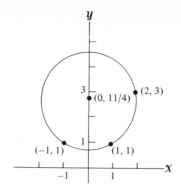

FIGURE 4.47

Thus, an equation for the circle through the points $(1, 1)$, $(2, 3)$, and $(-1, 1)$ is

$$x^2 + y^2 - \tfrac{11}{2}y + \tfrac{7}{2} = 0.$$

If we complete the square and put the equation in standard form, we have

$$x^2 + (y - \tfrac{11}{4})^2 = 65/16.$$

From this, we see that the circle has center $(0, \tfrac{11}{4})$ and radius $\sqrt{65}/4$. (See Figure 4.47.)

EXERCISES 4.8

1. Graph each of the following degenerate conics.
    a. $2x^2 + 3y^2 = 0$.   b. $2x^2 - 3y^2 = 0$.
    c. $y^2 = 4$.   d. $x^2 - 2x = 0$.

2. Write a second-degree equation that describes the given set.
    a. $\{(x, y) : x = 3\} \cup \{(x, y) : x = -1\}$.
    b. $\{(x, y) : y = 5x\} \cup \{(x, y) : y = -5x\}$.
    c. $\{(x, y) : y = 2x\} \cup \{(x, y) : y = -2x + 8\}$.

3. Graph the following surfaces in three space.
    a. $x^2 + y^2 = z^2$ (elliptic cone).   b. $x^2 - y^2 = z^2$.
    c. $4x^2 + 9z^2 = 36$.   d. $x^2 = y - 1$.

4. Find a constraining equation for a circle containing the three points given. Find the center and the radius of the circle.
    a. $(2, 3)$, $(-1, -1)$, $(1, 1)$.   b. $(5, 0)$, $(0, 6)$, $(-2, 1)$.
    c. $(4, 4)$, $(-6, -6)$, $(3, -1)$.   d. $(1, 3)$, $(7, 7)$, $(-3, 1)$.

of real numbers. Now with a point A having coordinate triple (x, y, z) we associate a *position vector* $\mathbf{A} = (O, A)$ from the origin to the point A. (See Figure 5.1.)

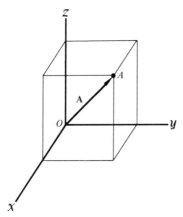

FIGURE 5.1

The position vector $\mathbf{A}$ will also be denoted by $(\mathbf{x}, \mathbf{y}, \mathbf{z})$. The *sum* of two such position vectors is defined coordinatewise:

$$(\mathbf{x}, \mathbf{y}, \mathbf{z}) + (\mathbf{u}, \mathbf{v}, \mathbf{w}) = (\mathbf{x} + \mathbf{u}, \mathbf{y} + \mathbf{v}, \mathbf{z} + \mathbf{w}).$$

The *scalar product* is similarly defined;

$$\alpha(\mathbf{x}, \mathbf{y}, \mathbf{z}) = (\alpha\mathbf{x}, \alpha\mathbf{y}, \alpha\mathbf{z}).$$

Also, *subtraction* is given by $\mathbf{A} - \mathbf{B} = \mathbf{A} + (-1)\mathbf{B}.$

Example: $(1, 1, 1) + (2, -1, 3) = (3, 0, 4)$, $2(2, -1, 3) = (4, -2, 6)$, and $(5, 2, -4) - (2, 3, 1) = (3, -1, -5).$

Remark: If a nonzero vector $\mathbf{A}$ is given, the set

$$\{\alpha\mathbf{A} : \alpha \in \mathbf{R}\}$$

of all scalar multiples of A is a line in space passing through the origin and the point A. (See Figure 5.2.)

It is easy to verify that the various commutative, associative, and distributive properties of vector addition established for vectors in the plane hold for vectors in space (Exercise 4). Let us now define the *standard basis* vectors for space.

5.1-1 Definition: Let $\mathbf{I} = (1, 0, 0)$, $\mathbf{J} = (0, 1, 0)$, and $\mathbf{K} = (0, 0, 1)$. The vectors $\mathbf{I}$, $\mathbf{J}$, and $\mathbf{K}$ are called *standard basis vectors* for space (with respect to the given coordinatization).

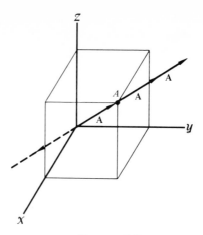

FIGURE 5.2

Remark: Recall that the symbols **I** and **J** were also used for vectors in the plane. We shall depend on the context to make clear in a given situation whether **I** denotes **(1, 0)** or **(1, 0, 0)**, and similarly for **J**. Note that graphically, the standard basis vectors are unit vectors that lie along the three axes in our Cartesian coordinate system (see Figure 5.3).

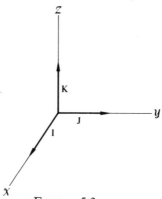

FIGURE 5.3

The concept of basis vectors in space is useful because we can decompose any vector **(x, y, z)** into a sum of *component* vectors along the three axes. Indeed,

$$x\mathbf{I} + y\mathbf{J} + z\mathbf{K} = x(1, 0, 0) + y(0, 1, 0) + z(0, 0, 1)$$
$$= (x, 0, 0) + (0, y, 0) + (0, 0, z) = (x, y, z).$$

The distance between a point with coordinate (x, y, z) and the origin is defined consistently with the two-dimensional case using the Pythagorean theorem (assuming a Cartesian coordinatization of space). We thus have the *length* of a vector.

5.1-2 Definition: The *length* of the vector $A = aI + bJ + cK$ is denoted by $|A|$ and is given by

$$|A| = \sqrt{a^2 + b^2 + c^2}.$$

As for vectors in the plane, the distance between two points A and B in space is thus given by $|A - B|$ (see Figure 5.4).

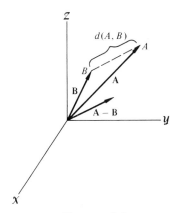

FIGURE 5.4

That is, if $A = (a, b, c)$ and $B = (u, v, w)$, then

$$|A - B| = |(a, b, c) - (u, v, w)| = |(a - u, b - v, c - w)|$$
$$= \sqrt{(a - u)^2 + (b - v)^2 + (c - w)^2} = d(A, B).$$

The Dot Product

We now extend the *dot product* to vectors in space.

5.1-3 Definition: The *dot product* of two vectors (x, y, z) and (u, v, w) is given by

$$(x, y, z) \cdot (u, v, w) = xu + yv + zw.$$

As in the two-dimensional case, the dot product is a mapping of pairs of vectors to scalars ($\cdot : \mho \times \mho \rightarrow R$). In the exercises (Exercise 7) you are asked to establish some elementary properties of the dot product such as the commutative and distributive laws. Notice, in particular, that if $A = (a, b, c)$, then

$$A \cdot A = a^2 + b^2 + c^2 = |A|^2.$$

It follows that the length of the vector A may be given in terms of the dot product by

$$|A| = \sqrt{A \cdot A}.$$

This relation is quite useful, both because it is easily extended to higher-dimensional spaces and because it may be used to establish properties of length such as $|\alpha \mathbf{A}| = |\alpha|\,|\mathbf{A}|$.

One of the most useful results concerning the dot product is the following analogue of Derivation 3.3-7.

5.1-4 Derivation: If $\mathbf{A}$ and $\mathbf{B}$ are position vectors in space $(\mathbf{A} \neq 0, \mathbf{B} \neq 0)$, then

$$\mathbf{A} \cdot \mathbf{B} = |\mathbf{A}|\,|\mathbf{B}|\cos\theta,$$

where θ is the *angle between vectors* $\mathbf{A}$ and $\mathbf{B}$. (As stated earlier, this should actually serve as a definition for the *angle between vectors*.)

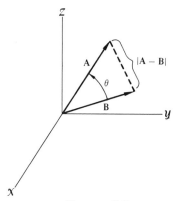

FIGURE 5.5

Proof: (See Figure 5.5.)
By the law of cosines

$$|\mathbf{A} - \mathbf{B}|^2 = |\mathbf{A}|^2 + |\mathbf{B}|^2 - 2|\mathbf{A}|\,|\mathbf{B}|\cos\theta.$$

Also

$$|\mathbf{A} - \mathbf{B}|^2 = (\mathbf{A} - \mathbf{B}) \cdot (\mathbf{A} - \mathbf{B}) = \mathbf{A} \cdot \mathbf{A} + \mathbf{B} \cdot \mathbf{B} - 2\mathbf{A} \cdot \mathbf{B}.$$
$$= |\mathbf{A}|^2 + |\mathbf{B}|^2 - 2\mathbf{A} \cdot \mathbf{B}.$$

The result follows by equating and simplifying.

From this, we have the following definition.

5.1-5 Definition: Two vectors $\mathbf{A}$ and $\mathbf{B}$ are said to be *orthogonal* (perpendicular) iff $\mathbf{A} \cdot \mathbf{B} = 0$.

Example: $(1, -2, 3)$ and $(2, -2, -2)$ are perpendicular (orthogonal) since $(1, -2, 3) \cdot (2, -2, -2) = 2 + 4 - 6 = 0$. (See Figure 5.6.)

Example: Find a vector (x, y, z) perpendicular to $(1, 1, 4)$ such that $x = y$ and $z = 2$.

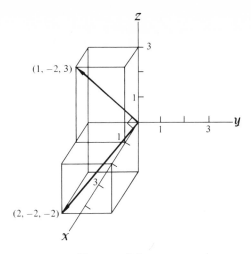

FIGURE 5.6

Solution: Compute $(x, x, 2) \cdot (1, 1, 4) = x + x + 8$, and set $2x + 8 = 0$. Hence, $(-4, -4, 2)$ is such a vector.

EXERCISES 5.1

1. Graph each vector in space and find its length.
   a. $(2, 4, -1)$.   b. $(1, 4, 2)$.
   c. $(-2, -1, -3)$.   d. $(-4, 1, 3)$.

2. Graph all scalar multiples of **A** where
   a. $\mathbf{A} = (1, 4, 2)$.   b. $\mathbf{A} = (-3, -1, 2)$.
   c. $\mathbf{A} = (2, 2, -1)$.   d. $\mathbf{A} = (-1, 2, 3)$.

3. Compute the dot product of the given pair of vectors.
   a. $(1, 3, -2)$, $(2, 3, -4)$.   b. $(5, -1, 3)$, $(1, 3, 1)$.
   c. $(-2, 3, 6)$, $(4, -2, 4)$.   d. $(-5, -5, 0)$, $(2, 4, 1)$.

4. Suppose (x, y, z) and (u, v, w) are vectors and let α, β be real numbers. Show that
   a. $(x, y, z) + (u, v, w) = (u, v, w) + (x, y, z)$.
   b. Vector addition is associative.
   c. $(\alpha + \beta)(x, y, z) = \alpha(x, y, z) + \beta(x, y, z)$.
   d. $\alpha((x, y, z) + (u, v, w)) = \alpha(x, y, z) + \alpha(u, v, w)$.

5. Verify that the set of all position vectors in space forms a vector space over the field of real numbers (that is, verify that each of the properties of Definition 3.2-3 is satisfied.)

6. Show that $\mathbf{I} \cdot \mathbf{J} = \mathbf{I} \cdot \mathbf{K} = \mathbf{J} \cdot \mathbf{K} = 0$ and $\mathbf{I} \cdot \mathbf{I} = \mathbf{J} \cdot \mathbf{J} = \mathbf{K} \cdot \mathbf{K} = 1$.

7. For vectors in space, verify each of the following.
   a. $\mathbf{A} \cdot \mathbf{B} = \mathbf{B} \cdot \mathbf{A}$.   b. $\alpha(\mathbf{A} \cdot \mathbf{B}) = (\alpha\mathbf{A}) \cdot \mathbf{B} = \mathbf{A} \cdot (\alpha\mathbf{B})$.
   c. $\mathbf{A} \cdot (\mathbf{B} + \mathbf{C}) = \mathbf{A} \cdot \mathbf{B} + \mathbf{A} \cdot \mathbf{C}$.

8. Find a vector $\mathbf{A} = (a, b, c)$ such that:
   a. $a = b$, $c = 4$, and **A** is perpendicular to $(1, 3, -2)$;

b. $a = 2$, $b = 3c$, and **A** is perpendicular to $(4, -1, 1)$;

c. $a = 5b$, $c = 2$, and **A** is orthogonal to $(-3, 1, 2)$.

9. Find a unit vector **A** ($|\mathbf{A}| = 1$) that is perpendicular to both vectors given.

    a. $(1, 4, 2)$, $(1, -2, 3)$.   b. $(-2, -2, 1)$, $(3, 3, -4)$.

    c. $(-2, 3, 1)$, $(1, 4, 1)$.   d. $(4, -2, 7)$, $(-1, -2, 5)$.

10. Investigate (prove or disprove). Assume $\mathbf{A} \neq \mathbf{0}$, and $\mathbf{B} \neq \mathbf{0}$, and for all $\alpha \in \mathbf{R}$, $\mathbf{A} \neq \alpha\mathbf{B}$. If $\mathbf{X} \cdot \mathbf{A} = 0$ and $\mathbf{X} \cdot \mathbf{B} = 0$, and also $\mathbf{Y} \cdot \mathbf{A} = 0$ and $\mathbf{Y} \cdot \mathbf{B} = 0$, then $\mathbf{X} = \beta\mathbf{Y}$ for some $\beta \in \mathbf{R}$.

5.2 PLANES AND LINES IN SPACE

Free Vectors as Equivalence Classes of Fixed Vectors

As in the case for vectors in the plane, we shall find it useful to consider vectors in space that have their "tails" at points other than the origin. We now describe fixed vectors and free vectors in space, and discuss some of their applications in describing certain subsets of space. Since the notation and interpretation are consistent with our development in two dimensional space, we will not formalize the definitions.

Consider an arrow from the point (a, b, c) to the point (x, y, z). This is a *fixed vector* and may be denoted by $((a, b, c), (x, y, z))$. (See Figure 5.7.) The

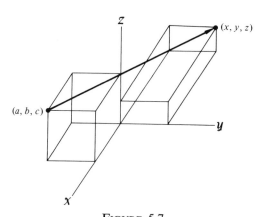

FIGURE 5.7

fixed vector $((0, 0, 0), (x, y, z))$ is exactly the position vector $(\mathbf{x}, \mathbf{y}, \mathbf{z})$. Clearly, the length of a fixed vector (A, B) is the distance $d(A, B)$.

Now define an equivalence relation $\sim$ on the set of all fixed vectors as follows:

$$((a, b, c), (x, y, z)) \sim ((d, e, f), (u, v, w))$$

provided that

$$(\mathbf{x}, \mathbf{y}, \mathbf{z}) - (\mathbf{a}, \mathbf{b}, \mathbf{c}) = (\mathbf{u}, \mathbf{v}, \mathbf{w}) - (\mathbf{d}, \mathbf{e}, \mathbf{f}).$$

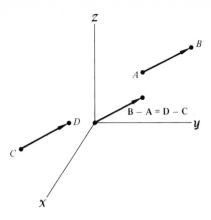

FIGURE 5.8

(See Figure 5.8.) Equivalent vectors have the same length and point the same direction. We call the equivalence classes induced by $\sim$, *free vectors*. Since

$$((a, b, c), (x, y, z)) \sim ((0, 0, 0), (x - a, y - b, z - c))$$

for any fixed vector $((a, b, c), (x, y, z))$ in the *equivalence class*

$$((\mathbf{a}, \mathbf{b}, \mathbf{c}), (\mathbf{x}, \mathbf{y}, \mathbf{z})),$$

it follows that each free vector contains as a member a position vector $(\mathbf{u}, \mathbf{v}, \mathbf{w})$. This representative position vector is unique, and we denote the corresponding free vector by $[\mathbf{u}, \mathbf{v}, \mathbf{w}]$. That is,

$$((\mathbf{a}, \mathbf{b}, \mathbf{c}), (\mathbf{x}, \mathbf{y}, \mathbf{z})) = [\mathbf{x} - \mathbf{a}, \mathbf{y} - \mathbf{b}, \mathbf{z} - \mathbf{c}].$$

For any $\alpha \neq 0$, we call αu, αv, and αw *direction numbers* of the free vector $[\mathbf{u}, \mathbf{v}, \mathbf{w}]$.

We define *addition, subtraction, scalar multiplication,* and *dot products* of free vectors in terms of their unique representative position vectors. A free vector can easily be expressed in terms of a fixed vector representative with tail at any convenient point F, since

$$(\mathbf{O}, \mathbf{A}) = (\mathbf{F}, \mathbf{A} + \mathbf{F}).$$

Example: Let $A = (1, 1, -1)$, $B = (2, -1, 3)$, and $C = (1, 3, 2)$. Then

$$(\mathbf{A}, \mathbf{B}) = ((\mathbf{1}, \mathbf{1}, -\mathbf{1}), (\mathbf{2}, -\mathbf{1}, \mathbf{3})) = [\mathbf{1}, -\mathbf{2}, \mathbf{4}],$$

and

$$(\mathbf{A}, \mathbf{C}) = ((\mathbf{1}, \mathbf{1}, -\mathbf{1}), (\mathbf{1}, \mathbf{3}, \mathbf{2})) = [\mathbf{0}, \mathbf{2}, \mathbf{3}].$$

So

$$
\begin{aligned}
((1, 1, -1), (2, -1, 3)) + ((1, 1, -1), (1, 3, 2)) &= [1, -2, 4] + [0, 2, 3] \\
&= [1, 0, 7] \\
&= ((1, 1, -1), (2, 1, 6)).
\end{aligned}
$$

Also

$$3((1, 1, -1), (1, 3, 2)) = 3[0, 2, 3] = [0, 6, 9]$$

and

$$((1, 1, -1), (2, -1, 3)) \cdot ((1, 1, -1), (1, 3, 2)) = [1, -2, 4] \cdot [0, 2, 3]$$
$$= 0 - 4 + 12 = 8.$$

Since $|[1, -2, 4]| = \sqrt{21}$ and $|[0, 2, 3]| = \sqrt{13}$, if we use the fact that $\mathbf{A} \cdot \mathbf{B} = |\mathbf{A}|\,|\mathbf{B}|\cos\theta$, it follows that the angle between these vectors (see Figure 5.9) is given by

$$8 = \sqrt{21}\,\sqrt{13}\,\cos\theta.$$

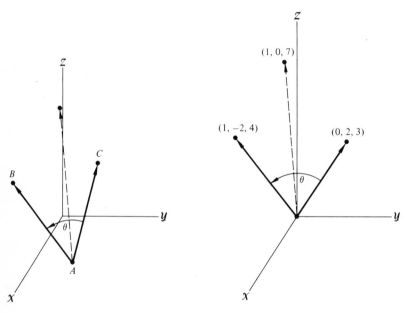

FIGURE 5.9

Thus $\cos\theta = \dfrac{8}{\sqrt{21}\,\sqrt{13}} \cong 0.484$, from which $\theta \cong 1.066$ radians.

Remark: Frequently we shall fail to distinguish clearly between position vectors and points, and fixed vectors and free vectors, but rely on the context to make clear which is meant.

Planes

Let us consider now how vector notions may be used in determining definitions and equations for planes in space. First, suppose $\mathbf{A} = a\mathbf{I} + b\mathbf{J} + c\mathbf{K}$

is a nonzero position vector. The set of all position vectors perpendicular to **A** forms a plane passing through *O* perpendicular to **A** (see Figure 5.10).

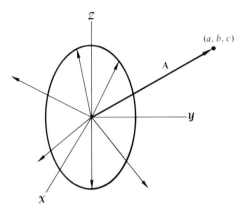

FIGURE 5.10

If a fixed vector (A, B) is given, then there exists a unique *normal* (perpendicular) plane passing through *A* consisting of all points *X* such that $(\mathbf{A}, \mathbf{X}) \cdot (\mathbf{A}, \mathbf{B}) = 0$. (See Figure 5.11.)

5.2-1   **Definition:** A set of points $\mathcal{P}$ in space such that

$$\mathcal{P} = \{X : (\mathbf{A}, \mathbf{X}) \cdot (\mathbf{A}, \mathbf{B}) = 0\}$$

is called a plane passing through the point *A* and having the vector $(\mathbf{A}, \mathbf{B})$ as a *normal*. (We assume $A \neq B$.)

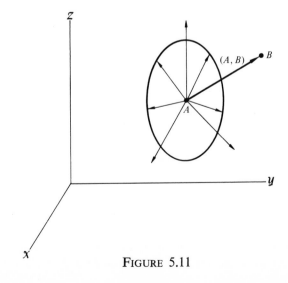

FIGURE 5.11

Example: The set of points given by

$$\{(x, y, z) : (\mathbf{x}, \mathbf{y}, \mathbf{z}) \cdot \mathbf{K} = 0\} = \{(x, y, z) : z = 0\}$$

is simply the *x–y* plane, and the vector **K** is a unit normal to the plane.

We may now determine the general constraining equation for a plane in space containing the origin in terms of a position vector normal to the plane. Consider the vector $\mathbf{N} = (\mathbf{a}, \mathbf{b}, \mathbf{c})$ normal to a plane $\mathcal{P}$. For any point $(x, y, z) \in \mathcal{P}$, the vector $(\mathbf{x}, \mathbf{y}, \mathbf{z})$ is perpendicular to **N**; that is,

$$\mathcal{P} = \{(x, y, z) : (\mathbf{x}, \mathbf{y}, \mathbf{z}) \cdot (\mathbf{a}, \mathbf{b}, \mathbf{c}) = 0\}$$
$$= \{(x, y, z) : ax + by + cz = 0\} .$$

Thus, the equation of any plane containing the origin must be of the form

$$ax + by + cz = 0,$$

where $(\mathbf{a}, \mathbf{b}, \mathbf{c})$ is a vector normal to the plane.

Let us now find an equation of a plane $\mathcal{P}'$ normal to $\mathbf{N} = [\mathbf{a}, \mathbf{b}, \mathbf{c}]$ (parallel to $\mathcal{P}$), but not necessarily passing through the origin. Suppose $\mathcal{P}'$ contains the point $F = (d, e, f)$. Then each vector in $\mathcal{P}'$ may be determined as a vector $\mathbf{U} = (\mathbf{u}, \mathbf{v}, \mathbf{w})$ in $\mathcal{P}$ plus the vector $\mathbf{F} = (\mathbf{d}, \mathbf{e}, \mathbf{f})$, as shown in Figure 5.12.

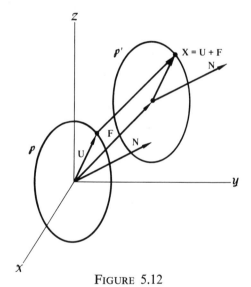

FIGURE 5.12

Thus, we have

$$\mathcal{P}' = \{(x, y, z) : (\mathbf{x}, \mathbf{y}, \mathbf{z}) = (\mathbf{u}, \mathbf{v}, \mathbf{w}) + (\mathbf{d}, \mathbf{e}, \mathbf{f}) \text{ and } (u, v, w) \in \mathcal{P}\}$$
$$= \{(x, y, z) : (\mathbf{x}, \mathbf{y}, \mathbf{z}) = (\mathbf{u} + \mathbf{d}, \mathbf{v} + \mathbf{e}, \mathbf{w} + \mathbf{f}) \text{ and } au + bv + cw = 0\}$$
$$= \{(x, y, z) : (\mathbf{x} - \mathbf{d}, \mathbf{y} - \mathbf{e}, \mathbf{z} - \mathbf{f}) = (\mathbf{u}, \mathbf{v}, \mathbf{w}) \text{ and } au + bv + cw = 0\}$$
$$= \{(x, y, z) : a(x - d) + b(y - e) + c(z - f) = 0\} .$$

This equation can also be derived using the fact that X is in $\mathcal{P}'$ iff $(\mathbf{F}, \mathbf{X}) \cdot \mathbf{N} = 0$. That is,

$$((d, e, f), (x, y, z)) \cdot [a, b, c] = [x - d, y - e, z - f] \cdot [a, b, c]$$
$$= a(x - d) + b(y - e) + c(z - f) = 0.$$

We summarize this as a theorem.

5.2-2 Theorem: The plane containing the point (d, e, f) and normal to the nonzero vector $[a, b, c]$ is given by the constraining equation

$$a(x - d) + b(y - e) + c(z - f) = 0.$$

The general form of an equation of a plane is thus a linear equation of the form

$$ax + by + cz = k,$$

where k is some constant and the vector $[a, b, c]$ is normal to the plane.

If $k = 0$, the plane contains the origin, otherwise, it contains the points $(k/a, 0, 0)$, $(0, k/b, 0)$, $(0, 0, k/c)$ for those coefficients a, b, c that are nonzero. These are the points at which the plane intersects the coordinate axes, and they are called *intercepts* of the plane.

Question: How is the number k related to the distance the plane is from the origin. (See Exercise 11.)

Example: An equation of the plane through the point $(5, 3, -1)$, such that the vector from $(5, 3, -1)$ to $(2, -2, -2)$ is normal to it is given by

$$((5, 3, -1), (2, -2, -2)) \cdot ((5, 3, -1), (x, y, z))$$
$$= [-3, -5, -1] \cdot [x - 5, y - 3, z + 1]$$
$$= -3(x - 5) + -5(y - 3) + -1(z + 1) = 0.$$

That is, $3x + 5y + z = 29$.

Lines

Let us develop equations for lines in space. As noted earlier, if (a, b, c) is a nonzero position vector, then the set

$$\{(x, y, z) : (x, y, z) = \alpha(a, b, c) \text{ for some } \alpha \in \mathbf{R}\}$$

of all scalar multiples of (a, b, c) is a line through the origin containing the point (a, b, c). Thus, equations for a line through the origin containing the point (a, b, c) may be given in *parametric* form by

$$x = \alpha a, \, y = \alpha b, \, z = \alpha c.$$

On elimination of the parameter α, we obtain

$$\alpha = \frac{x}{a} = \frac{y}{b} = \frac{z}{c},$$

assuming *a*, *b*, and *c* are nonzero. Thus, in this case, the line is given by the equations

$$\frac{x}{a} = \frac{y}{b} = \frac{z}{c}.$$

(Work Exercise 12 to analyze the cases in which at least one of numbers *a*, *b*, or *c* is zero.)

We may obtain equations for lines not necessarily containing the origin by adding a certain given vector to each position vector in a line through the origin. We demonstrate this with an example.

Example: Find the equations of a line $\mathcal{L}$ containing the points $(1, 3, -1)$ and $(4, -2, 3)$ [or equivalently, determined by the fixed vector $((1, 3, -1), (4, -2, 3))$].

Solution: The position vector $(\mathbf{4 - 1, -2 - 3, 3 - (-1)}) = (\mathbf{3, -5, 4})$ is parallel to the given line; thus so is the line $\mathcal{L}_o$ through the origin given by

$$\mathcal{L}_o = \{(x, y, z) : (\mathbf{x, y, z}) = \alpha(\mathbf{3, -5, 4}); \alpha \in \mathbf{R}\}.$$

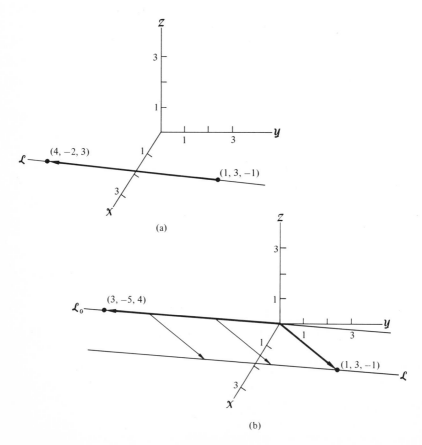

(a)

(b)

FIGURE 5.13

(See Figure 5.13(a) and (b).) Since the point $(1, 3, -1)$ is in the line $\mathcal{L}$, we may obtain the position vectors with terminal points in $\mathcal{L}$ by adding $(1, 3, -1)$ to each vector in $\mathcal{L}_o$. Thus,

$$\mathcal{L} = \{(x, y, z) : (\mathbf{x}, \mathbf{y}, \mathbf{z}) = \alpha(3, -5, 4) + (1, 3, -1); \alpha \in \mathbf{R}\}.$$

Hence, constraining equations for $\mathcal{L}$ are given parametrically by

$$x = 3\alpha + 1, \qquad y = -5\alpha + 3, \qquad z = 4\alpha - 1,$$

and, on elimination of the parameter (solving for α in each of these);

$$\frac{x - 1}{3} = \frac{y - 3}{-5} = \frac{z + 1}{4}$$

are nonparametric equations of the line. Adding the vector $(1, 3, -1)$ to each point of $\mathcal{L}_o$ can be viewed as shifting or translating $\mathcal{L}_o$ into $\mathcal{L}$ using vector addition.

We formalize this with a definition and a theorem.

5.2-3   Definition: A set of points $\mathcal{L}$ in space such that

$$\mathcal{L} = \{X : X = \alpha(\mathbf{B} - \mathbf{A}) + \mathbf{A}, \text{ for some } \alpha \in \mathbf{R}\}$$

is called a *line* passing through A and B. This line may also be called the *line determined by the fixed vector* (A, B). (See Figure 5.14.)

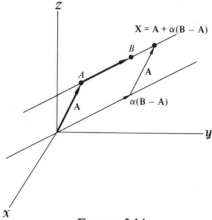

FIGURE 5.14

5.2-4   Theorem: The line in space containing the points (a, b, c) and (d, e, f) may be given parametrically by the equations

$$x = (a - d)\alpha + d, \qquad y = (b - e)\alpha + e, \qquad z = (c - f)\alpha + f.$$

If the coefficients of α are all nonzero, this parameter may be eliminated so that constraining equations of the line are

$$\frac{x-d}{a-d} = \frac{y-e}{b-e} = \frac{z-f}{c-f}.$$

PROOF: Let $A = (a, b, c)$ and $B = (d, e, f)$. The line

$$\mathcal{L}_o = \{Y : Y = \alpha(A - B) \text{ for some } \alpha \in R\}$$

is a line through the origin parallel to the desired line. By adding **B** to each vector with terminal point in $\mathcal{L}_o$, we have

$$\mathcal{L} = \{X : X = \alpha(A - B) + B; \alpha \in R\}.$$

(Note that $A \in \mathcal{L}$ (take $\alpha = 1$) and $B \in \mathcal{L}$ (take $\alpha = 0$).) Writing this in component form, we have

$$\mathcal{L} = \{(x\ y, z) : (x, y, z) = \alpha((a, b, c) - (d, e, f)) + (d, e, f); \alpha \in R\}$$
$$= \{(x, y, z) : (x, y, z) = (\alpha(a - d) + d, \alpha(b - e) + e, \alpha(c - f) + f)\}.$$

The nonparametric equations are obtained by solving each component equation for α and equating to eliminate α.

EXERCISES 5.2

1. Express each free vector given in terms of its position vector representative. Graph both the given representative and the position vector representative.
   a. $((1, 1, 3), (4, 6, 2))$.
   b. $((2, 4, -2), (3, 1, 1))$.
   c. $((-1, 0, 6), (2, 1, -3))$.
   d. $((2, 5, -3), (-7, 6, 2))$.

2. Determine the sum of the free vectors given, and express this sum both by the position vector representative and a representative at the point given.
   a. $((2, 1, 7), (2, 2, -1))$, $((2, 1, 7), (5, 1, -2))$; $(2, 1, 7)$.
   b. $((3, -1, 2), (4, 3, 1))$, $((-1, 2, 1), (2, 3, 5))$; $(1, 1, 1)$.
   c. $((5, 4, 3), (1, 4, 6))$, $((6, 2, -3), (4, 4, 4))$; $(2, 1, -6)$.
   d. $((-1, -2, 4), (-1, 6, 2))$, $((3, 4, 6), (1, 2, -1))$; $(6, 1, 7)$.

3. Determine the equation of the plane passing through the origin and normal to the indicated vector. Graph the vector and the plane.
   a. $(1, 2, 4)$.
   b. $(-2, 3, 1)$.
   c. $(5, -1, -2)$.
   e. $(2, -3, 4)$.

4. Determine the equation of the plane passing through the given point and normal to the given vector. Graph the vector with a representative having tail at the point given, and graph the plane.
   a. $(1, 5, 6)$, $[3, 4, 1]$.
   b. $(2, -1, 3)$, $[-1, -4, 1]$.
   c. $(3, 2, -1)$, $[2, 3, 4]$.
   d. $(0, -2, 1)$, $[-2, 2, 4]$.

5. A plane $ax + by + cz = k$, $k \neq 0$ is a plane that does not pass through $(0, 0, 0)$. Determine the distance (perpendicular) from $(0, 0, 0)$ to the plane. (HINT: (a, b, c) is normal to the plane, but (a, b, c) is not necessarily in the plane. However, for some α, $\alpha(a, b, c)$ has head in the plane.)

6. Determine parametric and nonparametric equations of the line containing the two points given.
   a. $(1, 2, 4)$, $(-1, 2, 3)$.
   b. $(3, 6, -1)$, $(5, 4, 2)$.
   c. $(7, -1, 2)$, $(3, 1, -4)$.
   d. $(1, 1, 1)$, $(3, 3, 4)$.
   e. $(5, 1, 3)$, $(-4, 2, -1)$.
   f. $(-2, -2, 1)$, $(2, 3, 1)$.

7. Show that the set of all position vectors in space normal to a given vector $(\mathbf{a}, \mathbf{b}, \mathbf{c})$ forms a vector space. That is, let $\mathcal{U} = \{(\mathbf{x}, \mathbf{y}, \mathbf{z}) : (\mathbf{x}, \mathbf{y}, \mathbf{z}) \cdot (\mathbf{a}, \mathbf{b}, \mathbf{c}) = 0\}$, and show that $\langle \mathcal{U}, \mathbf{R} \rangle$ satisfies the conditions of a vector space.

8. Why must a plane not containing the origin have at least one nonzero intercept? Under what graphical conditions will a plane have exactly one nonzero intercept? Exactly two? Exactly three?

9. Show that the set of all linear combinations of two noncollinear position vectors is a plane through the origin.

10. Give a definition of *parallel planes* using the concept of vectors normal to the planes.

11. Consider the planes $ax + by + cz = d_i$, for several choices of constants d_i. Explain how these planes differ. For what values of d_i does the plane contain $(0, 0, 0)$? For what value does it contain (α, β, γ)? (HINT: For any value of d_i, the vector $[\mathbf{a}, \mathbf{b}, \mathbf{c}]$ is normal to the plane.)

12. Consider the line described parametrically by $x = \alpha a$, $y = \alpha b$, $z = \alpha c$.
    a. Verify that the line passes through the points $(0, 0, 0)$ and (a, b, c).
    b. Eliminate the parameter to obtain equations for the line when (i) $a = 0$, $b \neq 0$, $c \neq 0$; (ii) $a = 0$, $b = 0$, $c \neq 0$. Give geometric descriptions of these lines.
    c. Eliminate the parameter in the parametric equations of Theorem 5.2-4 when not all of the coefficients are nonzero.

13. Show that the intersection of two nonparallel planes is a line.

14. Find the lengths of the medians of the triangle whose vertices are $(0, 4, -11)$, $(-3, 8, 1)$, $(7, 2, -3)$.

15. Show that $(2, -3, 8)$, $(-9, 0, 3)$, $(7, 4, -1)$ are vertices of an isosceles triangle.

16. Show that $(1, -3, 2)$, $(4, -2, 6)$, $(2, 2, 0)$ are the vertices of a right triangle.

5.3 PROJECTION OF VECTORS ON A LINE AND ON A PLANE. CUTTING A RIGHT CIRCULAR CONE WITH A PLANE

Projection on a Line

We have discussed how a vector in the plane can be projected on a line in that plane, and now wish to extend this notion to three-dimensional space. First, given two vectors $\mathbf{X}$ and $\mathbf{V}$, the projection of $\mathbf{X}$ on $\mathbf{V}$ (or the line $\mathcal{L}$ containing $\mathbf{V}$) denoted by $\mathbf{X}_\mathcal{L}$ or by $\mathbf{X}_\mathbf{V}$ is a scalar multiple of $\mathbf{V}$, as shown in Figure 5.15. The length of this projection, $|\mathbf{X}_\mathbf{V}|$, is given by

$$\pm |\mathbf{X}| \cos \theta,$$

where θ is the angle between $\mathbf{V}$ and $\mathbf{X}$. (If $\theta \in (\pi/2, 3\pi/2)$, the sign is $-$, otherwise it is $+$.) Since $\mathbf{X} \cdot \mathbf{V} = |\mathbf{X}| |\mathbf{V}| \cos \theta$, it follows that

$$|\mathbf{X}_\mathbf{V}| = \pm \frac{|\mathbf{X} \cdot \mathbf{V}|}{|\mathbf{V}|},$$

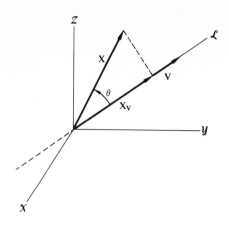

FIGURE 5.15

and since $\cos \theta$ is negative for $\theta \in (\pi/2, 3\pi/2)$, the projection itself is given as follows.

5.3-1 Definition: The projection of **X** onto **V** is given by

$$\mathbf{X_V} = \left(\frac{\mathbf{X} \cdot \mathbf{V}}{|\mathbf{V}|\,|\mathbf{V}|}\right) \mathbf{V} = \left(\frac{\mathbf{X} \cdot \mathbf{V}}{\mathbf{V} \cdot \mathbf{V}}\right) \mathbf{V}.$$

Example: Determine the projection of the vector $\mathbf{A} = ((1, 1, 1), (2, 1, 3))$ on the line determined by the fixed vector $V = ((2, 1, 3), (4, 2, 1))$.

Solution: First, translate the vectors to position vector representation: $\mathbf{A} = [1, 0, 2]$, and $\mathbf{V} = [2, 1, -2]$. The projection is given by

$$(|\mathbf{A}| \cos \theta)\frac{\mathbf{V}}{|\mathbf{V}|} = |\mathbf{A}|\,\frac{\mathbf{A} \cdot \mathbf{V}}{|\mathbf{A}|\,|\mathbf{V}|}\,\frac{\mathbf{V}}{|\mathbf{V}|} = \frac{\mathbf{A} \cdot \mathbf{V}}{\mathbf{V} \cdot \mathbf{V}}\,\mathbf{V} = -\tfrac{2}{9}[2, 1, -2]$$

$$= [-\tfrac{4}{9}, -\tfrac{2}{9}, \tfrac{4}{9}].$$

If one wishes to view this as emanating from the point $(2, 1, 3)$, we have

$$((2, 1, 3), (14/9, 7/9, 31/9)).$$

Projection on a Plane

Now suppose we are given the plane $\mathcal{P}$ described by the equation $ax + by + cz = d$ and we wish to find the projection $\mathbf{X}_{\mathcal{P}}$ of a vector **X** on the plane $\mathcal{P}$. (See Figure 5.16.) We proceed as follows. The vector **X** may be decomposed into a sum of two components, one along the normal to $\mathcal{P}$ and one lying in $\mathcal{P}$. The latter is precisely the projection we seek. (Since the vector we seek is a free vector, there is no loss of generality in assuming that the plane passes

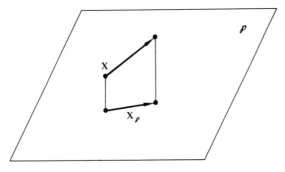

FIGURE 5.16

through the origin.) The component of X along the normal to $\mathcal{P}$ is the projection of X on $A = [a, b, c]$, which is given by

$$X_A = \frac{A \cdot X}{A \cdot A} A.$$

(See Figure 5.17.)

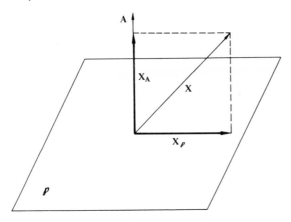

FIGURE 5.17

Hence, we desire a vector $X_{\mathcal{P}}$ such that

$$X_A + X_{\mathcal{P}} = X \qquad \text{and} \qquad X_{\mathcal{P}} \cdot A = 0.$$

The first equation represents the decomposition of X into two components, and the second condition ensures that the vector $X_{\mathcal{P}}$ lies in $\mathcal{P}$ (that is, X_A and $X_{\mathcal{P}}$ are mutually orthogonal). Solving for $X_{\mathcal{P}}$, we have

$$X_{\mathcal{P}} = X - X_A = X - \frac{A \cdot X}{A \cdot A} A.$$

This vector also satisfies the second equation and hence lies in the plane:

$$\left(X - \frac{A \cdot X}{A \cdot A}A\right) \cdot A = X \cdot A - A \cdot X\frac{A \cdot A}{A \cdot A} = X \cdot A - X \cdot A = 0.$$

5.3-2 **Definition:** The projection of a vector X on a plane with normal A is the vector

$$X_\mathcal{P} = X - \frac{X \cdot A}{A \cdot A}A.$$

One can easily apply this procedure to finding the fixed vector projection of a fixed vector onto a plane.

Example: Let us find the fixed vector projection of $((1, 2, 1), (3, 4, 2))$ on the plane $3x + 2y + 4z = 1$. We apply the procedure above to the free vector $[2, 2, 1]$, the plane $3x + 2y + 4z = 0$ and its normal $[3, 2, 4]$. Thus,

$$X_\mathcal{P} = [2, 2, 1] - \tfrac{14}{29}[3, 2, 4] = [16/29, 30/29, -27/29].$$

To find the particular fixed vector we seek, we need to know the point at which a normal passing through the point $(1, 2, 1)$ pierces the plane. Thus, if $((1, 2, 1), (x, y, z))$ is to be normal to the plane, then

$$[x - 1, y - 2, z - 1] = \alpha[3, 2, 4]$$

for some α, and if (x, y, z) satisfies the equation $3x + 2y + 4z = 1$, then (x, y, z) is in the plane. We have the equations

$$x - 1 = 3\alpha, \qquad y - 2 = 2\alpha, \qquad \text{and} \qquad z - 1 = 4\alpha,$$

or equivalently

$$x = 3\alpha + 1, \qquad y = 2\alpha + 2, \qquad \text{and} \qquad z = 4\alpha + 1.$$

Thus,

$$3(3\alpha + 1) + 2(2\alpha + 2) + 4(4\alpha + 1) = 1,$$

from which $\alpha = -\tfrac{10}{29}$. Hence, the point in the plane we desire is $(-\tfrac{1}{29}, \tfrac{38}{29}, -\tfrac{11}{29})$, and thus by shifting our free vector to this point, we have the desired fixed vector

$$((-\tfrac{1}{29}, \tfrac{38}{29}, -\tfrac{11}{29}), (\tfrac{15}{29}, \tfrac{68}{29}, -\tfrac{38}{29})).$$

Angle between a Line and a Plane

The *angle θ between a line and a plane* is defined to be the angle between a vector in the line and its projection in the plane. (See Figure 5.18.) Hence, if A is any nonzero vector in the line and N is a vector normal to the plane, the projection of A on the plane is given by

$$A_\mathcal{P} = A - \frac{N \cdot A}{|N|^2}N,$$

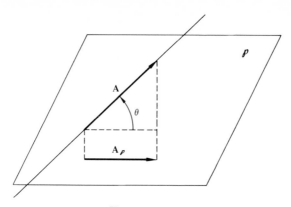

FIGURE 5.18

so that

$$\cos \theta = \frac{\mathbf{A} \cdot \mathbf{A}_{\varphi}}{|\mathbf{A}| \, |\mathbf{A}_{\varphi}|}$$

$$= \frac{\mathbf{A} \cdot \mathbf{A} - [(\mathbf{N} \cdot \mathbf{A})^2/|\mathbf{N}|^2]}{\sqrt{(\mathbf{A} \cdot \mathbf{A})} \sqrt{\left\{ \mathbf{A} - [(\mathbf{N} \cdot \mathbf{A})/|\mathbf{N}|^2] \mathbf{N} \right\} \cdot \left\{ \mathbf{A} - \left[\frac{(\mathbf{N} \cdot \mathbf{A})}{|\mathbf{N}|^2} \right] \mathbf{N} \right\}}},$$

(which after considerable computation)

$$= \sqrt{\frac{(\mathbf{N} \cdot \mathbf{N})(\mathbf{A} \cdot \mathbf{A}) - (\mathbf{N} \cdot \mathbf{A})^2}{(\mathbf{N} \cdot \mathbf{N})(\mathbf{A} \cdot \mathbf{A})}} = \sqrt{1 - \frac{(\mathbf{N} \cdot \mathbf{A})^2}{(\mathbf{N} \cdot \mathbf{N})(\mathbf{A} \cdot \mathbf{A})}}.$$

Example: The angle between the line $x = y = z$ and the plane $z = 0$ is easily interpreted geometrically. Let us verify the major steps in the derivation of $\cos \theta$ for this case. A normal to the plane is $\mathbf{N} = \mathbf{K} = (0, 0, 1)$ and a vector along the line is $\mathbf{A} = (1, 1, 1)$. Hence the projection of $\mathbf{A}$ on the plane is given by

$$\mathbf{A}_{\varphi} = (1, 1, 1) - \frac{(0, 0, 1) \cdot (1, 1, 1)}{(0, 0, 1) \cdot (0, 0, 1)} (0, 0, 1)$$

$$= (1, 1, 1) - (0, 0, 1) = (1, 1, 0),$$

(as one might have guessed). (See Figure 5.19.)
Thus,

$$\mathbf{A} \cdot \mathbf{A}_{\varphi} = |\mathbf{A}| \, |\mathbf{A}_{\varphi}| \cos \theta,$$

so

$$(1, 1, 1) \cdot (1, 1, 0) = \sqrt{3} \sqrt{2} \cos \theta,$$

and so

$$\cos \theta = \frac{2}{\sqrt{3} \sqrt{2}} = \sqrt{\frac{2}{3}}.$$

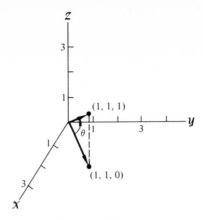

FIGURE 5.19

Note that we could apply the formula from the above derivation and have

$$\cos \theta = \sqrt{1 - \frac{((1, 1, 1) \cdot (0, 0, 1))^2}{3}} = \sqrt{\frac{2}{3}}.$$

Distance from a Point to a Plane

By the distance from a point A to a plane $\mathcal{P}$ is meant the distance from A to the point in $\mathcal{P}$ nearest A. This is the length of a fixed vector normal to $\mathcal{P}$ with head at A and tail in the plane. The length of this vector is the length of the projection of any vector from a point X of $\mathcal{P}$ to A upon a vector normal to the plane. (See Figure 5.20.) We illustrate the method of finding this distance with an example.

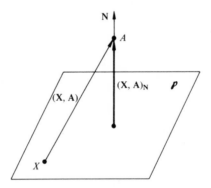

FIGURE 5.20

Example: Find the distance from the point $(5, -2, -4)$ to the plane $2x - 3y + z = 10$.

Solution: Since the point $(1, -1, 5)$ is in the plane, the fixed vector $((1, -1, 5), (5, -2, -4))$ is from the plane to the point. We thus seek the length of the projection of $((1, -1, 5), (5, -2, -4)) = [4, -1, -9]$ upon the vector $[2, -3, 1]$ normal to the plane. This projection has length given by

$$\left| \frac{[2, -3, 1] \cdot [4, -1. -9]}{|[2, -3, 1]|} \right| = \left| \frac{8 + 3 - 9}{\sqrt{4 + 9 + 1}} \right| = \frac{2}{\sqrt{14}}.$$

Incidentally, the projection itself is the vector

$$\frac{2}{\sqrt{14}} \frac{[2, -3, 1]}{|[2, -3, 1]|} = \frac{1}{7} [2, -3, 1].$$

Cutting a Right Circular Cone with a Plane

Let us take this opportunity to justify calling curves in the plane that have Cartesian equations of the form

$$Ax^2 + Bxy + Cy^2 + Dx + Ey + F = 0,$$

conic sections.

We will consider a *right circular cone* in $\mathbf{R}^3$ and determine the equation of the curve which results from cutting the cone with the x–y plane.

In order to describe a cone, let us specify a point A for the *vertex*, a vector $\mathbf{N}$ to specify the direction of the axis, and an angle θ called the *half-angle* of the cone (see Figure 5.21). Any point X on the cone must satisfy one of the following vector equations:

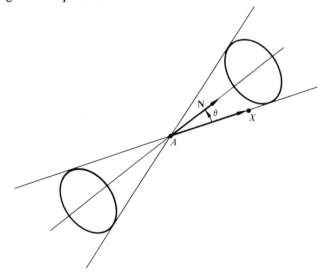

FIGURE 5.21

$$(\mathbf{A}, \mathbf{X}) \cdot \mathbf{N} = |(\mathbf{A}, \mathbf{X})| \; |\mathbf{N}| \cos \theta,$$
$$(\mathbf{A}, \mathbf{X}) \cdot (-\mathbf{N}) = |(\mathbf{A}, \mathbf{X})| \; |\mathbf{N}| \cos \theta.$$

This can be written as the single equation

$$|(\mathbf{A}, \mathbf{X}) \cdot \mathbf{N}| = |(\mathbf{A}, \mathbf{X})| \; |\mathbf{N}| \; |\cos \theta|.$$

We are able to use this information to define formally what is meant by a cone in $\mathbf{R}^3$.

5.3-3   Definition: A *right circular cone* with *vertex* at the point A, and axis in the direction of $\mathbf{N}$ is the set

$$\{X : |(\mathbf{A}, \mathbf{X}) \cdot \mathbf{N}| = |(\mathbf{A}, \mathbf{X})|\lambda\},$$

where $0 < \lambda$. The line $\mathbf{A} + t\mathbf{N}$ is called the *axis*, and θ is called the *half-angle* of the cone where $\cos \theta = \dfrac{\lambda}{|\mathbf{N}|}$.

Let us put this information in terms of coordinatized space. We can write this vector equation in terms of the components where $(x, y, z) = X$, $(a, b, c) = A$, and $[\alpha, \beta, \gamma] = \mathbf{N}$, to obtain

$$|((\mathbf{a}, \mathbf{b}, \mathbf{c}), (\mathbf{x}, \mathbf{y}, \mathbf{z})) \cdot [\alpha, \beta, \gamma]| = |((\mathbf{a}, \mathbf{b}, \mathbf{c}), (\mathbf{x}, \mathbf{y}, \mathbf{z}))|\lambda,$$

or equivalently

$$|[\mathbf{x} - \mathbf{a}, \mathbf{y} - \mathbf{b}, \mathbf{z} - \mathbf{c}] \cdot [\alpha, \beta, \gamma]| = \lambda|[\mathbf{x} - \mathbf{a}, \mathbf{y} - \mathbf{b}, \mathbf{z} - \mathbf{c}]|.$$

Thus,

$$|(x - a)\alpha + (y - b)\beta + (z - c)\gamma| = \lambda\sqrt{(x - a)^2 + (y - b)^2 + (z - c)^2},$$

and by squaring both sides, we have the general equation for a cone in three dimensional space:

$$((x - a)\alpha + (y - b)\beta + (z - c)\gamma)^2 = \lambda^2((x - a)^2 + (y - b)^2 + (z - c)^2).$$

The equation for the plane curve that results from the intersection of the cone with the x–y plane is given by setting $z = 0$. Thus, the equation of a conic section is given by

$$((x - a)\alpha + (y - b)\beta - c\gamma)^2 = \lambda^2((x - a)^2 + (y - b)^2 + c^2).$$

It is easy to show that this results in an equation of the form

$$Ax^2 + Bxy + Cy^2 + Dx + Ey + F = 0.$$

Question: Why is it sufficiently general to consider only the case in which a cone is cut by the x–y plane?

Example: Let us find the equation of the conic section obtained by cutting with the x–y plane, the cone with vertex $(1, 2, 1)$, half angle $\pi/3$, and whose axis is the line determined by the fixed vector $((1, 2, 1), (3, 2, 2))$. The equation of the cone is

$$|((\mathbf{x}, \mathbf{y}, \mathbf{z}) - (1, 2, 1)) \cdot ((3, 2, 2) - (1, 2, 1))|$$
$$= |(\mathbf{x} - 1, \mathbf{y} - 2, \mathbf{z} - 1)| \; |(2, 0, 1)| \cos \pi/3.$$

On squaring both sides we have

$$(2(x - 1) + 0(y - 2) + 1(z - 1))^2$$
$$= ((x - 1)^2 + (y - 2)^2 + (z - 1)^2)5(\tfrac{1}{2})^2.$$

Setting $z = 0$, and simplifying, we have

$$11x^2 - 5y^2 - 58x + 20y + 6 = 0.$$

Applying Theorem 4.4-3, we see that this is a hyperbola since

$$\begin{vmatrix} 11 & 0 \\ 0 & -5 \end{vmatrix} = -55 < 0$$

(See Figure 5.22.)

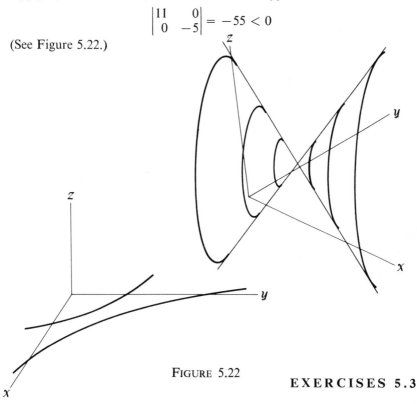

FIGURE 5.22

EXERCISES 5.3

1. Find the projection of the vector **A** on the line determined by the fixed vector *V*. Express this as a vector with tail at the tail of *V*.
    a. $\mathbf{A} = [2, 3, -1]$; $V = ((0, 0, 0), (4, 1, 1))$.
    b. $\mathbf{A} = [5, 1, -1]$; $V = ((2, 1, 3), (6, -1, 4))$.
    c. $\mathbf{A} = ((1, 3, 1), (4, 2, 3))$; $V = ((2, 1, 7), (6, 4, -1))$.
    d. $\mathbf{A} = ((4, 6, 1), (2, 3, 7))$; $V = ((1, 1, 1), (6, 4, 7))$.

2. Find the projection of the vector **A** onto the plane whose equation is given. Represent the vector with tail at *O*. Find the cosine of the angle between the vector and the plane.
    a. $\mathbf{A} = [2, 3, 4]$; $3x + 2y + 4z = 0$.
    b. $\mathbf{A} = [-1, 4, -2]$; $2x + 2y + 3z = 2$.
    c. $\mathbf{A} = ((2, 1, 2), (5, 3, 1))$; $6x + y - z = 1$.
    d. $\mathbf{A} = ((5, 1, 3), (2, -1, 1))$; $-2x - 3y + z = 7$.

3. Find the fixed vector projection of the given fixed vector onto the given plane.
   a. $((2, 1, 3), (5, 7, 1))$; $2x + 2y - 3z = 4$.
   b. $((0, 1, 7), (2, 4, 2))$; $5x - y + 2z - 1$.
   c. $((3, 1, 2), (4, 1, 6))$; $2x + y - 7z = 6$.
   d. $((1, 2, 1), (5, 3, 4))$; $z = 0$.

4. Under what geometrical conditions will the projection of a vector $\mathbf{A}$ on a plane be (a) the zero vector? (b) the vector $\mathbf{A}$?

5. Find the distance from the given point to the given plane.
   a. $(2, -2, 3)$, $6x + 3y + 7z = 0$.   b. $(5, 1, -7)$, $2x - 7y - 3z = 5$.
   c. $(2, 3, -6)$, $-6x + 2y + z = 7$.   d. $(-1, 4, 5)$, $x - y - z = 2$.

6. Find the equation of the conic section determined by cutting with the x–y plane the cone having vertex A, half-angle θ, and axis in the direction of the vector $\mathbf{N}$. (Sketch the cone and guess in advance whether the result will be an ellipse, a hyperbola, or a parabola. Use Theorem 4.4-3 to test the guess.)
   a. $A = (1, -1, 2)$, $\mathbf{N} = [1, 1, 1]$, $\theta = \mathrm{Cos}^{-1}\,\tfrac{1}{3}$.
   b. $A = (2, 1, -1)$, $\mathbf{N} = [1, 2, -2]$, $\theta = \pi/3$.
   c. $A = (-1, 3, 0)$, $\mathbf{N} = [2, -3, 1]$, $\theta = \mathrm{Cos}^{-1}\,\tfrac{1}{4}$.
   d. $A = (2, -2, 3)$, $\mathbf{N} = [-1, 2, -3]$, $\theta = \mathrm{Cos}^{-1}\,\tfrac{3}{5}$.

7. For what value of θ will the intersection of the x–y plane with the cone having vertex $(3, 3, 3)$, half-angle θ, and axis containing the point $(4, 5, 4)$ be a parabola?

8. Suppose $\mathbf{A} = (a, b, c)$ makes angles α, β, γ with $\mathbf{I}$, $\mathbf{J}$, and $\mathbf{K}$, respectively. Then $\cos \alpha$, $\cos \beta$, and $\cos \gamma$ are called the *direction cosines* of $\mathbf{A}$.

   a. Show that $\cos \alpha = \dfrac{a}{\sqrt{a^2 + b^2 + c^2}}$.

   b. State and prove similar formulas for $\cos \beta$ and $\cos \gamma$.
   c. Verify that
   $$\cos^2 \alpha + \cos^2 \beta + \cos^2 \gamma = 1,$$
   and hence show that
   $$\cos \alpha\, \mathbf{I} + \cos \beta\, \mathbf{J} + \cos \gamma\, \mathbf{K}$$
   is a unit vector having the same direction as $\mathbf{A}$. (Explain how this reduces to the trigonometric identity $\cos^2 \theta + \sin^2 \theta = 1$ in the two-dimensional case.)

5.4 SYSTEMS OF EQUATIONS AND MATRIX NOTATION. DETERMINANTS

We have seen that a linear equation
$$ax + by + cz = d$$
defines a plane in space. It should be the case that the intersection of two sets of points described by linear equations is a set described by equations of the form
$$\frac{x - \alpha}{a} = \frac{y - \beta}{b} = \frac{z - \gamma}{c},$$

since the intersection of two nonparallel planes is a line. Similarly, the intersection of three planes, no two of which are parallel, is a point. We are thus led to the problem of finding such intersections of planes, which from an analytic point of view is the problem of "solving systems of linear equations."

In dealing with systems of linear equations, it is convenient to use matrix notation. We thus pause to discuss 3×3 matrices and their addition and multiplication.

Matrices

A 3×3 matrix A is an array consisting of three rows and three columns of numbers in the form

$$A = \begin{bmatrix} a_{11} & a_{12} & a_{13} \\ a_{21} & a_{22} & a_{23} \\ a_{31} & a_{32} & a_{33} \end{bmatrix}.$$

The ijth component of A is the element a_{ij} in the ith row and jth column of A. Two matrices A and B are equal iff their corresponding components are equal. We add matrices componentwise:

$$A + B = \begin{bmatrix} a_{11} & a_{12} & a_{13} \\ a_{21} & a_{22} & a_{23} \\ a_{31} & a_{32} & a_{33} \end{bmatrix} + \begin{bmatrix} b_{11} & b_{12} & b_{13} \\ b_{21} & b_{22} & b_{23} \\ b_{31} & b_{32} & b_{33} \end{bmatrix}$$

$$= \begin{bmatrix} a_{11} + b_{11} & a_{12} + b_{12} & a_{13} + b_{13} \\ a_{21} + b_{21} & a_{22} + b_{22} & a_{23} + b_{23} \\ a_{31} + b_{31} & a_{32} + b_{32} & a_{33} + b_{33} \end{bmatrix}.$$

A scalar times a matrix A is also defined componentwise:

$$\alpha A = \alpha \begin{bmatrix} a_{11} & a_{12} & a_{13} \\ a_{21} & a_{22} & a_{23} \\ a_{31} & a_{32} & a_{33} \end{bmatrix} = \begin{bmatrix} \alpha a_{11} & \alpha a_{12} & \alpha a_{13} \\ \alpha a_{21} & \alpha a_{22} & \alpha a_{23} \\ \alpha a_{31} & \alpha a_{32} & \alpha a_{33} \end{bmatrix}.$$

In the exercises, you are asked to verify that the set $\mathfrak{M}$ of all 3×3 matrices forms a vector space $\langle \mathfrak{M}, R \rangle$ under these operations.

In addition to these operations, we define *matrix multiplication* as follows: the ijth element of the product AB of A and B is the dot product of the ith row of A with the jth column of B, where these rows and columns are viewed as vectors in $\langle R^3, R \rangle$.

5.4-1 Definition: The component c_{ij} in the matrix $C = AB$ is computed by taking the dot product

$$[a_{i1}\, a_{i2}\, a_{i3}] \cdot \begin{bmatrix} b_{1j} \\ b_{2j} \\ b_{3j} \end{bmatrix} = a_{i1}b_{1j} + a_{i2}b_{2j} + a_{i3}b_{3j}$$

of the ith row of A and the jth column of B.

For example, the component in the first row and first column of $C = AB$ is

$$c_{11} = [a_{11}\ a_{12}\ a_{13}] \cdot \begin{bmatrix} b_{11} \\ b_{21} \\ b_{31} \end{bmatrix} = a_{11}b_{11} + a_{12}b_{21} + a_{13}b_{31}.$$

Example: Suppose

$$A = \begin{bmatrix} 1 & 2 & 3 \\ 0 & -1 & 1 \\ 2 & 5 & 2 \end{bmatrix} \quad \text{and} \quad B = \begin{bmatrix} -1 & 2 & 0 \\ 1 & 3 & 6 \\ 10 & -6 & -6 \end{bmatrix}.$$

Then

$$2A = 2\begin{bmatrix} 1 & 2 & 3 \\ 0 & -1 & 1 \\ 2 & 5 & 2 \end{bmatrix} = \begin{bmatrix} 2 & 4 & 6 \\ 0 & -2 & 2 \\ 4 & 10 & 4 \end{bmatrix}$$

$$A + B = \begin{bmatrix} 0 & 4 & 3 \\ 1 & 2 & 7 \\ 12 & -1 & -4 \end{bmatrix}$$

$$AB = \begin{bmatrix} -1+2+30 & 2+6-18 & 0+12-18 \\ 0-1+10 & 0-3-6 & 0-6-6 \\ -2+5+20 & 4+15-12 & 0+30-12 \end{bmatrix}$$

$$= \begin{bmatrix} 31 & -10 & -6 \\ 9 & -9 & -12 \\ 23 & 7 & 18 \end{bmatrix}.$$

Incidentally, since

$$BA = \begin{bmatrix} -1 & -4 & -1 \\ 13 & 29 & 18 \\ -2 & -4 & 12 \end{bmatrix} \neq AB,$$

we know that matrix multiplication is not a commutative operation.

5.4-2   Theorem: Matrix multiplication is associative; that is, if A, B, and C are 3×3 matrices, then $(AB)C = A(BC)$.

PROOF: Although there are more sophisticated ways to establish this result, for 3×3 matrices it should not be beyond the skill of the student to show this simply by computing.

An examination of our definition of matrix multiplication reveals that we can define the product of two matrices C and D whenever the number of columns of C equals the number of rows of D.

Example:

$$\begin{bmatrix} 1 & 2 & 3 \\ 0 & -1 & 1 \\ 2 & 5 & 2 \end{bmatrix}\begin{bmatrix} -1 & 2 \\ 1 & 3 \\ 10 & -6 \end{bmatrix} = \begin{bmatrix} 31 & -10 \\ 9 & -9 \\ 23 & 7 \end{bmatrix}$$

and

$$\begin{bmatrix} 1 & 2 & 3 \\ 0 & -1 & 1 \\ 2 & 5 & 2 \end{bmatrix} \begin{bmatrix} -1 \\ 1 \\ 10 \end{bmatrix} = \begin{bmatrix} 31 \\ 9 \\ 23 \end{bmatrix}.$$

Remark: We find it convenient to identify matrices of the form

$$\begin{bmatrix} a \\ b \\ c \end{bmatrix} \quad \text{and} \quad [a\,b\,c]$$

with vectors in $\langle \mathbf{R}^3, \mathbf{R} \rangle$. Indeed, we have anticipated this by using the same

notation for both. We shall sometimes refer to $\begin{bmatrix} a \\ b \\ c \end{bmatrix}$ as a *column vector*

and $[a\,b\,c]$ as a *row vector* when dealing with a context involving matrices.

A System of Equations Written as a Matrix Equation

We now use the idea of matrix multiplication in connection with the descriptions of systems of equations in three unknowns. Consider the system of equations

$$\begin{aligned} a_{11}x + a_{12}y + a_{13}z &= c_1 \\ a_{21}x + a_{22}y + a_{23}z &= c_2 \\ a_{31}x + a_{32}y + a_{33}z &= c_3. \end{aligned} \qquad (1)$$

A vector $\begin{bmatrix} x \\ y \\ z \end{bmatrix}$ is a solution of the system if and only if the matrix $\begin{bmatrix} x \\ y \\ z \end{bmatrix}$ satisfies

the matrix equation

$$\begin{bmatrix} a_{11} & a_{12} & a_{13} \\ a_{21} & a_{22} & a_{23} \\ a_{31} & a_{32} & a_{33} \end{bmatrix} \begin{bmatrix} x \\ y \\ z \end{bmatrix} = \begin{bmatrix} c_1 \\ c_2 \\ c_3 \end{bmatrix}.$$

We see that a system of linear equations can be described by a matrix equation $AX = C$, where A is the matrix of coefficients of the unknowns, X is the matrix (vector) of unknowns, and C is the matrix of "constant coefficients."

Example: We may write the system

$$\begin{aligned} 3x + 2y + z &= 4 \\ x + 3y - z &= 0 \\ 2x + 7y \phantom{{}- z} &= 0 \end{aligned}$$

in matrix form by the matrix equation

$$\begin{bmatrix} 3 & 2 & 1 \\ 1 & 3 & -1 \\ 2 & 7 & 0 \end{bmatrix} \begin{bmatrix} x \\ y \\ z \end{bmatrix} = \begin{bmatrix} 4 \\ 0 \\ 0 \end{bmatrix}.$$

Consider the three planes described by the equations in the system (1). These three planes intersect in a unique point provided that no one plane is parallel to the line of intersection of the other two, or equivalently, provided that the three normal vectors $[\mathbf{a}_{11}, \mathbf{a}_{12}, \mathbf{a}_{13}]$, $[\mathbf{a}_{21}, \mathbf{a}_{22}, \mathbf{a}_{23}]$, and $[\mathbf{a}_{31}, \mathbf{a}_{32}, \mathbf{a}_{33}]$ are linearly independent. Since intersection of the planes in a unique point is the geometric analogue of a unique solution to the corresponding system of equations, we have the following theorem.

5.4-3   Theorem: The system of linear equations $AX = C$, where A, X, and C are as described above, has a unique solution iff the rows of A are linearly independent.

The Determinant

Let us now examine the property of Theorem 5.4-3 a bit further. By definition, the rows of A (expressed as vectors) are linearly independent iff there are no constants α, β, γ, not all zero, such that

$$\alpha(a_{11}, a_{12}, a_{13}) + \beta(a_{21}, a_{22}, a_{23}) + \gamma(a_{31}, a_{32}, a_{33}) = (0, 0, 0).$$

This is equivalent to the statement that the matrix equation

$$\begin{bmatrix} a_{11} & a_{21} & a_{31} \\ a_{12} & a_{22} & a_{32} \\ a_{13} & a_{23} & a_{33} \end{bmatrix} \begin{bmatrix} \alpha \\ \beta \\ \gamma \end{bmatrix} = \begin{bmatrix} 0 \\ 0 \\ 0 \end{bmatrix},$$

has only the solution $\begin{bmatrix} 0 \\ 0 \\ 0 \end{bmatrix}$.

Suppose for a moment that this matrix equation has a solution other than $\begin{bmatrix} 0 \\ 0 \\ 0 \end{bmatrix}$, where $\alpha \neq 0$ (this can be accomplished by interchanging equations if necessary). Then on dividing through each equation by α, we obtain

$$a_{21}\frac{\beta}{\alpha} + a_{31}\frac{\gamma}{\alpha} = -a_{11}$$

$$a_{22}\frac{\beta}{\alpha} + a_{32}\frac{\gamma}{\alpha} = -a_{12}$$

$$a_{23}\frac{\beta}{\alpha} + a_{33}\frac{\gamma}{\alpha} = -a_{13}.$$

We can solve the first two equations to obtain

$$\begin{bmatrix} \dfrac{\beta}{\alpha} \\ \dfrac{\gamma}{\alpha} \end{bmatrix} = \begin{bmatrix} \dfrac{-a_{11}a_{32} + a_{12}a_{31}}{a_{21}a_{32} - a_{31}a_{22}} \\ \dfrac{a_{11}a_{22} - a_{12}a_{21}}{a_{21}a_{32} - a_{31}a_{22}} \end{bmatrix},$$

provided

$$\begin{vmatrix} a_{21} & a_{31} \\ a_{22} & a_{32} \end{vmatrix} \neq 0$$

(otherwise solve a different pair of equations; if all three 2×2 determinants involved are zero, then the result we are leading to is automatic). Since this solution for β/α and γ/α must also satisfy the third equation

$$a_{23} \frac{\beta}{\alpha} + a_{33} \frac{\gamma}{\alpha} = -a_{13},$$

we have

$$-a_{23}a_{11}a_{32} + a_{23}a_{12}a_{31} + a_{33}a_{11}a_{22} - a_{33}a_{12}a_{21} + a_{13}a_{21}a_{32} - a_{13}a_{31}a_{22} = 0.$$

The expression on the left of this equation can be written using 2×2 determinants as

$$a_{11}\begin{vmatrix} a_{22} & a_{23} \\ a_{32} & a_{33} \end{vmatrix} - a_{12}\begin{vmatrix} a_{21} & a_{23} \\ a_{31} & a_{33} \end{vmatrix} + a_{13}\begin{vmatrix} a_{21} & a_{22} \\ a_{31} & a_{32} \end{vmatrix}, \tag{2}$$

which as we have just shown is zero if the row vectors in question are linearly dependent. Conversely, if this expression is zero, we can reverse our computation and find many nonzero solutions for our equation, thus showing that the row vectors are dependent.

5.4-4 Definition: The *determinant* of the 3×3 matrix

$$A = \begin{bmatrix} a_{11} & a_{12} & a_{13} \\ a_{21} & a_{22} & a_{23} \\ a_{31} & a_{32} & a_{33} \end{bmatrix}$$

is the number given in expression (2). It is denoted by $\det A$ or by $|A|$.

Remark: Notice that each term in the determinant expression (2) is plus or minus the product of one component of the top row vector and the determinant of the 2×2 matrix gotten by removing the top row and the column containing the component. For example, the first term is gotten by

$$\begin{bmatrix} \boxed{a_{11}} & a_{12} & a_{13} \\ a_{21} & \boxed{\begin{matrix} a_{22} & a_{23} \\ a_{32} & a_{33} \end{matrix}} \\ a_{31} & \end{bmatrix}.$$

We have shown that the row vectors are linearly dependent iff $|A| = |0|$.

5.4-5 Theorem: The rows of a 3×3 matrix A are linearly dependent iff $|A| = 0$.

5.4-6 Corollary: The system of linear equations $AX = C$ has a unique solution iff $|A| \neq 0$.

We conclude this discussion by extending the notion of the transpose of a matrix to 3×3 matrices.

5.4-7 Definition: The transpose of the 3×3 matrix A shown in 5.4-4 is the matrix A^t obtained from A by interchanging rows and columns. That is

$$A^t = \begin{bmatrix} a_{11} & a_{21} & a_{31} \\ a_{12} & a_{22} & a_{32} \\ a_{13} & a_{23} & a_{33} \end{bmatrix}.$$

5.4-8 Theorem: $|A| = |A^t|$.

Proof left as an exercise.

EXERCISES 5.4

1. Show that the set of 3×3 matrices forms a vector space where addition and scalar multiplication is as given in this section.

2. Use matrix multiplication and determine AB and BA (whenever possible), where:

   a. $A = \begin{bmatrix} 1 & 2 \\ 1 & 1 \end{bmatrix}$, $B = \begin{bmatrix} 2 & 2 \\ 1 & 4 \end{bmatrix}$.

   b. $A = \begin{bmatrix} 1 & 2 & 2 \end{bmatrix}$, $B = \begin{bmatrix} 2 & 1 \\ 3 & 1 \\ 1 & 1 \end{bmatrix}$.

   c. $A = \begin{bmatrix} 0 & 1 & 4 \\ 2 & 1 & 1 \\ 4 & 0 & 2 \end{bmatrix}$, $B = \begin{bmatrix} 1 & 4 & 1 \\ 1 & 3 & 6 \end{bmatrix}$.

   d. $A = \begin{bmatrix} 1 & 0 & 0 \\ 0 & 1 & 0 \\ 0 & 0 & 1 \end{bmatrix}$, $B = \begin{bmatrix} 2 & 4 \\ 1 & 2 \\ 4 & 3 \end{bmatrix}$.

   e. $A = \begin{bmatrix} 0 & 1 & 0 \\ 1 & 0 & 0 \\ 0 & 0 & 0 \end{bmatrix}$, $B = \begin{bmatrix} 1 & 4 & 7 \\ 9 & 9 & 3 \\ 2 & 8 & 0 \end{bmatrix}$.

3. Write each of the following systems of equations as a matrix equation.

a. $2x - y + z = 1$	b. $x - 2y + z = 4$	c. $3x - 2y = 1$
$x - y - z = 2$	$2x - 3y + z = 1$	$x - y - z = 4$
$3x - 2y - z = -1.$	$3x - 2y - z = 2.$	$3x + y = -4.$

4. Write each of the following matrix equations as a system of equations without using matrices.

   a. $\begin{bmatrix} 3 & -6 & 5 \\ 2 & -1 & 1 \\ 1 & -2 & 4 \end{bmatrix} \begin{bmatrix} x \\ y \\ z \end{bmatrix} = \begin{bmatrix} 9 \\ -1 \\ 3 \end{bmatrix}$.   b. $\begin{bmatrix} 1 & 1 & 1 \\ 1 & -1 & 0 \\ 3 & 1 & 0 \end{bmatrix} \begin{bmatrix} x \\ y \\ z \end{bmatrix} = \begin{bmatrix} 3 \\ 4 \\ 6 \end{bmatrix}$.

5. The 3×3 matrix

   $$I = \begin{bmatrix} 1 & 0 & 0 \\ 0 & 1 & 0 \\ 0 & 0 & 1 \end{bmatrix}$$

   is called an *identity matrix*. Show that $BI = IB = B$ for any 3×3 matrix B.

6. Suppose

$$A = \begin{bmatrix} a & 0 & 0 \\ 0 & a & 0 \\ 0 & 0 & a \end{bmatrix},$$

where $a > 0$.

  a. Compute $AA = A^2$ and $A^3 = AA^2$.   b. How would you define $A^{1/2}$?

7. Consider the matrix

$$A = \begin{bmatrix} 2 & 1 & 1 \\ 3 & 1 & 4 \\ 1 & 2 & -1 \end{bmatrix}.$$

  a. Find a matrix B such that

$$BA = \begin{bmatrix} 2 & 1 & 1 \\ 1 & 2 & -1 \\ 3 & 1 & 4 \end{bmatrix},$$

that is, interchanges the last two rows of A). (HINT: Try the identity matrix with the last two rows interchanged.)

  b. Find a matrix B such that

$$BA = \begin{bmatrix} 2 & 1 & 1 \\ 3 & 1 & 4 \\ 2 & 4 & -2 \end{bmatrix}.$$

  c. Find a matrix B such that

$$BA = \begin{bmatrix} 6 & 3 & 3 \\ 3 & 1 & 4 \\ 2 & 4 & -2 \end{bmatrix}.$$

  d. Find a matrix B such that

$$BA = \begin{bmatrix} 2 & 1 & 1 \\ 6 & 2 & 8 \\ 2 & 4 & -2 \end{bmatrix}.$$

  e. Find a matrix B such that

$$BA = \begin{bmatrix} 2 & 1 & 1 \\ 6 & 2 & 8 \\ 2 & -1 & 5 \end{bmatrix}.$$

8. Show that matrix multiplication of 3×3 matrices (a) is associative and (b) distributes over matrix addition.

9. Show that $|I| = 1$, where I is the 3×3 identity matrix.

10. Let

$$A = \begin{bmatrix} 1 & -1 & 4 \\ -1 & 2 & 0 \\ 0 & 1 & 1 \end{bmatrix}$$

  a. List the column vectors of A.
  b. List the row vectors.
  c. Are the column vectors independent?
  d. Are the row vectors independent?

11. Show geometrically that the following system of equations has no solution.

$$\begin{aligned} x + y + z &= 0 \\ 2x + 2y + 2z &= 1 \\ x + 2y - z &= 2 \\ x + 2y - z &= 0. \end{aligned}$$

12. Describe the set of solutions for the following system.

$$2x + y + z = 0$$
$$x - y + 2z = 3.$$

13. Compute $|A|$ where

a.
$$A = \begin{bmatrix} 1 & 3 & 4 \\ -1 & 2 & -1 \\ 6 & 1 & 1 \end{bmatrix}$$

b.
$$A = \begin{bmatrix} 2 & 1 & 1 \\ 3 & -1 & 4 \\ 4 & 2 & 2 \end{bmatrix}$$

c.
$$A = \begin{bmatrix} 3 & -1 & -1 \\ 1 & 4 & 2 \\ 1 & 1 & 1 \end{bmatrix}$$

^{t} d.
$$A = \begin{bmatrix} 1 & 2 & 1 \\ 3 & 1 & 1 \\ 4 & 3 & 2 \end{bmatrix}.$$

14. Show that the determinant of a 3×3 matrix with a column or row of zeros has determinant 0.

15. Show that the equation $AX = C$ has a unique solution iff the column vectors are independent. (HINT: The existence of a solution is exactly the statement that some linear combination of the columns gives C.)

16. Investigate (prove or disprove): If the rows of a 3×3 matrix are linearly dependent, then so are the columns.

17. a. Draw the three planes in three-dimensional space given by the following three constraining equations.

$$2x - 3y + z = 0$$
$$x + y + z = 1$$
$$3x - 2y + 2z = 1.$$

b. Write the system of equations in the form $AX = C$ and show that $|A| = 0$.

c. Graph the solution set for the equation $AX = C$.

18. Show that $|A^t| = |A|$.

19. Is it possible to find matrices B and C such that $BAC = A^t$?

5.5 THREE BY THREE MATRIX INVERSES AND CRAMER'S RULE

In the preceding section, we show how a system of three linear equations in three unknowns,

$$a_{11}x + a_{12}y + a_{13}z = c_1$$
$$a_{21}x + a_{22}y + a_{23}z = c_2$$
$$a_{31}x + a_{32}y + a_{33}z = c_3,$$

may be written as the matrix equation $AX = C$, where

$$A = \begin{bmatrix} a_{11} & a_{12} & a_{13} \\ a_{21} & a_{22} & a_{23} \\ a_{31} & a_{32} & a_{33} \end{bmatrix}, \quad X = \begin{bmatrix} x \\ y \\ z \end{bmatrix}, \quad C = \begin{bmatrix} c_1 \\ c_2 \\ c_3 \end{bmatrix}.$$

In order that we may find a solution vector $\begin{bmatrix} x \\ y \\ z \end{bmatrix}$ for the system, it suffices to find the inverse of A, that is a matrix A^{-1} such that $A^{-1}A = I$, where I is the 3×3 identity matrix. This is clear since, if such a matrix A^{-1} exists, multiplying both sides of $AX = C$ on the left by A^{-1} yields

$$A^{-1}(AX) = (A^{-1}A)X = IX = X = A^{-1}C.$$

The solution is thus the vector $A^{-1}C$.

As in the 2×2 case studied earlier, a matrix is called *nonsingular* when it has an inverse; otherwise it is said to be *singular*. For 2×2 matrices, we found that a condition that characterizes singularity is that the determinant of the matrix should be zero. This in turn was interpreted geometrically as meaning that the rows of the corresponding matrix were linearly dependent. In the present section, we shall establish similar properties for 3×3 matrices and their inverses. In order to establish our result, we shall find it convenient first to develop some additional properties of the determinant function.

5.5-1 Theorem: Let A be a 3×3 matrix. Then

a. $|AB| = |A|\,|B|$, where B is any 3×3 matrix.
b. If A is nonsingular, then $|A^{-1}| = 1/|A|$.
c. If A^* is obtained from A by interchanging two adjacent rows of A, then $|A^*| = -|A|$.
d. If A^* is obtained from A by multiplying any row of A by a scalar k, then $|A^*| = k|A|$.
e. $|kA| = k^3|A|$ for any $k \in R$.
f. If A^* is obtained from A by adding to any row of A a scalar multiple of any other row of A, then $|A^*| = |A|$.

PROOF: We leave the proof mostly for the reader. In most cases, the result is easily established by expanding the determinants involved. Others can be established by using parts that have been established. For example, Part e follows from Part d. Part b follows from Part a by the following argument: If A^{-1} exists, we know that $AA^{-1} = I$, so by Part a, $|AA^{-1}| = |A|\,|A^{-1}| = |I| = 1$; then it follows that $|A^{-1}| = 1/|A|$. (We shall shortly see that $|A| \neq 0$ whenever A^{-1} exists.)

Example: Suppose

$$A = \begin{bmatrix} 1 & 2 & -1 \\ 0 & 2 & 2 \\ 3 & -1 & -5 \end{bmatrix}.$$

Then

$$|A| = 1 \begin{vmatrix} 2 & 2 \\ -1 & -5 \end{vmatrix} - 2 \begin{vmatrix} 0 & 2 \\ 3 & -5 \end{vmatrix} + (-1) \begin{vmatrix} 0 & 2 \\ 3 & -1 \end{vmatrix}$$

$$= (-10 + 2) - 2(-6) - (1)(-6) = 10.$$

$$|3A| = \begin{vmatrix} 3 & 6 & -3 \\ 0 & 6 & 6 \\ 9 & -3 & -15 \end{vmatrix} = 3(-90 + 18) - 6(-54) - 3(-54) = 270$$

$$= 3^3(10) = 3^3|A|.$$

If

$$B = \begin{bmatrix} 1 & 0 & 1 \\ -1 & -1 & 0 \\ 3 & 2 & -2 \end{bmatrix},$$

then

$$AB = \begin{bmatrix} -4 & -4 & 3 \\ 4 & 2 & -4 \\ -11 & -9 & 13 \end{bmatrix} \quad \text{and} \quad |B| = 3.$$

Now

$$|AB| = -4(26 - 36) + 4(52 - 44) + 3(-36 + 22) = 40 + 32 - 42$$
$$= 30 = 10 \cdot 3 = |A| |B|.$$

Interchanging the top two rows of A to form A^*, we obtain

$$|A^*| = \begin{vmatrix} 0 & 2 & 2 \\ 1 & 2 & -1 \\ 3 & -1 & -5 \end{vmatrix} = -2(-2) + 2(-7) = -10 = -|A|.$$

Multiplying the second row of A by 3 to form A^*, we obtain

$$|A^*| = \begin{vmatrix} 1 & 2 & -1 \\ 0 & 6 & 6 \\ 3 & -1 & -5 \end{vmatrix} = 1(-24) - 2(-18) - 1(-18) = 30 = 3|A|.$$

Adding twice the third row of A to its second row to form A^*, we obtain

$$|A^*| = \begin{vmatrix} 1 & 2 & -1 \\ 6 & 0 & -8 \\ 3 & -1 & -5 \end{vmatrix} = 1(-8) - 2(-6) - 1(-6) = 10 = |A|.$$

We now establish our characterization of singularity.

5.5-2 Theorem: A^{-1} exists iff $|A| \neq 0$.

PROOF: (only if) Suppose A is nonsingular. Then $I = AA^{-1}$, which implies that

$$1 = |I| = |AA^{-1}| = |A| |A^{-1}|,$$

which in turn implies that $|A| \neq 0$ (as well as that $|A^{-1}| \neq 0$).

(if) Suppose A is a 3×3 matrix with $|A| \neq 0$. We must show that there is a 3×3 matrix B such that $AB = I$. We shall give a constructive proof of this fact as follows. Consider a matrix B constructed of select 2×2 determinants.

$$B = \begin{bmatrix} b_{11} & b_{12} & b_{13} \\ b_{21} & b_{22} & b_{23} \\ b_{31} & b_{32} & b_{33} \end{bmatrix}$$

$$
=
\begin{bmatrix}
\begin{vmatrix} a_{22} & a_{23} \\ a_{32} & a_{33} \end{vmatrix}
& -\begin{vmatrix} a_{12} & a_{13} \\ a_{32} & a_{33} \end{vmatrix}
& \begin{vmatrix} a_{12} & a_{13} \\ a_{22} & a_{23} \end{vmatrix} \\[6pt]
-\begin{vmatrix} a_{21} & a_{23} \\ a_{31} & a_{33} \end{vmatrix}
& \begin{vmatrix} a_{11} & a_{13} \\ a_{31} & a_{33} \end{vmatrix}
& -\begin{vmatrix} a_{11} & a_{13} \\ a_{21} & a_{23} \end{vmatrix} \\[6pt]
\begin{vmatrix} a_{21} & a_{22} \\ a_{31} & a_{32} \end{vmatrix}
& -\begin{vmatrix} a_{11} & a_{12} \\ a_{31} & a_{32} \end{vmatrix}
& \begin{vmatrix} a_{11} & a_{12} \\ a_{21} & a_{22} \end{vmatrix}
\end{bmatrix}.
$$

We now show that $AB = |A|I$. First, consider a *main diagonal* entry in the product AB. For example, the entry in the second row and second column is obtained by the dot product

$$
\begin{bmatrix} a_{21} & a_{22} & a_{23} \end{bmatrix} \cdot
\begin{bmatrix} b_{12} \\ b_{22} \\ b_{32} \end{bmatrix}
= -a_{21}\begin{vmatrix} a_{12} & a_{13} \\ a_{32} & a_{33} \end{vmatrix}
+ a_{22}\begin{vmatrix} a_{11} & a_{13} \\ a_{31} & a_{33} \end{vmatrix}
- a_{23}\begin{vmatrix} a_{11} & a_{12} \\ a_{31} & a_{32} \end{vmatrix}.
$$

We recognize this to be $-|A^*|$, where A^* is obtained from A by interchanging the first two rows. Thus, the entry in the second row and second column of AB is the number $|A|$. A similar argument may be given for the other diagonal entries of AB.

Next consider an off-diagonal element of AB, say that in the first row and second column. This is given by

$$
\begin{bmatrix} a_{11} & a_{12} & a_{13} \end{bmatrix} \cdot
\begin{bmatrix} b_{12} \\ b_{22} \\ b_{32} \end{bmatrix}
= -a_{11}\begin{vmatrix} a_{12} & a_{13} \\ a_{32} & a_{33} \end{vmatrix}
+ a_{12}\begin{vmatrix} a_{11} & a_{13} \\ a_{31} & a_{33} \end{vmatrix}
- a_{13}\begin{vmatrix} a_{11} & a_{12} \\ a_{31} & a_{32} \end{vmatrix},
$$

which upon expansion is seen to be zero. A similar argument for the other entries off the main diagonal of AB shows that they are zero. Hence, we have that

$$
AB = \begin{bmatrix} |A| & 0 & 0 \\ 0 & |A| & 0 \\ 0 & 0 & |A| \end{bmatrix} = |A|I.
$$

Since we assume that $|A| \neq 0$, it follows that

$$
\frac{1}{|A|}(AB) = A\left[\frac{1}{|A|}B\right] = I,
$$

so that

$$
A^{-1} = \frac{1}{|A|}B.
$$

The matrix B defined in the proof furnishes us with a way of constructing A^{-1} from A whenever $|A| \neq 0$.

Cofactors

The 2×2 determinants that appear in B in the proof of Theorem 5.5-2 are determinants of matrices sometimes called *cofactors* of certain entries of A.

These matrices are usually denoted by subscripted capital letters. For example, the cofactor A_{32} is obtained from A by deleting the row and columns of A containing a_{32}; that is,

$$A_{32} = \begin{bmatrix} a_{11} & a_{13} \\ a_{21} & a_{23} \end{bmatrix} = \begin{bmatrix} & \vdots & \\ a_{11} & a_{12} & a_{13} \\ & \vdots & \\ a_{21} & a_{22} & a_{23} \\ & \vdots & \\ \cdots a_{31} \cdots & a_{32} \cdots & a_{33} \cdots \end{bmatrix}.$$

If A^* is a matrix constructed by replacing each entry of A by the determinant of its corresponding cofactor, and taking $+$ or $-$ depending on whether the sum of the subscripts is even or odd, then the matrix B in Theorem 5.5-2 is given by $(A^*)^t$. Thus, in terms of cofactors of elements of A, we may give A^{-1} as

$$A^{-1} = \frac{1}{|A|} \begin{bmatrix} |A_{11}| & -|A_{21}| & |A_{31}| \\ -|A_{12}| & |A_{22}| & -|A_{32}| \\ |A_{13}| & -|A_{23}| & |A_{22}| \end{bmatrix}.$$

Example: If

$$A = \begin{bmatrix} -2 & 0 & 4 \\ 5 & 2 & 1 \\ -3 & 2 & -1 \end{bmatrix}$$

we compute $|A| = 72$, so A^{-1} exists, and is obtained by

$$\frac{1}{|A|} B = \frac{1}{72} \begin{bmatrix} -4 & 8 & -8 \\ 2 & 14 & 22 \\ 16 & 4 & -4 \end{bmatrix} = \begin{bmatrix} \dfrac{-4}{72} & \dfrac{8}{72} & \dfrac{-8}{72} \\[2mm] \dfrac{2}{72} & \dfrac{14}{72} & \dfrac{22}{72} \\[2mm] \dfrac{16}{72} & \dfrac{4}{72} & \dfrac{-4}{72} \end{bmatrix}$$

$$= \begin{bmatrix} -\dfrac{1}{18} & \dfrac{1}{9} & -\dfrac{1}{9} \\[2mm] \dfrac{1}{36} & \dfrac{7}{36} & \dfrac{11}{36} \\[2mm] \dfrac{2}{9} & \dfrac{1}{18} & -\dfrac{1}{18} \end{bmatrix}.$$

Example: Find the solution to the system

$$\begin{array}{rcrcrcr} -2x & & & + & 4z & = & 72 \\ 5x & + & 2y & + & z & = & 144 \\ -3x & + & 2y & - & z & = & 24. \end{array}$$

Solution: This system can be written in matrix form by $AX = C$, where the coefficient matrix A is the 3×3 matrix of the preceding example,

$$X = \begin{bmatrix} x \\ y \\ z \end{bmatrix} \quad \text{and} \quad C = \begin{bmatrix} 72 \\ 144 \\ 24 \end{bmatrix}.$$

Thus, the solution is obtained by

$$\begin{bmatrix} x \\ y \\ z \end{bmatrix} = X = A^{-1}AX = A^{-1}C.$$

That is,

$$\begin{bmatrix} -\dfrac{1}{18} & \dfrac{1}{9} & -\dfrac{1}{9} \\ \dfrac{1}{36} & \dfrac{7}{36} & \dfrac{11}{36} \\ \dfrac{2}{9} & \dfrac{1}{18} & -\dfrac{1}{18} \end{bmatrix} \begin{bmatrix} 72 \\ 144 \\ 24 \end{bmatrix} = \begin{bmatrix} \dfrac{28}{3} \\ \dfrac{112}{3} \\ \dfrac{68}{3} \end{bmatrix},$$

so

$$x = 28/3, \qquad y = 112/3, \qquad z = 68/3,$$

is the solution.

Although this may not be the most efficient method for solving systems with two or three unknowns, it can be useful. Further, it gives us a general method for computing specific components of the inverse of a matrix.

Cramer's Rule

We close this section with a statement of a technique of solving consistent systems of linear equations by using the determinant function.

5.5-3   Theorem: (Cramer's rule). Given the system $AX = C$, where A is nonsingular, the solution is given by

$$X = A^{-1}C = \begin{bmatrix} \dfrac{|A_1|}{|A|} \\ \dfrac{|A_2|}{|A|} \\ \dfrac{|A_3|}{|A|} \end{bmatrix},$$

where A_j denotes the matrix formed by replacing the jth column of A by the column C.

We shall defer a proof of this theorem to the next section. It should be noted that a similar result holds for systems in which the coefficient matrix is 2×2 as well as for systems of more than three equations. Note that if the system is *homogeneous*, that is, if

$$C = \begin{bmatrix} 0 \\ 0 \\ 0 \end{bmatrix},$$

then each of the matrices A_j has a column of zeros so that $|A_j|/|A| = 0$. Thus, homogeneous systems with nonsingular coefficient matrices have only the trivial solution

$$X = \begin{bmatrix} 0 \\ 0 \\ 0 \end{bmatrix}.$$

Example: In order to solve the system

$$\begin{bmatrix} 0 & 1 & 1 \\ 1 & 0 & 1 \\ 2 & -1 & 0 \end{bmatrix} \begin{bmatrix} x \\ y \\ z \end{bmatrix} = \begin{bmatrix} 2 \\ 1 \\ -1 \end{bmatrix},$$

we can write the solution as

$$\begin{bmatrix} \dfrac{|A_1|}{|A|}, & \dfrac{|A_2|}{|A|}, & \dfrac{|A_3|}{|A|} \end{bmatrix}.$$

That is, we have

$$x = \frac{\begin{vmatrix} 2 & 1 & 1 \\ 1 & 0 & 1 \\ -1 & -1 & 0 \end{vmatrix}}{|A|}, \quad y = \frac{\begin{vmatrix} 0 & 2 & 1 \\ 1 & 1 & 1 \\ 2 & -1 & 0 \end{vmatrix}}{|A|}, \quad z = \frac{\begin{vmatrix} 0 & 1 & 2 \\ 1 & 0 & 1 \\ 2 & -1 & -1 \end{vmatrix}}{|A|}.$$

The solution is thus

$$\begin{bmatrix} x \\ y \\ z \end{bmatrix} = \begin{bmatrix} 0 \\ 1 \\ 1 \end{bmatrix}.$$

Example: Use Cramer's rule to solve the following system of equations:

$$\begin{aligned} x - y + 2z &= 1 \\ 3x + 2y - z &= 2 \\ x + y + 2z &= -1. \end{aligned}$$

That is, the matrix equation $AX = \begin{bmatrix} 1 \\ 2 \\ -1 \end{bmatrix}$, where

$$A = \begin{bmatrix} 1 & -1 & 2 \\ 3 & 2 & -1 \\ 1 & 1 & 2 \end{bmatrix}.$$

We have $|A| = 14$, and

$$|A_1| = \begin{vmatrix} 1 & -1 & 2 \\ 2 & 2 & -1 \\ -1 & 1 & 1 \end{vmatrix} = 16,$$

$$|A_2| = \begin{vmatrix} 1 & 1 & 2 \\ 3 & 2 & -1 \\ 1 & -1 & 2 \end{vmatrix} = -14,$$

and

$$|A_3| = \begin{vmatrix} 1 & -1 & 1 \\ 3 & 2 & 2 \\ 1 & 1 & -1 \end{vmatrix} = -8.$$

Hence, we have the solution

$$x = \frac{16}{14} = \frac{8}{7}, \qquad y = \frac{-14}{14} = -1, \qquad z = \frac{-8}{14} = \frac{-4}{7}.$$

EXERCISES 5.5

1. Find an inverse for each matrix by the method described in this section

a. $\begin{bmatrix} 1 & 2 & 0 \\ 0 & 1 & 1 \\ 0 & 2 & 1 \end{bmatrix}$.   b. $\begin{bmatrix} 2 & 3 & -1 \\ 1 & -1 & 2 \\ 1 & 2 & 1 \end{bmatrix}$.   c. $\begin{bmatrix} 1 & 2 & 3 \\ 1 & 1 & 2 \\ 2 & 3 & -1 \end{bmatrix}$.

d. $\begin{bmatrix} 2 & 2 & 1 \\ 1 & -4 & 1 \\ 2 & 1 & 1 \end{bmatrix}$.   e. $\begin{bmatrix} -1 & 6 & 4 \\ 3 & 1 & 7 \\ 4 & 2 & -3 \end{bmatrix}$.

2. Solve the following equations by first finding an inverse matrix and then multiplying on both sides of the equation.

a. $\begin{bmatrix} 2 & 3 & 1 \\ 4 & 1 & -1 \\ 2 & -1 & 3 \end{bmatrix} \begin{bmatrix} x \\ y \\ z \end{bmatrix} = \begin{bmatrix} 1 \\ 2 \\ 0 \end{bmatrix}$.   b. $\begin{bmatrix} -1 & 3 & -4 \\ 2 & -1 & 2 \\ 3 & -2 & 6 \end{bmatrix} \begin{bmatrix} x \\ y \\ z \end{bmatrix} = \begin{bmatrix} 0 \\ 1 \\ -2 \end{bmatrix}$.

c. $x + 3y - 4z = 2$
$\quad 2x - y + 2z = 0$
$\quad 4x - 6y + z = 1.$

3. Show that computing $A^{-1} = D$ by the method of this section yields a matrix such that $DA = I$. (We showed that $AD = I$.)

4. Use Cramer's rule to solve the following systems of equations

a. $\begin{bmatrix} -2 & 1 & 0 \\ 1 & -2 & 1 \\ 0 & 1 & -2 \end{bmatrix} \begin{bmatrix} x \\ y \\ z \end{bmatrix} = \begin{bmatrix} 1 \\ -1 \\ 2 \end{bmatrix}$.   b. $\begin{bmatrix} 8 & 0 & 0 \\ 0 & -7 & 0 \\ 0 & 0 & 3 \end{bmatrix} \begin{bmatrix} x \\ y \\ z \end{bmatrix} = \begin{bmatrix} 2 \\ -2 \\ 0 \end{bmatrix}$.

c. $\begin{bmatrix} 0 & 1 & -2 \\ -1 & 1 & 3 \\ 2 & -3 & 0 \end{bmatrix} \begin{bmatrix} x \\ y \\ z \end{bmatrix} = \begin{bmatrix} 1 \\ 1 \\ 1 \end{bmatrix}$.

d. $2x + y - z = 2$
   $4x - y + 2z = 0$
   $x + 2y + z = 1$.

e. $x + y + z = 2$
   $x + y - z = 3$
   $x - y + z = -1$.

5. Solve the systems of equations in Exercises 3 and 4 of Section 5.4.

6. Show that Cramer's rule holds when the matrices involved are 2×2.

7. Define cofactors for the entries in a 2×2 matrix A in such a way that

$$A^{-1} = \frac{1}{|A|} \begin{bmatrix} |A_{11}| & -|A_{21}| \\ -|A_{12}| & |A_{22}| \end{bmatrix}.$$

8. Investigate (prove or disprove):
   a. Given the matrix equation $AB = AC$, then it follows that $B = C$.
   b. If the matrix equations

$$AX = I \quad \text{and} \quad XA = I$$

have a solution X, then there is only one solution.

5.6 INTRODUCTION TO CROSS PRODUCTS AND APPLICATIONS

We shall now combine the computational properties of 3×3 determinants with the notion of basis vectors $\mathbf{I}, \mathbf{J}, \mathbf{K}$ to study the properties of a second kind of product of vectors, the *cross product*.

5.6-1 Definition: The *cross product* of two vectors (a_1, a_2, a_3) and (b_1, b_2, b_3), denoted by $(a_1, a_2, a_3) \times (b_1, b_2, b_3)$ is the *vector*

$$(a_2b_3 - a_3b_2)\mathbf{I} + (a_3b_1 - a_1b_3)\mathbf{J} + (a_1b_2 - a_2b_1)\mathbf{K}.$$

Remark: We may formally write this cross product as the determinant

$$(a_1, a_2, a_3) \times (b_1, b_2, b_3) = \begin{vmatrix} \mathbf{I} & \mathbf{J} & \mathbf{K} \\ a_1 & a_2 & a_3 \\ b_1 & b_2 & b_3 \end{vmatrix},$$

where it is understood that this symbol means

$$\begin{vmatrix} a_2 & a_3 \\ b_2 & b_3 \end{vmatrix} \mathbf{I} - \begin{vmatrix} a_1 & a_3 \\ b_1 & b_3 \end{vmatrix} \mathbf{J} + \begin{vmatrix} a_1 & a_2 \\ b_1 & b_2 \end{vmatrix} \mathbf{K},$$

analogous to the computation of an ordinary determinant of the form

$$\begin{vmatrix} i & j & k \\ a_1 & a_2 & a_3 \\ b_1 & b_2 & b_3 \end{vmatrix}.$$

It immediately follows that if the vectors $\mathbf{A}$ and $\mathbf{B}$ are linearly dependent, then the cross product is the zero vector. This follows since

$$\mathbf{A} \times (\alpha\mathbf{A}) = (a_1, a_2, a_3) \times (\alpha a_1, \alpha a_2, \alpha a_3)$$

$$= \begin{vmatrix} \mathbf{I} & \mathbf{J} & \mathbf{K} \\ a_1 & a_2 & a_3 \\ \alpha a_1 & \alpha a_2 & \alpha a_3 \end{vmatrix}$$

$$= \alpha \begin{vmatrix} a_2 & a_3 \\ a_2 & a_3 \end{vmatrix} \mathbf{I} - \alpha \begin{vmatrix} a_1 & a_3 \\ a_1 & a_3 \end{vmatrix} \mathbf{J} + \alpha \begin{vmatrix} a_1 & a_2 \\ a_1 & a_2 \end{vmatrix} \mathbf{K}$$

$$= 0\mathbf{I} - 0\mathbf{J} + 0\mathbf{K} = \mathbf{0}.$$

Remark: Since the cross product of two vectors in $\langle \mathbf{R}^3, \mathbf{R} \rangle$ is a vector in $\langle \mathbf{R}^3, \mathbf{R} \rangle$, this operation is sometimes called the *vector product* (or, occasionally, the *outer product*, as distinct from the *inner* (dot) product).

Example:

$$(1, 1, 1) \times (2, -5, 1) = \begin{vmatrix} \mathbf{I} & \mathbf{J} & \mathbf{K} \\ 1 & 1 & 1 \\ 2 & -5 & 1 \end{vmatrix}$$

$$= \begin{vmatrix} 1 & 1 \\ -5 & 1 \end{vmatrix} \mathbf{I} - \begin{vmatrix} 1 & 1 \\ 2 & 1 \end{vmatrix} \mathbf{J} + \begin{vmatrix} 1 & 1 \\ 2 & -5 \end{vmatrix} \mathbf{K}$$

$$= 6\mathbf{I} + \mathbf{J} - 7\mathbf{K} = (6, 1, -7).$$

Example:

$$\mathbf{I} \times \mathbf{J} = \begin{vmatrix} \mathbf{I} & \mathbf{J} & \mathbf{K} \\ 1 & 0 & 0 \\ 0 & 1 & 0 \end{vmatrix} = 0\mathbf{I} - 0\mathbf{J} + 1\mathbf{K} = \mathbf{K}.$$

The first observation we make concerning the cross product vector is that it is normal to both vectors entering into the product.

5.6-2 Theorem: The cross product $\mathbf{A} \times \mathbf{B}$ of two vectors $\mathbf{A}$ and $\mathbf{B}$ is a vector perpendicular to both $\mathbf{A}$ and $\mathbf{B}$.

PROOF: It suffices to show that $(\mathbf{A} \times \mathbf{B}) \cdot \mathbf{A} = 0$, and similarly for $\mathbf{B}$. Let $\mathbf{A} = (a_1, a_2, a_3)$ and $\mathbf{B} = (b_1, b_2, b_3)$. Then $\mathbf{A} \times \mathbf{B} \cdot \mathbf{A}$ (we may omit grouping symbols without fear of confusion) is given by

$$\mathbf{A} \times \mathbf{B} \cdot \mathbf{A} = \left[\begin{vmatrix} a_2 & a_3 \\ b_2 & b_3 \end{vmatrix} \mathbf{I} - \begin{vmatrix} a_1 & a_3 \\ b_1 & b_3 \end{vmatrix} \mathbf{J} + \begin{vmatrix} a_1 & a_2 \\ b_1 & b_2 \end{vmatrix} \mathbf{K} \right] \cdot (a_1\mathbf{I} + a_2\mathbf{J} + a_3\mathbf{K})$$

$$= a_1 \begin{vmatrix} a_2 & a_3 \\ b_2 & b_3 \end{vmatrix} - a_2 \begin{vmatrix} a_1 & a_3 \\ b_1 & b_3 \end{vmatrix} + a_3 \begin{vmatrix} a_1 & a_2 \\ b_1 & b_2 \end{vmatrix}$$

$$= \begin{vmatrix} a_1 & a_2 & a_3 \\ a_1 & a_2 & a_3 \\ b_1 & b_2 & b_3 \end{vmatrix},$$

which is zero because of the repeated rows. We leave the case $\mathbf{A} \times \mathbf{B} \cdot \mathbf{B}$ as an exercise.

Theorem 5.6-2 has an immediate application in finding an equation of a plane containing three noncollinear points. Suppose $A = (a_1, a_2, a_3)$, $B =$

(b_1, b_2, b_3), and $C = (c_1, c_2, c_3)$ are three points in a plane. The vectors $\mathbf{B} - \mathbf{A}$ and $\mathbf{C} - \mathbf{A}$ form a basis for the subspace (plane passing through O) parallel to the given plane, and so $(\mathbf{B} - \mathbf{A}) \times (\mathbf{C} - \mathbf{A})$ is a vector normal to the plane. Of course, once a normal vector is found, it is a simple matter to write an equation for the plane. (See Figure 5.23.)

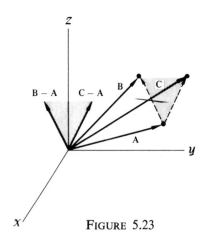

FIGURE 5.23

Example: Find an equation for the plane containing the points $(1, 1, 2)$, $(-1, 1, 0)$, $(2, -1, 3)$.

Solution: A vector normal to the desired plane is given by

$$((-1, 1, 0) - (1, 1, 2)) \times ((2, -1, 3) - (1, 1, 2))$$

$$= (-2, 0, -2) \times (1, -2, 1) = \begin{vmatrix} \mathbf{I} & \mathbf{J} & \mathbf{K} \\ -2 & 0 & -2 \\ 1 & -2 & 1 \end{vmatrix}$$

$$= -4\mathbf{I} + 0\mathbf{J} + 4\mathbf{K} = (-4, 0, 4).$$

Hence a plane parallel to the one desired is described by

$$-4 + 0y + 4z = 0,$$

or equivalently

$$-x + z = 0.$$

It follows that the desired plane can be given by an equation of the form $-x + z = d$. Since $(-1, 1, 0)$ is a point in the plane, we must in particular have $-(-1) + 0 = d$, or $d = 1$. Finally, we obtain the equation

$$-x + z = 1.$$

(You should verify that the three given points do satisfy this equation.)

Example: Find the equation of a plane containing the points $(2, -1, 3)$, $(1, 2, -2)$ and $(2, 2, -1)$. A normal is given by

$$((2, -1, 3) - (1, 2, -2)) \times ((2, 2, -1) - (1, 2, -2))$$

$$= (1, -3, 5) \times (1, 0, 1) = \begin{vmatrix} \mathbf{I} & \mathbf{J} & \mathbf{K} \\ 1 & -3 & 5 \\ 1 & 0 & 1 \end{vmatrix} = -3\mathbf{I} + 4\mathbf{J} + 3\mathbf{K}.$$

Thus, the equation may take the form

$$-3x + 4y + 3z = d.$$

Upon substitution of the components of one ordered triple in the plane, for example, $(2, -1, 3)$, we have

$$-3(2) + 4(-1) + 3(3) = -6 - 4 + 9 = -1 = d.$$

The plane can therefore be described by the equation

$$-3x + 4y + 3z = -1.$$

Algebraic Properties

The next theorem shows that the cross-product operation is not commutative, but it does have a very interesting property with respect to a change of order.

5.6-3   Theorem: $\mathbf{A} \times \mathbf{B} = -\mathbf{B} \times \mathbf{A}$ (anti-commutative law).

PROOF: Formally,

$$\mathbf{A} \times \mathbf{B} = \begin{vmatrix} \mathbf{I} & \mathbf{J} & \mathbf{K} \\ a_1 & a_2 & a_3 \\ b_1 & b_2 & b_3 \end{vmatrix} = -\begin{vmatrix} \mathbf{I} & \mathbf{J} & \mathbf{K} \\ b_1 & b_2 & b_3 \\ a_1 & a_2 & a_3 \end{vmatrix}$$

since these determinants differ only by interchange of the second and third rows. But the second determinant is $\mathbf{B} \times \mathbf{A}$.

Example: We have seen that $\mathbf{I} \times \mathbf{J} = \mathbf{K}$. Note also that

$$\mathbf{J} \times \mathbf{I} = \begin{vmatrix} \mathbf{I} & \mathbf{J} & \mathbf{K} \\ 0 & 1 & 0 \\ 1 & 0 & 0 \end{vmatrix} = -\mathbf{K}.$$

We devote the next few paragraphs to an investigation of some additional algebraic properties of the cross-product operation. First note that

$$(\alpha\mathbf{A}) \times \mathbf{B} = \alpha(\mathbf{A} \times \mathbf{B}),$$

since

$$\begin{vmatrix} \mathbf{I} & \mathbf{J} & \mathbf{K} \\ \alpha a_1 & \alpha a_2 & \alpha a_3 \\ b_1 & b_2 & b_3 \end{vmatrix} = \begin{vmatrix} \alpha a_2 & \alpha a_3 \\ b_2 & b_3 \end{vmatrix} \mathbf{I} - \begin{vmatrix} \alpha a_1 & \alpha a_3 \\ b_1 & b_2 \end{vmatrix} \mathbf{J} + \begin{vmatrix} \alpha a_1 & \alpha a_2 \\ b_1 & b_2 \end{vmatrix} \mathbf{K}$$

$$= \alpha \begin{vmatrix} a_2 & a_3 \\ b_2 & b_3 \end{vmatrix} \mathbf{I} - \alpha \begin{vmatrix} a_1 & a_3 \\ b_1 & b_3 \end{vmatrix} \mathbf{J} + \alpha \begin{vmatrix} a_1 & a_3 \\ b_1 & b_2 \end{vmatrix} \mathbf{K}$$

$$= \alpha \begin{vmatrix} \mathbf{I} & \mathbf{J} & \mathbf{K} \\ a_1 & a_2 & a_3 \\ b_1 & b_2 & b_3 \end{vmatrix}.$$

Next, consider a distributive property. Let us compute $\mathbf{A} \times (\mathbf{B} + \mathbf{C})$ with the objective of comparing it with $(\mathbf{A} \times \mathbf{B}) + (\mathbf{A} \times \mathbf{C})$. Making obvious notation conventions, we have

$\mathbf{A} \times (\mathbf{B} + \mathbf{C})$

$$= \begin{vmatrix} \mathbf{I} & \mathbf{J} & \mathbf{K} \\ a_1 & a_2 & a_3 \\ b_1 + c_1 & b_2 + c_2 & b_3 + c_3 \end{vmatrix}$$

$$= \begin{vmatrix} a_2 & a_3 \\ b_2 + c_2 & b_3 + c_3 \end{vmatrix} \mathbf{I} - \begin{vmatrix} a_1 & a_3 \\ b_1 + c_1 & b_3 + c_3 \end{vmatrix} \mathbf{J} + \begin{vmatrix} a_1 & a_2 \\ b_1 + c_1 & b_2 + c_2 \end{vmatrix} \mathbf{K} .$$

Now, since

$$\begin{vmatrix} a_2 & a_3 \\ b_2 + c_2 & b_3 + c_3 \end{vmatrix} = a_2(b_3 + c_3) - a_3(b_2 + c_2)$$

$$= (a_2 b_3 - a_3 b_2) + (a_2 c_3 - a_3 c_2)$$

$$= \begin{vmatrix} a_2 & a_3 \\ b_2 & b_3 \end{vmatrix} + \begin{vmatrix} a_2 & a_3 \\ c_2 & c_3 \end{vmatrix}$$

and similarly for the other 2×2 determinants, we have

$$\left[\begin{vmatrix} a_2 & a_3 \\ b_2 & b_3 \end{vmatrix} \mathbf{I} - \begin{vmatrix} a_1 & a_3 \\ b_1 & b_3 \end{vmatrix} \mathbf{J} + \begin{vmatrix} a_1 & a_2 \\ b_1 & b_2 \end{vmatrix} \mathbf{K} \right]$$

$$+ \left[\begin{vmatrix} a_2 & a_3 \\ c_2 & c_3 \end{vmatrix} \mathbf{I} - \begin{vmatrix} a_1 & a_3 \\ c_1 & c_3 \end{vmatrix} \mathbf{J} + \begin{vmatrix} a_1 & a_2 \\ c_1 & c_2 \end{vmatrix} \mathbf{K} \right] = (\mathbf{A} \times \mathbf{B}) + (\mathbf{A} \times \mathbf{C}).$$

Thus, the cross product is "left" distributive over vector addition. In the exercises you are asked to establish a "right" distributive law,

$$(\mathbf{A} + \mathbf{B}) \times \mathbf{C} = (\mathbf{A} \times \mathbf{C}) + (\mathbf{A} \times \mathbf{C}).$$

We have seen that the cross-product operation is not commutative. Let us investigate whether it has the associative property. Notice, the simple case

$$\mathbf{I} \times (\mathbf{J} \times \mathbf{J}) = \mathbf{I} \times \mathbf{0} = \mathbf{0},$$

whereas

$$(\mathbf{I} \times \mathbf{J}) \times \mathbf{J} = \mathbf{K} \times \mathbf{J} = -\mathbf{I}.$$

Hence, we must abandon any hope that the cross-product operation is associative. However, if further investigation is carried out with regard to the product $\mathbf{A} \times (\mathbf{B} \times \mathbf{C})$, one discovers that it can be written as a certain linear combination of the vectors $\mathbf{B}$ and $\mathbf{C}$, and thus lies in the plane determined by $\mathbf{B}$ and $\mathbf{C}$.

5.6-4 Theorem: (The triple cross product identity). If $\mathbf{A}$, $\mathbf{B}$, and $\mathbf{C}$ are vectors in space, then

$$\mathbf{A} \times (\mathbf{B} \times \mathbf{C}) = (\mathbf{A} \cdot \mathbf{C})\mathbf{B} - (\mathbf{A} \cdot \mathbf{B})\mathbf{C}.$$

PROOF:

$$\mathbf{A} \times (\mathbf{B} \times \mathbf{C}) = \mathbf{A} \times \begin{vmatrix} \mathbf{I} & \mathbf{J} & \mathbf{K} \\ b_1 & b_2 & b_3 \\ c_1 & c_2 & c_3 \end{vmatrix} = \begin{vmatrix} \mathbf{I} & \mathbf{J} & \mathbf{K} \\ a_1 & a_2 & a_3 \\ \begin{vmatrix} b_2 & b_3 \\ c_2 & c_3 \end{vmatrix} & \begin{vmatrix} b_1 & b_3 \\ c_1 & c_3 \end{vmatrix} & \begin{vmatrix} b_1 & b_2 \\ c_1 & c_2 \end{vmatrix} \end{vmatrix}$$

$$= \left[a_2 \begin{vmatrix} b_1 & b_2 \\ c_1 & c_2 \end{vmatrix} + a_3 \begin{vmatrix} b_1 & b_3 \\ c_1 & c_3 \end{vmatrix} \right] \mathbf{I} - \left[a_1 \begin{vmatrix} b_1 & b_2 \\ c_1 & c_2 \end{vmatrix} - a_3 \begin{vmatrix} b_2 & b_3 \\ c_2 & c_3 \end{vmatrix} \right] \mathbf{J}$$

$$+ \left[-a_1 \begin{vmatrix} b_1 & b_3 \\ c_1 & c_3 \end{vmatrix} - a_2 \begin{vmatrix} b_2 & b_3 \\ c_2 & c_3 \end{vmatrix} \right] \mathbf{K}$$

$$= (a_2 b_1 c_2 - a_2 b_2 c_1 + a_3 b_1 c_3 - a_3 b_3 c_1)\mathbf{I}$$
$$- (a_1 b_1 c_2 - a_1 b_2 c_1 - a_3 b_2 c_3 + a_3 b_3 c_2)\mathbf{J}$$
$$+ (-a_1 b_1 c_3 + a_1 b_3 c_1 - a_2 b_2 c_3 + a_2 b_3 c_2)\mathbf{K}$$
$$= b_1(a_2 c_2 + a_3 c_3)\mathbf{I} - c_1(a_2 b_2 + a_3 b_3)\mathbf{I} + b_1(a_1 c_1)\mathbf{I} - c_1(a_1 b_1)\mathbf{I}$$
$$+ b_2(a_1 c_1 + a_3 c_3)\mathbf{J} - c_2(a_1 b_1 + a_3 b_3)\mathbf{J} + b_2(a_2 c_2)\mathbf{J} - c_2(a_2 b_2)\mathbf{J}$$
$$+ b_3(a_1 c_1 + a_2 c_2)\mathbf{K} - c_3(a_1 b_1 + a_2 b_2)\mathbf{K} + b_3(a_3 c_3)\mathbf{K} - c_3(a_3 b_3)\mathbf{K}$$
$$= (a_1 c_1 + a_2 c_2 + a_3 c_3)(b_1 \mathbf{I} + b_2 \mathbf{J} + b_3 \mathbf{K})$$
$$- (a_1 b_1 + a_2 b_2 + a_3 b_3)(c_1 \mathbf{I} + c_2 \mathbf{J} + c_3 \mathbf{K})$$
$$= (\mathbf{A} \cdot \mathbf{C})\mathbf{B} - (\mathbf{A} \cdot \mathbf{B})\mathbf{C}.$$

Proof of Cramer's Rule

We shall now use the triple cross product identity to prove Cramer's rule.
Given the matrix equation

$$\begin{bmatrix} a_1 & b_1 & c_1 \\ a_2 & b_2 & c_2 \\ a_3 & b_3 & c_3 \end{bmatrix} \begin{bmatrix} x \\ y \\ z \end{bmatrix} = \begin{bmatrix} d_1 \\ d_2 \\ d_3 \end{bmatrix}$$

(that is, $AY = D$), where $|A| \neq 0$, we shall show that the unique solution is given by

$$x = \frac{|A_1|}{|A|}, \qquad y = \frac{|A_2|}{|A|}, \qquad \text{and} \qquad z = \frac{|A_3|}{|A|},$$

where A_j denotes the matrix obtained from A by replacing the jth column of A by the column in D.

Any solution

$$Y = \begin{bmatrix} x \\ y \\ z \end{bmatrix}$$

to the equation has the property that

$$\mathbf{Y} \cdot \mathbf{Z}_1 = d_1, \qquad \mathbf{Y} \cdot \mathbf{Z}_2 = d_2, \qquad \text{and} \qquad \mathbf{Y} \cdot \mathbf{Z}_3 = d_3,$$

where $\mathbf{Z}_i = (\mathbf{a}_i, \mathbf{b}_i, \mathbf{c}_i)$. (Why?)

Consider then, the cross product and an application of Theorem 5.6-4.

We have then

$$\mathbf{Y} \times (\mathbf{Z}_2 \times \mathbf{Z}_1) = (\mathbf{Y} \cdot \mathbf{Z}_1)\mathbf{Z}_2 - (\mathbf{Y} \cdot \mathbf{Z}_2)\mathbf{Z}_1 = d_1\mathbf{Z}_2 - d_2\mathbf{Z}_1$$
$$= (d_1 a_2 - d_2 a_1, \, d_1 b_2 - d_2 b_1, \, d_1 c_2 - d_2 c_1)$$
$$= \left\{ \begin{vmatrix} d_1 & d_2 \\ a_1 & a_2 \end{vmatrix}, \begin{vmatrix} d_1 & d_2 \\ b_1 & b_2 \end{vmatrix}, \begin{vmatrix} d_1 & d_2 \\ c_1 & c_2 \end{vmatrix} \right\}.$$

The left-hand side of this equation is given by

$$\mathbf{Y} \times \begin{vmatrix} \mathbf{I} & \mathbf{J} & \mathbf{K} \\ a_2 & b_2 & c_2 \\ a_1 & b_1 & c_1 \end{vmatrix} = \begin{vmatrix} \mathbf{I} & \mathbf{J} & \mathbf{K} \\ x & y & z \\ \begin{vmatrix} b_2 & c_2 \\ b_1 & c_1 \end{vmatrix} & \begin{vmatrix} a_2 & c_2 \\ a_1 & c_1 \end{vmatrix} & \begin{vmatrix} a_2 & b_2 \\ a_1 & b_1 \end{vmatrix} \end{vmatrix}.$$

Equating first components on the two sides of this equation gives

$$\begin{vmatrix} d_1 & d_2 \\ a_1 & a_2 \end{vmatrix} = y \begin{vmatrix} a_2 & b_2 \\ a_1 & b_1 \end{vmatrix} + z \begin{vmatrix} a_2 & c_2 \\ a_1 & c_1 \end{vmatrix}.$$

Applying the same process to the product

$$\mathbf{Y} \times (\mathbf{Z}_3 \times \mathbf{Z}_1)$$

gives a similar equation

$$\begin{vmatrix} d_1 & d_3 \\ a_1 & a_3 \end{vmatrix} = y \begin{vmatrix} a_3 & b_3 \\ a_1 & b_1 \end{vmatrix} + z \begin{vmatrix} a_3 & c_3 \\ a_1 & c_1 \end{vmatrix}.$$

If we multiply the first equation by $\begin{vmatrix} a_3 & c_3 \\ a_1 & c_1 \end{vmatrix}$ and the second by $\begin{vmatrix} a_2 & c_2 \\ a_1 & c_1 \end{vmatrix}$ and subtract, we have

$$\begin{vmatrix} a_3 & c_3 \\ a_1 & c_1 \end{vmatrix}\begin{vmatrix} d_1 & d_2 \\ a_1 & a_2 \end{vmatrix} - \begin{vmatrix} a_2 & c_2 \\ a_1 & c_1 \end{vmatrix}\begin{vmatrix} d_1 & d_3 \\ a_1 & a_3 \end{vmatrix} = y\left[\begin{vmatrix} a_3 & c_3 \\ a_1 & c_1 \end{vmatrix}\begin{vmatrix} a_2 & b_2 \\ a_1 & b_1 \end{vmatrix} - \begin{vmatrix} a_2 & c_2 \\ a_1 & c_1 \end{vmatrix}\begin{vmatrix} a_3 & b_3 \\ a_1 & b_1 \end{vmatrix} \right].$$

(Actually, we could have applied Cramer's rule to the case of two unknowns to arrive at this equation.)

Some simple computation reveals that this is equivalent to

$$a_1 \begin{vmatrix} a_1 & d_1 & c_1 \\ a_2 & d_2 & c_2 \\ a_3 & d_3 & c_3 \end{vmatrix} = a_1 y \begin{vmatrix} a_1 & b_1 & c_1 \\ a_2 & b_2 & c_2 \\ a_3 & b_3 & c_3 \end{vmatrix}.$$

We may assume WLOG that $a_1 \neq 0$ (explain!), thus obtaining

$$y = \frac{|A_2|}{|A|}$$

as promised. A similar process will yield the solution for x and z.

EXERCISES 5.6

1. Find $A \times B$, where
   a. $A = (1, 2, -3)$, $B = (2, -2, 5)$.   b. $A = (-2, 3, 1)$, $B = (5, 3, -1)$.
   c. $A = (2, 0, -2)$, $B = (2, 4, -2)$.   d. $A = (-2, -1, 1)$, $B = (3, 7, -5)$.

2. Show that $A \times B = 0$ iff $\alpha A + \beta B = 0$ for some α and β not both zero.

3. Verify that cross products are right distributive over vector addition, that is, that

$$(A + B) \times C = (A \times C) + (B \times C).$$

Does this property follow from the left distributive rule established in the text?

4. Use only the distributive laws, the anticommutative law, the fact that $(\alpha A \times B = \alpha(A \times B)$, and the fact that $I \times J = K$, $J \times K = I$, and $K \times I = J$, to compute $(a_1, a_2, a_3) \times (b_1, b_2, b_3)$.

5. Use the cross product to devise a procedure for determining whether three points A, B, and C are collinear.

6. Determine an equation for the plane containing the three points given.
   a. $(1, 3, 4)$, $(2, 2, 3)$, $(5, 1, 7)$.   b. $(5, 1, -1)$, $(-2, 1, 4)$, $(-1, -1, 3)$.
   c. $(6, -2, -3)$, $(4, 5, 6)$, $(-5, 7, 1)$.   d. $(6, 2, -4)$, $(-3, 2, 1)$, $(-4, 3, 3)$.

7. a. Show that $(A \times B) \times C = (A \cdot C)B - (B \cdot C)A$.
   b. Explain geometrically why $A \times (B \times C)$ should be a linear combination of B and C. (HINT: $A \times B$ is perpendicular to both A and B.)

8. Define the angle between two planes to be the angle between their normals. Find the cosine of the angle between the two planes given.
   a. $2x - 3y + z = 0$; $x + 2y - 3z = 0$.
   b. $3x + 3y - z = 1$; $2x + y + 4z = 2$.
   c. $5x - 2y + 2z = 5$; $-x + y - 3z = 3$.

9. Show the remaining parts of Cramer's rule

$$\left(x = \frac{|A_1|}{|A|}, \; z = \frac{|A_3|}{|A|} \right)$$

using the triple cross-product identity.

10. Show that the vector $(B \cdot B)A - (A \cdot B)B$ is perpendicular to B.

11. Show that

$$(A \times B) \cdot (A \times B) = \begin{vmatrix} A \cdot A & A \cdot B \\ A \cdot B & B \cdot B \end{vmatrix}.$$

12. Let P, Q, and S be points in space. Show that the vector

$$(P \times Q) + (Q \times S) + (S \times P)$$

is perpendicular to the plane containing P, Q, and S.

13. Define vectors $A = (a_1, a_2, a_3, a_4)$ and $B = (b_1, b_2, b_3, b_4)$ in $\langle R^4, R \rangle$ to be perpendicular provided that

$$A \cdot B = a_1 b_1 + a_2 b_2 + a_3 b_3 + a_4 b_4 = 0.$$

Define the "cross product" of three vectors in R^4 by

$$(ABC)^{\perp} = \begin{vmatrix} I & J & K & L \\ a_1 & a_2 & a_3 & a_4 \\ b_1 & b_2 & b_3 & b_4 \\ c_1 & c_2 & c_3 & c_4 \end{vmatrix},$$

where $I = (1, 0, 0, 0)$, $J = (0, 1, 0, 0)$, $K = (0, 0, 1, 0)$, and $L = (0, 0, 0, 1)$.
   a. Show that the vector $(ABC)^{\perp}$ is normal to each of the vectors A, B, C.
   b. Show that $(ABC)^{\perp}$ is the zero vector $(0, 0, 0, 0)$ if the vectors A, B, and C are linearly dependent.

14. a. State a version of Cramer's rule for systems of four equations in four unknowns.

b. Use the rule of Exercise 14a to solve the equation

$$\begin{bmatrix} 1 & 2 & -1 & 3 \\ 2 & 5 & 0 & 7 \\ 1 & 2 & 0 & 2 \\ 2 & 3 & -4 & 6 \end{bmatrix} \begin{bmatrix} x \\ y \\ z \\ w \end{bmatrix} = \begin{bmatrix} 1 \\ -1 \\ 0 \\ 2 \end{bmatrix}.$$

5.7 ADDITIONAL PROPERTIES AND APPLICATIONS OF CROSS PRODUCTS

The Length

Let us now consider the *length* of the cross-product vector $\mathbf{A} \times \mathbf{B}$.

5.7-1 Theorem: Suppose $\mathbf{A}$ and $\mathbf{B}$ are noncollinear and the angle measured from $\mathbf{A}$ to $\mathbf{B}$ (in the plane determined by $\mathbf{A}$ and $\mathbf{B}$) is θ. Then,

$$|\mathbf{A} \times \mathbf{B}|^2 = |\mathbf{A}|\,|\mathbf{B}|\,|\sin \theta|\,.$$

PROOF: We can show the equivalent fact that

$$|\mathbf{A} \times \mathbf{B}|^2 = |\mathbf{A}|^2|\mathbf{B}|^2 \sin^2 \theta = |\mathbf{A}|^2|\mathbf{B}|^2 - |\mathbf{A}|^2|\mathbf{B}|^2 \cos^2 \theta\,.$$

This is equivalent to showing that

$$(\mathbf{A} \times \mathbf{B}) \cdot (\mathbf{A} \times \mathbf{B}) = (\mathbf{A} \cdot \mathbf{A})(\mathbf{B} \cdot \mathbf{B}) - (\mathbf{A} \cdot \mathbf{B})^2\,.$$

On expanding both sides of this equation in component form, we may see how equality holds. (Also see Exercise 11 in the preceding section.)

The length of $\mathbf{A} \times \mathbf{B}$ has an interesting interpretation in terms of the parallelogram determined by $\mathbf{A}$ and $\mathbf{B}$. Suppose we imagine $\mathbf{A}$ and $\mathbf{B}$ with common initial point in a plane containing both $\mathbf{A}$ and $\mathbf{B}$ (Figure 5.24), and suppose $\theta \in [0, \pi)$ is the angle between $\mathbf{A}$ and $\mathbf{B}$. The area of the parallelogram with adjacent sides determined by $\mathbf{A}$ and $\mathbf{B}$ is given by $|\mathbf{A}|h$, where h

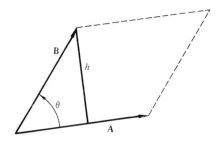

FIGURE 5.24

is the distance from the tip of **B** to the line containing **A**. Clearly, $h = |\mathbf{B}| \sin \theta$, so it follows that

$$|\mathbf{A}| \, |\mathbf{B}| \sin \theta = |\mathbf{A} \times \mathbf{B}|$$

is the *area* of the parallelogram formed by **A** and **B**. Note that if $\theta = 0$, the "parallelogram" is degenerate, and has zero area. But in such circumstances, we know that $\mathbf{A} \times \mathbf{B} = 0$, so even in this degenerate case, $|\mathbf{A} \times \mathbf{B}|$ is the area of the parallelogram formed by **A** and **B**.

The Right-Hand Rule

The vector $\mathbf{A} \times \mathbf{B}$ may be described geometrically as follows. Suppose **A** and **B** are noncollinear, so that **A** and **B** determine a plane $\mathcal{P}$, and suppose the angle from **A** to **B** is θ, where $0 \leqslant \theta \leqslant \pi$ (see Figure 5.25). Let **N** be a unit

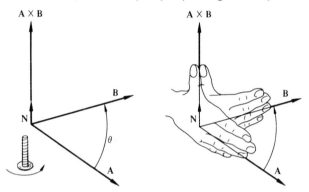

FIGURE 5.25

normal to $\mathcal{P}$ directed in the direction a right-hand threaded screw advances when its head is turned in the direction in which θ is measured (compare this with the notion of a right-handed coordinate system with regard to the vectors **I**, **J**, and **K**). Then

$$\mathbf{A} \times \mathbf{B} = (|\mathbf{A}| \, |\mathbf{B}| \sin \theta)\mathbf{N}.$$

This is called the *right-hand rule*. We have verified that $\mathbf{A} \times \mathbf{B}$ is orthogonal to both **A** and **B**, and we have verified that the length of $\mathbf{A} \times \mathbf{B}$ is $||\mathbf{A}| \, |\mathbf{B}| \sin \theta|$. We shall not, however, verify that a consistent right-hand rule results. A proof is slightly beyond the scope of this text. The student should verify this rule for some special cases (see Exercise 10).

The restriction $0 \leqslant \theta \leqslant \pi$ may be relaxed, provided that N is always directed in accordance with the right-hand rule described above. Suppose $\pi < \theta < 2\pi$, where θ measures the angle from **A** to **B**. (See Figure 5.26.) If **N** is directed in accordance with the direction of θ, by use of the right-hand screw rule, then $-\mathbf{N}$ corresponds to the right-hand rule for $\mathbf{A} \times \mathbf{B}$ if we

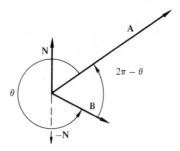

FIGURE 5.26

rotate **A** to **B** through $\varphi \leqslant \pi$, where $\varphi = 2\pi - \theta$. Since $\sin \theta = -\sin (2\pi - \theta)$, we have

$$\mathbf{A} \times \mathbf{B} = (|\mathbf{A}|\ |\mathbf{B}|\ \sin \theta)\mathbf{N}\ 3x = (|\mathbf{A}|\ |\mathbf{B}|\ \sin (2\pi - \theta)(-\mathbf{N})$$
$$= (|\mathbf{A}|\ |\mathbf{B}|\ \sin \varphi)(-\mathbf{N})).$$

The property $\mathbf{A} \times \mathbf{B} = -\mathbf{B} \times \mathbf{A}$ is easily verified through our geometric interpretation of cross products. We need only note that if θ is the angle from **A** to **B** with corresponding right-hand unit normal **N**, then the unit normal associated with the same angle θ from **B** to **A** is $-\mathbf{N}$. Thus,

$$\mathbf{B} \times \mathbf{A} = (|\mathbf{B}|\ |\mathbf{A}|\ \sin \theta)(-\mathbf{N}) = -(|\mathbf{A}|\ |\mathbf{B}|\ \sin \theta)\mathbf{N} = -\mathbf{A} \times \mathbf{B}.$$

Of course, $|\mathbf{B} \times \mathbf{A}| = |\mathbf{A} \times \mathbf{B}|$, which is consistent with the fact that this represents the area of the parallelogram formed by **A** and **B**.

The Box Product

We close this section with a brief discussion of the so-called *triple scalar product*, or *box product* $\mathbf{A} \times \mathbf{B} \cdot \mathbf{C}$ of three vectors **A**, **B**, and **C**.

Let **N** be the right-hand unit normal (corresponding to measuring the angle from **A** to **B**) to the plane $\mathcal{P}$ determined by **A** and **B**. For the moment, suppose that **C** is directed on the same side of $\mathcal{P}$ as **N** is, and let φ be the angle between **N** and **C** (see Figure 5.27). The volume v of the parallelepiped with adjacent edges formed by the vectors **A**, **B**, and **C** is given by the area of the base parallelogram formed by **A** and **B** times the height h. But $h = |\mathbf{C}| \cos \varphi$, and the angle between **C** and $\mathbf{A} \times \mathbf{B}$ is also φ, so

$$v = |\mathbf{A} \times \mathbf{B}|\ |\mathbf{C}| \cos \varphi = (\mathbf{A} \times \mathbf{B}) \cdot \mathbf{C}.$$

If **C** is directed to the side of the plane $\mathcal{P}$ opposite **N**, then $\mathbf{A} \times \mathbf{B} \cdot \mathbf{C}$ is negative, but in either case,

$$|\mathbf{A} \times \mathbf{B} \cdot \mathbf{C}|$$

is the volume of the parallelepiped with edges formed by **A**, **B**, and **C**. It is for this reason that this product is called the box product.

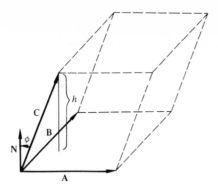

FIGURE 5.27

The box product may be given directly as a determinant, which in turn allows geometric interpretation of such determinants.

5.7-2 Theorem:

$$\mathbf{A} \cdot \mathbf{B} \times \mathbf{C} = \begin{vmatrix} a_1 & a_2 & a_3 \\ b_1 & b_2 & b_3 \\ c_1 & c_2 & c_3 \end{vmatrix}$$

PROOF: Since the vector $\mathbf{B} \times \mathbf{C}$ is given by

$$\mathbf{B} \times \mathbf{C} = \begin{vmatrix} \mathbf{I} & \mathbf{J} & \mathbf{K} \\ b_1 & b_2 & b_3 \\ c_1 & c_2 & c_3 \end{vmatrix},$$

it is clear that the dot product $\mathbf{A} \cdot \mathbf{B} \times \mathbf{C}$ is given by using the same determinant with $\mathbf{I}$ replaced by a_1, $\mathbf{J}$ replaced by a_2, and $\mathbf{K}$ replaced by a_3.

5.7-3 Corollary: A 3×3 determinant is zero iff the row vectors of the corresponding matrix are linearly dependent.

PROOF: This is exactly the condition that exists when the parallelepiped formed by the row vectors has zero volume.

5.7-4 Corollary:

$$\mathbf{A} \cdot \mathbf{B} \times \mathbf{C} = \mathbf{A} \times \mathbf{B} \cdot \mathbf{C}.$$

PROOF: The dot product is commutative, and $\mathbf{C} \cdot \mathbf{A} \times \mathbf{B}$ is given by two successive row changes in the above determinant.

5.7-5 Corollary: The rows of a 3×3 matrix are linearly dependent iff its columns are linearly dependent.

PROOF: $|A| = |A^t|$.

We now conclude this treatise of analytic geometry, although there are many marvelous topics yet to explore. We have attempted to make use of many elementary linear algebra notions to enhance the study of analytic geometry and to hint at some common generalizations. In most cases we barely scratched the surface, yet we feel we have accomplished two fundamental purposes: a study of traditional analytic geometry and the introduction of linear algebraic notions in the plane and in three space. We sincerely hope you have enjoyed it.

EXERCISES 5.7

1. Graph the vectors $\mathbf{A}$, $\mathbf{B}$, and $\mathbf{A} \times \mathbf{B}$, then observe the right-hand rule property.
   a. $\mathbf{A} = (1, 1, 1)$, $\mathbf{B} = (1, 1, 2)$. b. $\mathbf{A} = (1, 0, 2)$, $\mathbf{B} = (0, 0, 1)$.
   c. $\mathbf{A} = (-1, -2, 1)$, $\mathbf{B} = (2, 1, 3)$. d. $\mathbf{A} = (-1, -2, 0)$, $\mathbf{B} = (1, -3, 0)$.

2. Find the volume of the parallelepiped having adjacent edges formed by the given vectors. Graph.
   a. $(2, 1, 3)$, $(0, -2, 3)$, $(6, 1, 2)$. b. $(4, -1, 2)$, $(4, 7, 3)$, $(2, -1, 4)$.
   c. $(2, -2, 4)$, $(3, -3, 0)$, $(5, 2, -1)$.

3. Show that $\mathbf{A} \times \mathbf{B} \cdot \mathbf{C} = -\mathbf{B} \cdot \mathbf{A} \times \mathbf{C}$.

4. Explain why the normals $\mathbf{A}$ and $\mathbf{B}$ to two intersecting planes have a cross product parallel to the line of intersection of the two planes.

5. Find a position vector parallel to the line of intersection of the two planes given.
   a. $3x - 2y - z = 0$; $x - y + z = 2$.
   b. $5x + y + 2z = 2$; $x + y - 3z = 1$.
   c. $2x + y - z = 3$; $2x - y - z = 2$.
   d. $4x + y + z = 1$; $3x + 2y + 2z = 2$.

6. Find a parametric equation $\mathbf{V} = \mathbf{S}t + \mathbf{A}$ for the line of intersection of the planes in Exercise 5.

7. Suppose $O = (0, 0, 0)$ and $B = (1, 2, -2)$. Find the point $A = (a, a, 0)$ such that the vector $\mathbf{B} - \mathbf{A}$ is perpendicular to the line through O and A.

8. a. Show that
$$\mathbf{Z} = \frac{|\mathbf{X}|\mathbf{Y} + |\mathbf{Y}|\mathbf{X}}{|\mathbf{X}| + |\mathbf{Y}|}$$

   bisects the angle between $\mathbf{X}$ and $\mathbf{Y}$.
   b. Show that $|\mathbf{X}|\mathbf{Y} + |\mathbf{Y}|\mathbf{X}$ and $\mathbf{X}|\mathbf{Y}| - \mathbf{Y}|\mathbf{X}|$ are perpendicular. Graph the vectors.

9. Find the area of the triangle whose vertices are the points A, B, and C.
   a. $A = (1, 2, 4)$, $B = (-2, -3, 4)$, $C = (4, 1, -2)$.
   b. $A = (2, -1, 3)$, $B = (4, 1, -5)$, $C = (3, 6, -1)$.
   c. $A = (5, 1, 4)$, $B = (2, -3, 4)$, $C = (5, 2, -1)$.

10. Verify the right-hand rule in the case where $\mathbf{A}$ and $\mathbf{B}$ lie in the x-y plane. (HINT: For vectors $\mathbf{A} = (a, b)$ and $\mathbf{B}$ in the plane, $\mathbf{B} \cdot \mathbf{A}^\perp$ (where $\mathbf{A}^\perp = (-a, b)$) is either $+$ or $-$, depending on the rotational position of $\mathbf{B}$ from $\mathbf{A}$.)

INDEX

317

NOTATION

This index lists the principal notation used, together with the number of the page where each symbol first appears.